CW01082430

The Stirling Engine Manual

JAMES G. RIZZO

© James G. Rizzo 1995.

Parts of this book first appeared in "Modelling Stirling and Hot Air Engines" by James G Rizzo and published by Patrick Stephens Limited in 1985.

Layout and Design by Andrew Luckhurst, Bath, England.

All rights reserved. No part of this publication may be reproduced, stored in a retrevial system, transmitted in any form by any means electronic or manual or photocopied or recorded by any other information storage and retrieval system without prior permission in writing from the publishers.

British Library Cataloguing-in-Publication Data: a catalogue record for this book is held by the British Library.

ISBN No. 0 9519367 3 5

Published in Great Britain by
Camden Miniature Steam Services,
Barrow Farm,
Rode, Nr. Bath,
Somerset. BA3 6PS.

"Camden" stock one of the widest selections of engineering, technical and transportation books to be found anywhere. For a copy of their Booklist, write to the above address.

WARNING: in this book, the author and the publishers are only passing on information on how readers can model and enjoy hot air engines. *Safety is your responsibilty* and you must *always* be aware of the potential dangers inherent in using tools, machine tools and sources of heat.

Printed and Bound by Biddles Ltd.,
Guildford and Kings Lynn.

Contents

Introduction

In 1985 Patrick Stephens Ltd. (now part of Haynes Publishing Group Plc.) published "Modelling Stirling and Hot Air Engines". The book sold out, the demand remained and my new Publisher, Camden Miniature Steam Services, also a leading bookseller of a multitude of titles in most branches of hobby engineering, decided to republish the original text. In the course of events, it was mutually agreed that a few additions, to bring the hobby of STIRLING ENGINEERING more up to date, should make this edition more interesting.

It is still a book for beginners to the hobby of building STIRLING ENGINES. The hobby is still a fascinating one; there is now a greater degree of interest, and still a demand for a comprehensive coverage of an engine that has a rich historical background. My aim was, and still is, to introduce this branch of home engineering in simple and plain terms, and easily followed directions.

The same format has been retained. The first part of the book covers the history of the Stirling Engine, followed by a brief and elementary approach to the thermodynamic and practical principles of the cycle, a factual treatment of the more important engine parameters, workshop practice and, as a new addition, examples of Stirling Engines built by fellow model and home engineers.

The second part of the book deals with projects well within the capabilities of a beginner or a home engineer with modest workshop facilities. This section covers a range of examples from small, uncomplicated but highly instructive and entertaining engines, to two types of Stirling engines not previously covered, a Low Temperature Differential Stirling Engine, and a Pressurised Stirling Engine.

It is indeed a great source of satisfaction to meet so many fellow engineers who have read the first publication and an even greater satisfaction to see engines on Stands in Engineering Exhibitions, built from one or other of the plans set out in Part Two. As I had opined before, many beginners to the hobby have gone on to building more sophisticated engines, with more efficient mechanisms. These colleagues have shared their expertise and experiences with me and with others, and as a result so much of this information has come forward for inclusion in this book that it quickly became difficult to choose which material is to be included in this edition, and that which could be left over for the sequel - simply because of the shortage of space. We have already overrun the intended size by a large margin.

I happen to be a firm believer in three aspects of small scale Stirling engineering: first, this is an engine that still has scope for further development; secondly that the home engineer has much to offer in its development. Classic cases of this belief are there for the picking, particularly in the U.S.A. and in Germany, some examples of which are also mentioned herein. Thirdly, this need not be an expensive hobby, since a fair amount of the materials used can be obtained cheaply or from scrap yards. I am reminded of a quote I once read: "an engineer is one who can do for five bob what any fool can do for a quid". I venture to think that the home engineer can do it even cheaper than five bob.

This book is dedicated to those home and hobby engineers whose involvement may yet benefit mankind, particularly in those parts of the world where the need for utilisation of direct energy is greater than the proceeds of charity.

Acknowledgements

My previous publication "Modelling Stirling and Hot Air Engines" was made possible by the tremendous assistance and support I had received in the preparation stages. This assistance and encouragement was acknowledged then, and is repeated now with greater emphasis. The success of making the Stirling Eingine more reachable to budding engineers in home workshops is attributable to this support.

Two of these collaborators have come forward with even greater support - Andy Ross from Ohio U.S.A., and Mick Collins from Elstead, Surrey, stalwarts who inspire the right kind of confidence in broaching a subject which is normally dealt with by experts. I am just a hobbyist.

I have made new friends from whom I have obtained just as much support. Two in particular have made direct contributions to this book - Roy Darlington, of Worthing, Sussex, and Richard White, of Crawley, West Sussex. Roy has allowed me to write about his Low Temperature Differential Engine, which was the centre of attraction on the Stirling Engines Stand at the Model Engineering Exhibitions at Olympia in 1994 and 1995, as well as at Brighton's Modelworld in the same years. Richard White designed and constructed TUBA and described in it great detail in Chapter 22. These two additions to the family have almost completed the range of engines one would need to experiment with as a starting point towards further development.

Mick Collins has made a valuable contribution using the computer to create a power pressure indicator, thus placing the model Stirling Engine in the realm of computerisation.

Geoff Bartlett has sent me a wealth of information on his diaphragm-powered Stirling Engines, some of which is reproduced in this publication; the complete story will have to be held over to the sequel.

Professor James R. Senft of the University of Wisconsin, River Falls, U.S.A., has made it possible to make a proper, albeit simple, introduction to the Ringbom Stirling Engine, and to the Low Temperature Differential Engine, apart from allowing use of illustrations from his own highly interesting book "The Ringbom Stirling Engine".

John Annings, a friend of David and Jane Urwick, who now has possession of David's engines, gladly agreed to make them available for inclusion in this book. The photographs of David's engines on page 74 are the copyright of PHOTOSCENE, of South Molton, Devon, by whose permission they are reproduced.

My friends and colleagues from the University of Malta have once more come to my assistance on the theoretical and technical aspects of the Stirling Cycle Engine. They range from Professors to Technicians - too many to mention them all. The exchange of interest has motivated the Faculties of Engineering and Science to further research in solar-powered pressurised Stirling Engine development which may prove to be of tremendous value.

A number of engineering colleagues were kind enough to send me photographs of their engines for inclusion in Chapter 9, ".......Of Models and Modellers". Their valuable contributions are specially acknowledged since they are indicative of the high technical standard this engine has now reached. I should also like to express my appreciation for the wealth of photographs I have received; together they could easily fill a book of this size.

The line drawings on Page 73 are reproduced with the kind permission of New Cavendish Books, from their book "The Great Toys of Georges Carette".

The photographs of the Ericsson Engine constructed by Roy Key which appear on Page 79 and the colour section are reproduced by kind permission of Christie's Images.

The line drawings of the original 1818 Stirling Engine (after Dr. A.J. Organ) on Page 1, the Roper Engine on Page 4, and the solar powered concept by Ericsson on Page 7 were done by my friend Winston Attard.

I gratefully acknowledge the assistance and permission of the Director of the Science Museum, Kensington, London and of the Director of the Deutsches Museum, Munich, Germany to reproduce photographs of engines held at their respective Museums. In both cases they had allowed me to see other examples held in their depositories.

My sons, Adrian, Alex and Stephen, were not only supportive but actually assisted in several ways to get this project under way, and completed. My special thanks go to my daughter-in-law, Joanna, who spent long hours at the computer retyping the script, and to my Secretary, Mrs. Anna Pisani, who in her spare time looked after my huge correspondence and the multitude of paper work which is part and parcel of preparing a manuscript.

To all these kind persons, and to others who have in some way or other encouraged and supported me in my task, a mighty big "thank you". My sincere apologies go to anyone who, in the rush of things, may have escaped my memory.

James G. Rizzo,
Malta.
January 1995

CHAPTER ONE

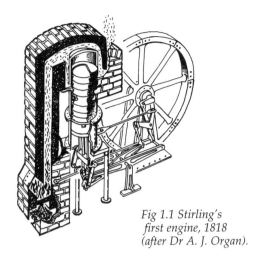

Fig 1.1 Stirling's first engine, 1818 (after Dr A. J. Organ).

What is a Stirling Cycle Engine?

The "Stirling-Cycle Engine", also known as the "STIRLING ENGINE" is the generic name given to a group of prime movers commonly known as "hot air engines". STIRLING ENGINES work on a "closed cycle" system where the working medium, that is air, hydrogen or helium, is used over and over again.

"Closed-cycle" and "open-cycle" hot air engines are externally heated to raise the temperature of the working medium to provide the required degree of volumetric expansion in order to provide force. These engines are therefore also known as "external combustion" engines. ("Open-cycle" hot air engines have fresh working medium induced during each cycle by means of valves).

HISTORICAL BACKGROUND

The Stirling-cycle engine bears the name of its developer the Reverend Robert Stirling, a Minister of the Church of Scotland, who with his brother James, an engineer by profession, developed the hot air engine and endowed it with an invention which in those days was very far advanced in concept.

The Rev. Stirling registered his "invention" in 1816 (patent No. 4081) but failed to follow up the registration and to enroll the specification, so his application lapsed. His first "hot air" engine, constructed in 1818 was quite successful and it is recorded that this engine, used as a quarry pump, ran continuously for over two years until it developed metal fatigue due to poor heat-resisting metals available at the time.

The Rev. Stirling's ideas were very advanced in concept. His 1816 specification *IMPROVEMENTS FOR DIMINISHING THE CONSUMPTION OF FUEL* makes excellent reading. His idea of regeneration, whereby heat was retained and re-used by the construction of "tubes, passages and plates made of metal, and any other substance that conducts and transmits heat easily" was an unusual one, which was not accepted for several generations. Its real purpose could not be understood, simply because it was so much in advance of scientific knowledge of that era. In retrospect, it can be considered as one of the most amazing inventions ever.

For almost a century the Rev. Stirling and his brother James were credited, erroneously, with two patents, one in 1827 and one in 1840. The 1816 specifications remained undiscovered until 1917, when the original documents were found and handed back to the Stirling family who passed them on to the Patent Office some 100 years after the date when they should have been enrolled in the official Blue Book series.

The Stirling engine of 1818 (Fig 1.1) had a displacer (known in those days as "transferer") and a power piston in the same cylinder. The one patented in 1827 (Fig 1.2) was a twin-displacer engine where the power piston was double acting, on the upward stroke receiving air in the lower half from the displacer cylinder on the left, and air in the upper half from the displacer cylinder on the right on the downward stroke. A fourth small cylinder, connected by a system of levers, was used as a pressure pump. This engine was modified several times in later years to provide better regeneration, better cooling and less dead space.

The engine patented in 1840 was an improvement on the 1827 model particularly where the regenerator was concerned. In this engine the regenerator was removed from around the displacer cylinder and placed in a separate container with a cooler on top of it. Heated air from the bottom of the displacer cylinder passed through the regenerator, through the cooler and on to the power cylinder. The engine in Fig. 1.3 shows in a compact form the main principles of Stirling's invention and illustrates better than any other type the construction of a near-perfect heat engine. It shows the source of heat (the furnace), the source of cooling (the water pipes) and between the two, the regenerator which abstracts heat as the air passes on its way to the cooler and returns heat to the air on its way to the source of heat.

Fig. 1.4 illustrates a converted steam engine in a Dundee foundry which started to run in March 1843. It appears to have been a satisfactory experiment for about two and half years, but in December 1845 a cylinder bottom overheated and failed. It was repaired twice and twice burnt out again. In the end the owners reconverted the motive power back to steam.

Although the Stirling brothers patented three types of engines, they preferred the later separate twin cylinder for the power piston and displacer to the first type where the displacer and power piston work in one common cylinder. Yet subsequent development showed that the first type of engine is in fact more efficient. Other types of engines suffered from a major defect by using separate cylinders, in that part of the enclosed air, known as the dead space, performs no useful work and so reduces the specific power of the engine.

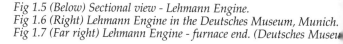

Fig 1.5 (Below) Sectional view - Lehmann Engine.
Fig 1.6 (Right) Lehmann Engine in the Deutsches Museum, Munich.
Fig 1.7 (Far right) Lehmann Engine - furnace end. (Deutsches Museum

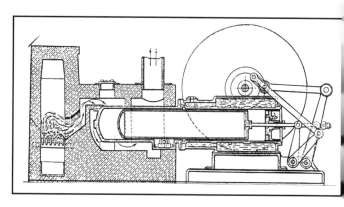

Most of the development that took place in later years was on the closed-cycle principle, following generally the Stirling designs, although there were some exceptions, notably the Ericsson engines. However, few of the developers who designed their engines on the closed-cycle included the regenerator. This was mainly because they could not understand the function of this component and therefore its usefulness. Open-cycle engine development also took place, but this type required a system of valves with levers, links or cams to move them. Invariably these valves opened directly to the hot chamber and just as invariably these valves burnt out with regular monotony. Obviously these engines were also very noisy.

Stirling's invention, the regenerator, has turned out to be the most essential component in the hot air engine. Scientists, mathematicians and engineers are now convinced that the efficiency of the modern Stirling-cycle engine is largely determined by the efficiency of the regenerator.

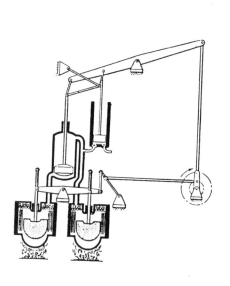

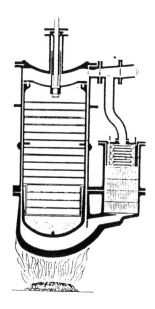

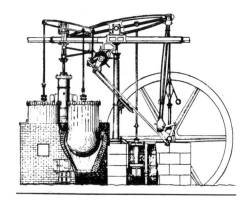

Fig 1.2 (Far left) Stirling engine of 1827.
Fig 1.3 (Left) Detail from Stirling specification of the 1840 engine.
Fig 1.4 (Above) Converted Stirling engine in a Dundee factory.

EARLY DEVELOPMENT OF THE HOT AIR ENGINE

Many early 19th century engineers believed that the hot air engine or "caloric" engine as it was also known, would eventually replace the steam engine which was then going through a difficult time, and considered a dangerous piece of machinery, claiming countless lives as a result of boiler explosions. It is not generally known that during the second half of the nineteenth century thousands of hot air engines were produced and used in factories as the alternative source of power to the steam engine. Their safety record made the hot air engines more attractive in spite of the low power they generated.

Engineers in Germany and France led the development of the caloric engine in Europe and a number of notable names left their imprint on the history of this fascinating engine; however almost all of them disregarded the Stirling regenerator principle. On the other hand Stirling engines were far superior in efficiency and output than other hot air engines and even some steam engines of that period.

It is interesting to note the development of hot air engines which were manufactured between the 1860's and 1890's. One of the more successful early engines was developed by Lehmann. The Lehmann engine followed the principle of the first Stirling engine, a single working cylinder containing both the displacer and the power piston, the notable difference being that the cylinder was laid horizontally and the linkage mechanism was more compact. There was no regenerator employed, but it is probable that the unusually long displacer served also, to a lesser degree, as a regenerator. The displacer cylinder had an internal dividing plate which probably served for different purposes - sealing two compartments which created an air cushion against the transmission of heat along the length of

the displacer, it strengthened the thin plated cylinder and also supported the displacer rod which extended beyond the wooden plug which sealed the displacer cylinder end.

Fig 1.5 taken from drawings made at the time give a very clear view of the compact linkage mechanism, the furnace, the large water jacket for cooling and the roller arrangement beneath the displacer which helped to support its weight. The brickwork surrounding the furnace and leading up to the chimney flue, was simple, pleasing to the eye and effective. The ducting for the flames and the intense heat generated enabled the hot end to obtain maximum heat transfer.

The original power piston of the Lehmann engine was a leather washer mounted on a metal plate, very similar to the bicycle pump plunger; later models had a barrel power piston with air intake valve (snifter valve) which allowed air into the cylinder whenever the internal pressure fell below atmospheric. The engine speed was reputed to be 95 to 100 RPM.

Fig 1.6 shows the Lehmann Engine installed at the Deutsches Museum, Munich and, with Fig 1.7

Fig 1.8 Details of the Lehmann Engine mechanism (Deutsches Museum).

*Fig 1.9 (Above left)
Cross-section
of the vertical Bailey
Engine.*

*Fig 1.10 (Above right)
Model of the Bailey
engine based on the
Lehmann design.
(Courtesy: The Science
Museum, London.)*

*Fig 1.11 (Below right)
Roper's hot air engine.*

*Fig 1.12 (Below left)
Details of the Bernier
hot air engine.*

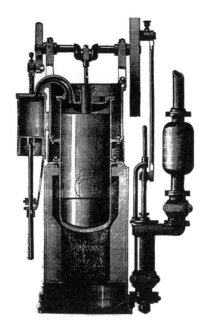

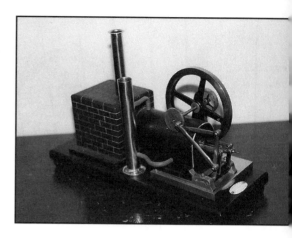

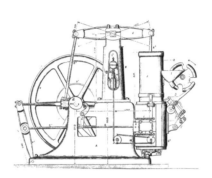

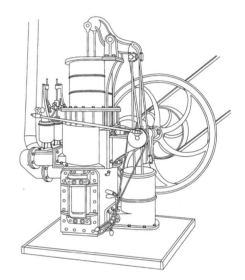

and Fig 1.8 is reproduced by kind permission of the Director of the Museum. Fig 1.7 is a close up of the brickwork surrounding the furnace and the hot end of the engine and Fig 1.8 is a close-up of the linkage system. (There are quite a number of different hot air engines on display and in the vaults of the Deutsches Museum, among them an Ericsson and two Heinrici Engines. The Ericsson Engine is similar to the one at the Science Museum in Kensington, London).

The Lehmann engine was also produced in other countries under license, with some minor modifications. In England the same engine with almost identical linkage was produced by W.H. Bailey & Co. and in Holland an "improved" design was manufactured by Stenberg of Helsingfors under the name of "CALORISCA". The main difference between the original Lehmann design and CALORISCA was the use of a cam-drive mechanism instead of the lever crank design, which probably made the engine less mechanically efficient.

Bailey and Co. produced a large number of engines of different sizes both on the Lehmann design, as well as on a design which differed marginally as a result of a simplified link mechanism and included an integral water pump (Fig 1.9). The advantage of few moving parts, the smooth and silent operation, easy maintenance and trouble free starting made them very popular, although their low power output limited their use to small industries and workshops. Curiously enough a number of scaled down, almost toy-like working models of the Bailey (Lehmann) design were produced and sold. One of these models is held by the Science Museum in Kensington (Fig 1.10), apparently presented to the Museum in 1894.

There were several other names linked with the development and production of different types of hot air engines of both open and closed-cycle type but few of these were of any real significance. Large engines were produced by such engineers as Laubereau, Laubereau and Schwarzkopoff, Churchill, Roper (Fig 1.11), Bernier (Fig 1.12), Belou (Fig 1.13) and Ericsson.

Few of these have survived even as museum pieces and we have to rely on engineering reports of the time for basic line illustrations and sketchy details.

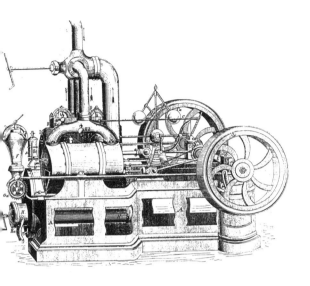

Fig 1.13 (Above left) Belou's Engine.

Fig 1.14 (Above right) Heinrici engine held in the Science Museum, London depository.

Fig 1.15 (Below left) Rider's hot air engine pump.

Fig 1.16 (Below right) Robinson hot air engine .

It is therefore difficult to estimate the efficiency of these huge engines, but their speed was abysmally slow, normally 30 to 50 RPM rarely reaching more than 80 RPM and one cannot fail to notice the complicated drive mechanisms , the lack of regeneration, the heavy materials used - all factors which will have reduced efficiency - and sales.

The other side of the picture is provided by three different designs of hot air engines, the Heinrici (Fig 1.14) produced in Germany, the Rider (Fig 1.15) originally manufactured in the USA and the Robinson (Fig 1.16) produced in Britain. These three types of engine require individual treatment in this Chapter, simply because of their impact on the development of the hot air engine in their time.

No study of the hot air engine is complete without an in depth reference to the Ericsson engine. The original Ericsson hot air engines were not of the closed-cycle type since they relied on a system of valves to regulate the intake and expulsion of the working gas.   Ericsson's experiments with the open-air cycle were doomed to fail mostly due to metal fatigue particularly in the use of valves.

Many years,failures and models later Ericsson finally reviewed his development and construction methods and brought out a single-cylinder hot air engine of the closed-cycle type, without valves, specifically designed as a water pump (Fig 1.17). The pump was an integral part of the engine; the early models using the water flow to cool the upper part of the cylinder, flowing through a water jacket, before discharging. Later models, the 8 inch and l0 inch size, had two pumps working from the main beam, a deep well pump and a surface pump, the former discharging into the water system while water from the surface pump was used first to cool the upper cylinder, the hot water then being used for domestic purposes.

Ericsson was a natural engineer whose reluctance to   accept   the   closed-cycle   principle,   and determination to continue the development of the open-cycle hot air engine, cost him dear. It also deprived the engineering world of a brilliant mind which could have greatly helped advance the Stirling regenerator in which he actually believed. During 1855 to 1857, Ericsson developed a number of different models of hot air engines of the open-cycle class, some with integral pumps. One of

Fig 1.17 (Near left) Sectional view of the Ericsson hot air engine pump.

Fig 1.18 (2nd left) The Ericsson engine held at the Science Museum, London.

Fig 1.19 (2nd right) Concept of the Solar-powered Ericsson hot air engine.

Fig 1.20 (Far right) A Rider hot air engine pump. (Science Museum, London).

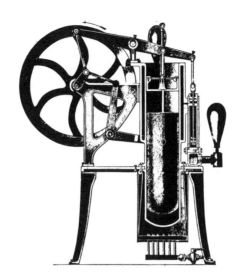

these engines can be seen at the Science Museum, Kensington (Fig 1.18) and another at the Deutsches Museum, Munich.

As early as 1864 Ericsson, who was also a brilliant inventor, attempted to make one of his engines work by solar power, using a reflector to heat the cylinder hot end (Fig 1.19). Nine years later he admitted that the use of valves was detrimental to the smaller engine and his new developments; thereafter he excluded valves and reverted to the closed-cycle system. Within a few years he developed a series of different sizes of pumping engines which became so popular that manufacturers under license in America and in Britain could not cope with the demand for a time.

It was about this time that A.K. Rider of Philadelphia, USA, invented and developed a type of closed-cycle hot air engine that was to bear his name and make it famous in engineering history. Thousands of these engines, used as water pumps, were sold. The *RIDER* (Fig 1.20) was an ingenious hot air engine, compact and handy, ideal for domestic use particularly for pumping water. It includes almost all the features of the early Stirling engine except that whereas Stirling was careful to keep the power cylinder cool, even in the single cylinder engine, in the Rider engine the motive power is not only generated, but produced and applied in the hot cylinder. The two parallel cylinders are connected by a passage holding a regenerator consisting of a number of very thin iron plates packed closely together.

The Rider engines became very popular, not only in the United States where they were sold by the tens of thousands, but also in England where they were manufactured, under license, by Hayward Tyler & Co. Like the Ericsson models, the Rider pumps used the water to cool one of the cylinders before it was discharged to serve its real purpose.

Three sizes of Rider engines were manufactured, a 6 inch engine with a 125 foot depth draw, an 8 inch engine with 300 foot depth draw and a 10 inch engine with a 500 foot depth draw.

Both the Rider and Ericsson engines were advertised as having an interchangeable furnace capable of using gas, paraffin, wood or coal depending on the client's choice. Production of these pumping engines continued into the twentieth century and examples can still be found at rallies and shows ready to turn on application of heat.

During the same period a range of small "domestic motors", as this size of hot air engine was then called, the Heinrici motor appeared, achieving what was probably the greatest sale of hot air engines in Europe. This famous "legs-in-the-air" engine had a simplified link drive which was quite graceful and attractive and also quite efficient for its size, (around 2' 6" to 3' tall). A large number of these motors were produced and exported to most European countries, and to Asia. The construction was sturdy and the materials used were, for the time, of very high standard. Some of the engines still in existence can be made to run efficiently with a minimum application of heat. A similar version was brought out in England in 1908 by Gardner Ltd.

In the 1880s an interesting development of the Stirling-cycle engine was taking place in England, in the shape of the Robinson engine, which made greater use of the regenerator that any other engine since the Stirling. The basic principle of the Robinson engine was a moving regenerator. This engine certainly had a distinctive appearance and an unusual design. It elicited comments from both ends of the descriptive epithets - from "squat and ugly" to "small and unusually attractive". Never had an engine from the days of the industrial

efficient than those of most other engines, with very few moving parts. Later generations of the Robinson engine had an improvement to the link mechanism whereby a roller was connected to the top end of the displacer rod and made to slide backwards and forwards along the power connecting rod, thus lengthening slightly the stroke and generally making this part of the mechanism more efficient. However the power output still remained low with an average speed of 200 RPM.

The last four engines in this overview, the Ericsson, Heinrici, Rider and Robinson, can be described as DOMESTIC MOTORS, their usage being in the household as well as in the small workshop, in the field as well as in the dentist's surgery. One particular popular use of the hot air engine came in the shape of cooling fans.

Many brand names of hot air fans stand out - *KYKO* manufactured in England, *JOST* manufactured in Germany and India and *AL COOL* and *LAKE BREEZE* produced in the States. There were other brand names manufactured in the Far East but details are sketchy. The mechanical drive employed differed from the single-cylinder concentric arrangement to the twin cylinder parallel "legs-in-the-air" configuration. The fan blades were either directly mounted on to the crankshaft boss or gear driven off a gear fitted on the crankshaft or belt driven by pulleys on the crankshaft with the fan mounted on a bracket.

These fans generally had a slow speed but created a beautiful breeze which was very welcome in tropical climates. Their ease of work and operation, their economy of usage with long hours between refills of the kerosene or spirit lamp, these and other advantages made then immensely popular with expatriates and well-to-do families in India and in the Far East in the first half of the

revolution come so close to an interpretation of the saying "beauty is in the eye of the beholder !" (Fig 1.21).

Yet in spite of the inclusion of the moving regenerator, the Robinson engine was not terribly efficient and its power output was markedly less than the Rider and the Heinrici. The main reasons for the relatively low efficiency were two basic design faults - dead space due to the positioning of the power cylinder away from the displacer cylinder with an unusually wide connecting passage, and a drive mechanism for the displacer which provided too short a stroke to the regenerator to enable it to conduct a proper transfer of heat. The regenerator was a hollow body consisting of two minutely perforated plates filled with a tight mass of thin wire, through which the hot air flowed on its way to the power piston placed at right angles to the displacer cylinder (See Fig 3.9 - Chapter 3).

The complete drive mechanism was certainly more

Fig 1.21 (Above) Robinson engine, with a cut-away view of the displacer held at the Science Museum, London.
Fig 1.22 (Right) Jost hot air fan.
Fig 1.23 (Far right) Kyko hot air fan.
(Figs 1.22 & 1.23 courtesy of John Wilkinson).

century. The *JOST* (Fig 1. 22) and *KYKO* (Fig 1.23) fans gave years of trouble free service and there are many still around that will work within a few minutes of lighting the lamp under the displacer.

The old drawings and woodcuts of these Stirling cycle engines and the other hot air engines are worth studying. One cannot help but admire the ingenuity of the great engineers of the last century, who had ideas far in advance of their times, yet had to battle and work with inadequate materials and tools.

Hot Air Engines started dropping out of fashion around the turn of the century, and although some were still being produced up till 1910, the small internal combustion engine, and especially the electric motor, quickly replaced the Stirling engine as a prime mover and for domestic puposes. By the 1920s most of the larger machines had gone and by the 1930s Hot Air Engines were a thing of the past - or so it seemed.

SUBSEQUENT DEVELOPMENT

The story of the hot air engine from the late 1930s is not unlike a fairy tale, with the charming prince in the shape of Philips of Eindhoven in the Netherlands bringing to life, with a kiss, the sleeping beauty, the Stirling engine. This success story cannot be told briefly. What is important to this review is that while looking for a small, simple and light engine to generate electricity in remote areas for radio receivers and transmitters, Philips chose to investigate and research into the Stirling engine.

The first task undertaken by the Philips scientists was to analyse the defects in the Stirling engine in order to improve its efficiency to a standard comparable with the internal combustion engine. The engine design, the construction of the regenerator, the problem of heat transfer, resistance of the air-flow and the mechanical drives were all closely studied and the results incorporated in the first of a series of single cylinder engines combining all the major improvements.

The single cylinder engine has in the lower part of the cylinder a power piston through which a rod moves the transfer piston (displacer) in the upper part. The hot space, the regenerator, and the cold space are annular in shape and built around the cylinder. This configuration allows the engine to be very compact. The engine has a closed crank-case containing a small pressure pump connected to the crank and used to elevate the internal working pressure of the gas, (Fig. 1. 24). The progression from this single-cylinder to the multi-cylinder engine would have been a natural one in the normal course of development. However in the case of the multi-cylinder, particu-

Fig 1.24 Philips Air Engine with Generator (by permission of Nederlandse Philips Bedrijven B.V.)

larly in four-cylinder engines, the progress was simply amazing. The Stirling engine, with its double-acting capacity, lent itself much more to this type of configuration than to any other form (see Chapter 2). In 1970 Philips developed a four-cylinder in-line engine with their famous rhombic drive (see Chapter 6), developing about 100 bhp at 3,000rpm. One of these experimental engines was fitted to a DAF coach and used with normal conventional transmission to drive the vehicle on the road.

Philips involvement and success aroused interest in a number of other firms. Moreover, Philips willingness to share their knowledge made it possible for engineers and model engineers to take another look at the hot air engine. In fact the air motor became a possibility for anyone who had modest technical ability and construction facilities. Among the interested larger combines, General Motors, USA, developed a 3 KW generator in conjunction with Philips and based on this engine a hybrid electric car powered by batteries and charged by the Stirling electric generator. Another large combine, the MAN-MWM Stirling Engine Development Group, jointly established by two major German diesel engine developers, joined Philips in building other experimental Stirling engines. United Stirling of Malmo, Sweden, was formed and licensed with the sole aim of manufacturing Stirling engines. This company, which has gone into development in a big way, produced large 200hp double acting engines. In 1972 the Ford Motor Company started a joint development programme with Philips to develop a passenger car engine of about 175 bhp. This was planned as a four-cylinder double-acting swashplate engine. At the same time Ford and United Stirling investigated another type of hot air engine of a slightly different technique. By 1976 Ford had installed a Philips engine in a Ford Pinto and a United Stirling engine in a Ford Taunus. Of interest to those who believe in the future of the Stirling engine is a report, prepared by a team of engineers and scientists funded by the Ford Motor Company, to investigate the technical feasibility of heavy investment in the production of an alternative power unit for the motor-car. The report concludes that the Stirling engine, at a development cost of $8000 million would save a minimum amount of two million barrels of oil per day by 1999. Of even greater interest and even more technologically feasible in the field of automotive propulsion are the hybrid-electric car units. This system will certainly gain more interest as car batteries increase in efficiency and decrease in size and weight, making it possible for a medium sized hot air engine to give the necessary topping up charge to a family size round-about-town electric car.

LATEST DEVELOPMENTS

Directly related to the Stirling-cycle engine have been at least four developments of interest to the model engineer. These are well within the means of an engineering society, a technical institute workshop or a higher education laboratory.

An amazing development of the Stirling engine which promises immense prospects for the future of the closed-cycle principle is the RINGBOM ENGINE. The Ringbom can be described as a "half-Stirling" - it has a power piston connected to the flywheel and a "free-acting" displacer, that is a displacer that is not connected to the drive mechanism, thereby reducing the number of moving parts by almost half while retaining the closed-cycle principle.

Ossian Ringbom invented this engine in 1905 and took out a patent in 1907. Thereafter and until a few years ago no further development took place. In the early 80s, a number of experiments were undertaken in various universities and laboratories leading to industrial development and solar applications for the Ringbom engine.

Professor James R. Seft of the University of Wisconsin, USA, has made an in-depth study of the Ringbom Engine and its derivatives, including the Low Temperature Differential Engines and has presented an excellent publication, "RINGBOM STIRLING ENGINES" published in 1993 by Oxford University Press (New York and Oxford).

THE BEALE FREE-PISTON ENGINE is a single cylinder engine without a crank case, crank-shaft or flywheel. This remarkable invention has only two moving parts, eliminating much hardware and hard work. It is simple in operation, compact, extremely quiet, and self-starting. This interesting development is the invention of Professor William Beale, of Athens, Ohio, USA. He made this discovery while professor of mechanical engineering at the University of Ohio. The engine requires heating and cooling. Between these two actions exists the dynamic equilibrium of three forces exerted within a sealed unit, pressure forces, spring forces and damping forces. The operation involves a heavy and accurate piston and a displacer. The piston, in combination with an effective gas spring, oscillates at a natural frequency when heat is applied. This type of engine requires absolute accuracy in construction. Beale engines are being developed for converting solar energy into electricity, total energy systems and water pumps amongst other developments. Although sealed, work can be extracted from the engine by attaching a load, such as a linear electric generator, to the reciprocating piston.

SOLAR ENGINES. Stirling engines driven directly by solar energy must, of necessity, be of great interest to countries where energy demand is high and solar energy is a ready commodity in unlimited quantity. The fact that for two-thirds of the day such engines are unoperative should not deter their development but rather serve as an impetus to find ways of converting energy, either into stored energy such as batteries, or stored potential energy, for example the use of water pumped to higher levels and used to power hydraulic generators on demand.

In terms of large scale development there has been no substantial breakthrough. The Beale engine mentioned above is an excellent example of the type of converter required to service this shortcoming. Whether this development can be extended scale-wise to be of any interest to developing countries is another matter.

In the field of model engineering, on the other hand, the scope is unlimited, once an enthusiast has become proficient in the construction of small engines, particularly single-cylinder concentric engines. With the aid of parabolic mirrors or Fresnel lenses sufficient heat can be generated at the hot end to enable the engine to develop relatively high speeds. Solar Engines of Phoenix, Arizona, has produced commercially a miniature sun motor (some 8in long) powered by a parabolic mirror, of 18in diameter, which when aimed at the sun produces a speed in excess of 1,000 RPM.

THE THERMO-MECHANICAL GENERATOR (TMG) is the first of two other important developments of the Stirling-cycle that should be described and considered here. Both are unconventional in the sense that they are a departure from the flywheel/crankshaft mechanical drive arrangement, yet in another sense both emerge from the same principle. Both developments originate from the Atomic Energy Research Establishment, Harwell, England.

The TMG was designed to generate low wattage electricity for equipment in remote locations where frequent maintenance and repairs are difficult. Therefore the prime requirement of this device is a continuous, efficient and highly reliable generator supplying electricity from a few tens of watts to a few hundred watts, depending on the equipment to be powered, whether it is a sea-buoy or a weather station radio, for long periods without servicing.

The main secret of the success of the thermo-mechanical generator lies in the restriction, to a large degree, of friction losses. A "normal" hot air engine works by volumetric changes in gas as a result of temperature changes brought about by displacing a fixed amount of gas to and from hot and cold chambers; to perform this work such an engine uses a displacer and a power piston to shift the gas from one end to the other. The thermo-mechanical generator uses a displacer and a semi-fixed substitute power piston, a diaphragm, to do the equivalent work. A linear alternator is necessary for the generation of electricity since the movement of the diaphragm is too small to be coupled to the crankshaft of a rotating engine.

A 120 watt version of the thermo-mechanical generator, was developed by Homach Systems Ltd. of Swindon, with a re-designed articulated diaphragm system invented by Mr. E.H. Cooke-Yarborough, one of Harwells leading scientists. The TMG has created a considerable interest in technical and scientific circles in view of its compact design and trouble-free maintenance.

THE "FLUIDYNE" ENGINE PUMP (Fig 1.25) is the other development that originally came from the Atomic Energy Research Laboratory and it too is related to the Stirling-cycle family. In the Fluidyne there are no metal working parts as we know them. No displacer, no power piston, no crankshaft or flywheel. Yet this "motor" can be made to pump water in a steady rhythmic flow when heat is applied to one end while the other end is kept cold. In principle it is a remarkable device and relatively easy to build in model form in a laboratory or workshop.

The device consists of two tubes containing a column of water topped by a pocket of air. The columns are joined at the top by an inverted open U-tube containing air (as the working gas) and joined at the bottom by a long tube connected to the pump body, a vertical tube which acts as the

pump and encloses the only mechanical items, an inlet and an outlet ball valve. The pump sucks water through the bottom valve and expels it in spurts through the top valve as the gas in the interconnected air space above the hot and cold chambers alternately expands and contracts. The Fluidyne engine-pump runs as long as heat is applied; it has a low thermal efficiency, but, conversely, since it can be powered by low cost heat, such as waste pipe heat and readily available crude combustible material, the efficiency factor does not matter much. The Fluidyne pump can be used in third world countries powered directly by free solar energy and that is where its real potential lies.

While the Fluidyne was being developed at Harwell, good results were being obtained with this ingenious device capable of pumping about 400 gallons per hour to a height of 10 feet with an efficiency of 4.7 per cent. Later, under development by the Metal Box Co. of Calcutta, India, it was reported to be able to pump 2500 gallons of water per hour at a head of 10 feet with an efficiency of 7 per cent.

The Fluidyne was devised at the AERE, Harwell by Dr. Colin West, who has written a very interesting book on this subject, "LIQUID-PISTON STIRLING ENGINES", published by Van Nostrand Reinhold Co. of New York, USA.

The search for power from the Stirling cycle now also extends to military and naval applications. Due to its silent mode of operation this engine has enormous advantages over the petrol and diesel engines and experimental

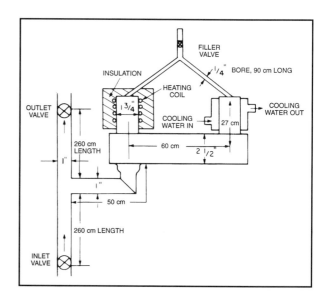

Fig 1.25 (above) The Fluidyne Engine Pump.
(courtesy Dr. Colin West).

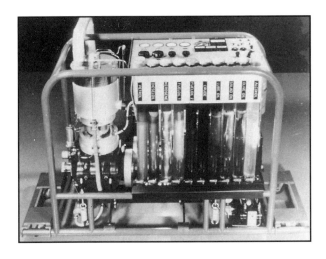

Fig 1.26 A multi-fuel demonstration of the Philips hot air engine, showing the engine's ability to work equally well with different fuels - in this case, alcohol, olive oil, salad oil, lubricating oil, two types of fuel oil, kerosene, diesel oil and petrol (by permission of Nederlands Philips Bedrijven B.V.)

development is currently ongoing to produce Stirling powered generators suitable for submarines and ground battle supporting positions.

FUTURE DEVELOPMENT

There now appears to be a good future for the Stirling engine. The use of heat resisting alloys and ceramics, better sealing techniques and the use of computers are all contributing factors in making this engine more efficient. Development in the past has been rather slow due to the fact that for many years it was more expedient to subsidize research into petrol and diesel engines. Now that these engines have been almost fully developed, it appears that it may be the turn of the Stirling engine to be given its proper place as a prime mover.

In many ways the Stirling engine is superior to other engines, steam, petrol or diesel. These reasons may be summarised as follows:

1. The Stirling is relatively less noisy; in many cases it is considered to be a quiet engine, comparatively free from vibration.

2. It creates no pollution problems. Since heat is applied externally there are no fumes or contamination and the exhaust or smoke is relatively clear.

3. It runs on a variety of fuels: oil, wood, coal, paraffin/kerosene, alcohol, gas, straw, sawdust and compressed paper are a few of the fuels which have been used. Also it is possible to change from one fuel to another without practical difficulties (Fig 1.26).

4. It is more economical to operate. Some of the fuels that can be used to generate heat are cheaper to obtain than oil-based products. The Stirling engine needs very little lubrication and this is also a substantial saver over a period of time.

5. There are fewer moving parts in Stirling engines than in petrol or diesel engines. Moreover there is less stress on the moving parts. These two factors combine to give longer life to these types of engines.

C H A P T E R   T W O

How the "Closed Cycle" Hot Air Engine works

"A Closed-Cycle Hot Air Engine works by volumetric changes of its working gas as a result of temperature changes. These volumetric changes are brought about by displacing a fixed amount of gas to and from hot and cold zones in an enclosed cylinder".

To a beginner who is thinking about building a Stirling engine the above may appear to be a formidable statement, but it is readily explainable by a series of diagrams.

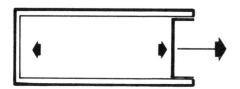

Fig 2.1 Expanding gas

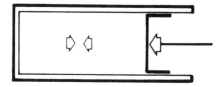

Fig 2.2 Contracting Gas

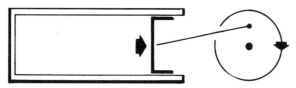

Fig 2.3 Expanding gas causing flywheel to turn.

1. If a pocket of gas (or air) enclosed in a cylinder is heated, the pressure inside the cylinder rises. If we assume that one end of the cylinder is a gas-tight fit and can move, the increased pressure will push that end until the expanded volume is accommodated (Fig 2.1).

2. If the same pocket of gas, in its expanded state, is cooled rapidly, the pressure falls, the volume contracts and the sliding end will move back to its original position mainly because the outside pressure is higher that the inside pressure which for a short while is below normal, and also because a partial vacuum is formed if the sliding end is a gas- tight fit (Fig 2.2).

3. If the process of stage 1 is repeated but the sliding end now becomes a gas-tight piston with a connecting rod to a flywheel, the increased pressure will force the piston outwards causing the flywheel to turn. (Fig 2.3). The "volumetric change" described above has occurred and has been converted into motion.

4. If we repeat the process of stage 2, rapid cooling, the piston is pushed back by the motion of the fly-wheel, the decreased pressure and partial vacuum.

In basic and very simplistic terms these are the two stages of the hot air principle as a result of heating and cooling.

It is evident that one cannot heat and cool a cylinder rapidly and repeatedly; on the other hand it is possible to heat one end of a cylinder and cool the other. A way therefore has to be found to move

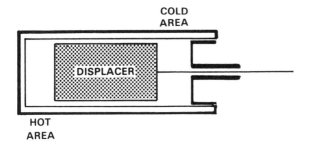

Fig 2.4 Displacer between hot area and cold area.

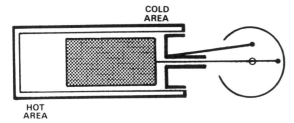

Fig 2.5 Displacer attachment to flywheel

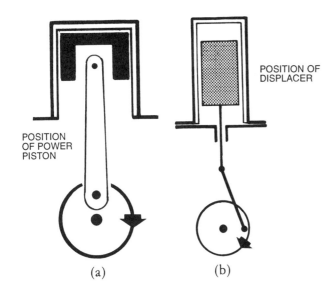

(a)   (b)

Fig 2.6 Positions of power piston and displacer (90°)

the pocket of gas from one side to the other - to the hot end to increase the pressure, expand the volume and create force, then transferring the same gas to the other end where it is cooled with opposite effect. A device is needed to transfer or shift the gas from one side to the other - we now call it a "displacer". In Stirling's days it was called a "transferer" which probably describes the actions better (Fig 2.4).

Again in basic terms, the displacer's work is to heat and cool the pocket of air alternately and rapidly by shifting it from one end to the other. Here it is important to describe the displacer - it is in effect a

loose fitting piston, not too tight so that it will allow gas to move in the annular space between it and the cylinder wall, not too loose as otherwise too much space will allow gas to escape and move too freely.

Let us now look at a cylinder which is sealed at one end and closed at the other end by a gas tight fitting piston (Fig 2.5). The displacer is connected to a flywheel by a connecting rod which passes through the piston crown in a way that no gas is allowed to escape from this end. We now heat the sealed end and cool the other end (where the piston is).

The complete cycle takes place in this manner:

Step 1 The DISPLACER is made to move outwards, i.e. towards the cold end. The pocket of gas is now at the hot end where it is heated and expands, the increased pressure applies force to the POWER PISTON, pushing it out as far as it can go at the same time turning the flywheel.

Step 2 The pocket of gas is shifted by the DISPLACER to the cold end where it is cooled, the pressure falls and as a result of flywheel momentum and reduced internal pressure (plus partial vacuum) the POWER PISTON moves back to its original position while compressing the gas.

The work of the Displacer is to transfer gas from one end of the cylinder to the other. The work of the Power Piston is to utilise the expansion of gas at high pressure and the compression of gas at low temperature and to transfer this utilisation into motion by means of a flywheel.

The DISPLACER and the POWER PISTON do not move backwards and forwards at the same time; rather there is calculated gap (both in time and in motion). This gap works out at a quarter of a turn of a circle, or as it is more commonly known, a 90° phase; the stroke of the DISPLACER always leading by approximately 90° (or a quarter of a turn) ahead of the POWER PISTON. (Figs 2.6[a] & 2.6[b]).

While the work of the engine appears to be a result of gas being pushed backwards and forwards, at the same time being heated and cooled, it is not easy to comprehend what is actually happening inside the engine, and no amount of theory or diagrams can really give a visual insight to the cycle. Unlike the internal combustion engine where each cycle of operation consists of four distinct and clearly defined phases, namely: induction, compression, combustion (ignition or power) and exhaust; the hot air engines phases are not so distinct and clear cut, with one phase lead-ing to another. A continuous movement of the

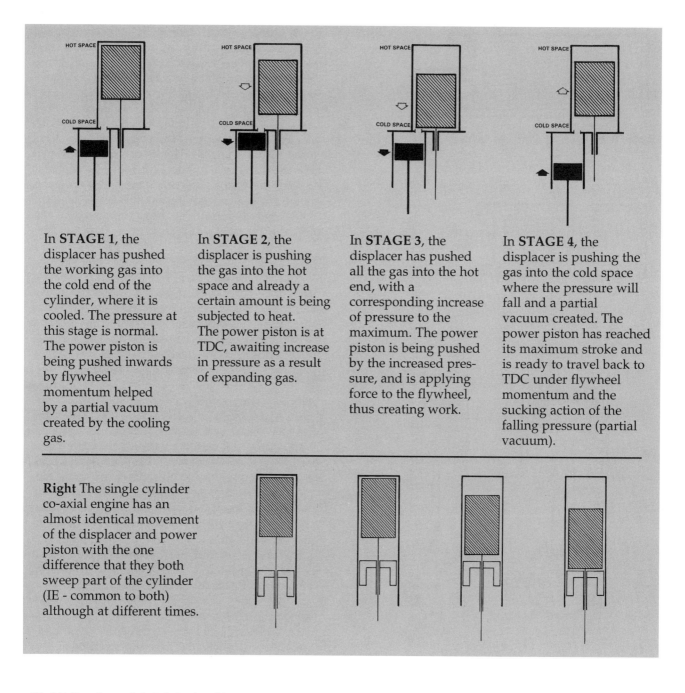

In **STAGE 1**, the displacer has pushed the working gas into the cold end of the cylinder, where it is cooled. The pressure at this stage is normal. The power piston is being pushed inwards by flywheel momentum helped by a partial vacuum created by the cooling gas.

In **STAGE 2**, the displacer is pushing the gas into the hot space and already a certain amount is being subjected to heat. The power piston is at TDC, awaiting increase in pressure as a result of expanding gas.

In **STAGE 3**, the displacer has pushed all the gas into the hot end, with a corresponding increase of pressure to the maximum. The power piston is being pushed by the increased pressure, and is applying force to the flywheel, thus creating work.

In **STAGE 4**, the displacer is pushing the gas into the cold space where the pressure will fall and a partial vacuum created. The power piston has reached its maximum stroke and is ready to travel back to TDC under flywheel momentum and the sucking action of the falling pressure (partial vacuum).

Right The single cylinder co-axial engine has an almost identical movement of the displacer and power piston with the one difference that they both sweep part of the cylinder (IE - common to both) although at different times.

Fig 2.7 Top: Stages 1, 2, 3 & 4 of working engine. Bottom: Positions of co-axial engine.

working gas is taking place between the closed side (hot end) of the cylinder and the side closed by the power piston (cold end). There is no sharp transition between the successive phases. The clearest picture one can get of the whole cycle would be to follow these four stages, on the understanding that there is no first and last stage and that one stage follows into the next in a continuous motion without any transition (Fig 2.7).

Two basic factors determine the efficiency of the Stirling-cycle engine. These are the sealing of the gas inside the cylinder between the closed end and the power piston end and secondly, the temperature difference between the hot and cold spaces of the cylinder.

SEALING effects efficiency in the following way. When gas inside the cylinder expands, the increased pressure pushes back against the side which gives the least resistance - in this case the power piston. The power piston in turn gives way as far as possible without allowing the gas to escape out of the cylinder. Technically and ideally, the amount of gas inside the cylinder should not alter. In practice, however, some gas does escape. When that happens the cycle efficiency drops and if the gas leak is substantial the engine fails to run, or if it runs, it does so for only a few minutes. It is therefore very important that the power piston should be gas tight.

TEMPERATURE DIFFERENCE also affects efficiency. The alternating expansion and contraction of gas (together with the increase and decrease of pressure) inside a cylinder is the real working force of the Stirling engine. This working force can only be effective if there is substantial difference in temperature between the hot end and the cold end of the cylinder. Therefore the higher the temperature at the hot end and the colder the temperature at the cold end, the more efficient the working force becomes. Both heating and cooling however create problems if they are to be carried out to extreme temperatures and for long periods. For example, most metals in common use, including steel, will distort if heat is applied to a high degree and for a long time. Research has been going on to find an alloy which can resist extreme temperatures. Ceramic has also been mentioned as a possibility. An engineer who is experimenting on model engines however, may use steel without difficulty and with good results.

It is relatively easier to provide cooling. Exposing a heated area to the surrounding atmosphere is one way. This is, of course, a slow process which can be hastened by enlarging the surface transfer area. The use of a cooler, whether a solid such as fins, or a part solid/part liquid such as a cooling tank, accelerates the dissipation of heat. Quite apart from this, the surrounding metal, cylinder, pistons, con-rod and regenerator (if any) together absorb an appreciable proportion of the heat. Methods of providing heating and cooling systems are discussed in Chapter 4, but there are also many other factors which have a direct bearing on the efficiency of the model or small engine.

REGENERATION of energy plays a great part in the design and construction of an engine. Heating and cooling the working gas several hundred times a minute is no mean feat for a small engine especially as the extremes of temperature can be a couple of hundred degrees or more apart. This work can be made easier by an arrangement whereby the hot gas on its way to the cold end loses its heat gradually while the cold gas, on its way to the hot end picks up heat along the way in order to reach the desired temperature and the necessary expansion in the hot chamber in the minimum of time, thus lessening to some degree the amount of heat application and allowing for greater speed in the transfer of gas.

Two basic methods have been used in model engines to assist in the way hot gas gradually loses its heat and cold gas gradually absorbs it. The first uses the displacer to do this heat transfer. The

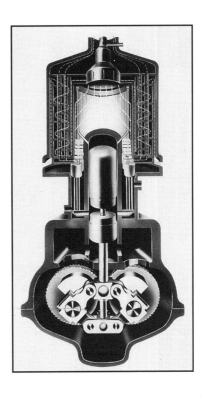

*Fig 2.8
Philips
rhombic drive
mechanism
(Philips)*

displacer body is made sufficiently long for the hot gas moving along it to transfer heat to the body of the displacer in what is termed a "temperature gradient". The body becomes hot at one end and tapering off in heat progressively towards the other end. The second method is more ingenious and in some model engines very effective. This involves the building of a regenerator outside or around the main cylinder through which the gas passes. The same principle of heat absorption applies to this kind of regenerator. Heat is absorbed in a gradient manner by a mass of metal, which makes up the regenerator and this heat is picked up again by cold gas on its way to the expansion chamber. (Further details on regenerators will be found in Chapter 3).

DRIVE MECHANISMS are a factor that can make or mar an engine. Many mechanical arrangements have been "invented" to provide the necessary 90° phase between the displacers and the power pistons. The most common arrangements in old days involved cumbersome systems of levers and cranks in order to achieve this "discrepancy" between the movements of the two pistons. The situation became even more complicated when the need arose to have different length of strokes for the two components.

Although the old engines are a delight to watch with all sorts of links, rocking levers, cranks and bell-cranks going in all directions, the engines were slow, rarely exceeding 200 rpm and very often in the region of 100 rpm. Back in the 1850s to 1900s these engines were used mainly to pump water. High revolutions were not important for this task

Figs 2.9 (Right) Configuration of engines.

A & A1 *- single cylinder co-axial configuration with the displacer and power piston working in the same space; also known as the :"Beta configuration" (Prova II, Dyna and Sunspot described in this book are built on this configuration).*

B & B1 *- twin-cylinder configuration with the displacer and power piston occupying and working in seperate areas - also known as the "Gamma Configuration" (Dolly, Lolly and Sturdy are built with this configuration).*

C & C1 *- twin-cylinder with power pistons each working in a separate space - also known as the "Alpha configuration", or sometimes as the "Rider configuration" after its developer. Some engines of this type are modified by the addition of an extension to the power piston on the hot side to keep the power piston at some distance from the hot cap.*

Fig 2.10 (Far right) V-type Rider engine configuration.

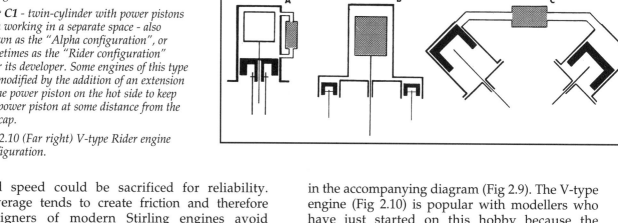

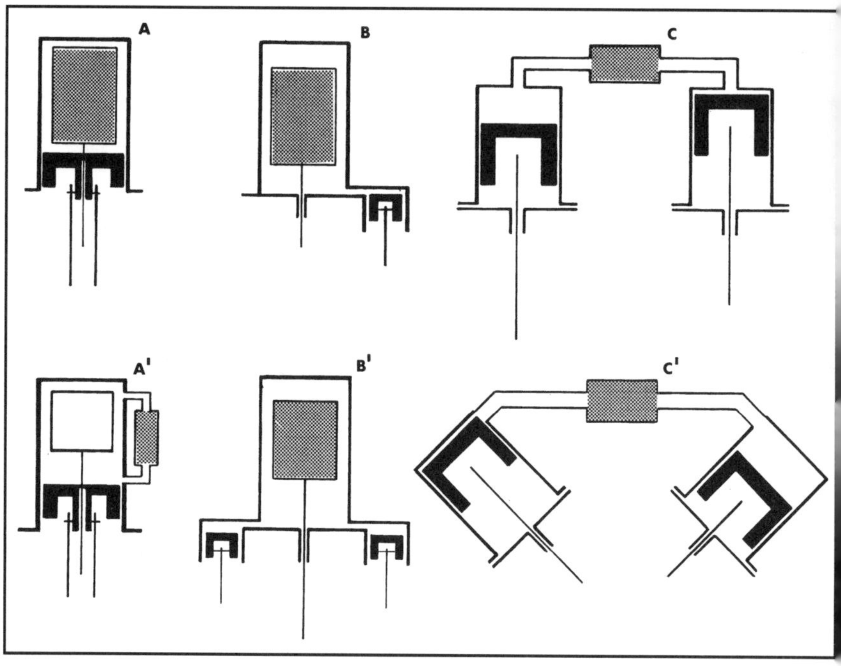

and speed could be sacrificed for reliability. Leverage tends to create friction and therefore designers of modern Stirling engines avoid complicated systems of levers and cranks.

One of the more brilliant and successful drives, the rhombic drive mechanism, was devised and perfected by Philips. With this method the displacer rod passes through the power piston rod without exerting lateral thrust on the power piston (Fig 2.8). It is a compact mechanism capable of sustained pressure. Another excellent design is the swashplate mechanism which drives a number of cylinders successively by a continuous circular motion. Such engines are designed to work horizontally and with a multiple of cylinders (usually four to six in number). There is still room for more inventiveness, however, when it comes to the mechanical arrangements of the Stirling engine and many a young engineer (and some not so young, too) have come forward with workable and commendable ideas. New drive arrangements are still being devised and some may yet become commercially viable. (Drive mechanisms are discussed at length in Chapter 6).

DESIGN VARIATIONS

Stirling engines can be broadly divided into two distinct groups: the single acting and the double acting.

SINGLE-ACTING engines are those which enclose in each cylinder a piston and a displacer, or two pistons with an expansion space and a compression space. The most common basic arrangements for single-acting engines are shown in the accompanying diagram (Fig 2.9). The V-type engine (Fig 2.10) is popular with modellers who have just started on this hobby because the configuration makes the drive mechanism fairly simple to construct with one parameter, the 90 degree phase already in place. Such engines can make use of an external regenerator.

DOUBLE-ACTING engines are those engines with two or more cylinders, the cylinders being connected in such a way that the expansion (hot) end of one is connected to the compression (cold) end of another, the connection passing through a regenerator. Each cylinder holds a single piston which serves as a power piston and displacer at the same time (Fig 2.11). The main advantage of this type of operation is that the number of elements per unit is halved. Thus if in a single-acting engine with four cylinders there are four power pistons and four displacers plus the complicated con-rod mechanism, a double-acting engine with four cylinders needs only four piston-displacers and a less complicated con-rod arrangement. The main disadvantage of the double-acting configuration lies in the lack of flexibility in design and the fact that one cannot experiment as with a single-acting engine.

Manufacturers of the larger type of hot air engines are attracted by the advantages of minimum working parts, and current development is now geared to double-acting engines. In the field of model engineering and small engine production the single-acting engine will continue to attract the greater development in view of the simplicity of design and the greater tolerance that these engines have to changes in parameters and mechanical conditions.

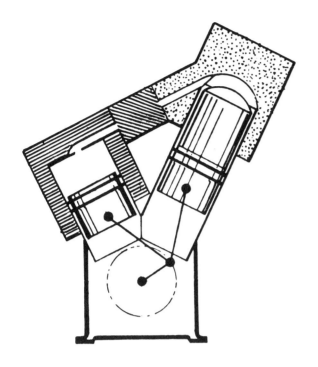

VARIATIONS OF THE STIRLING CYCLE

The THERMO-MECHANICAL GENERATOR works on the general principle of a hot air engine with the following mechanical alterations. The displacer is retained but the power piston is replaced by a fixed flexible metal diaphragm. The displacer is mounted on a flat circular spring attached to the main body casing which allows the displacer to move some ³⁄₃₂in without touching the body or the power diaphragm. A propane gas burner heats the cylinder base to some 800° F, and the engine self starts automatically on the application of heat. The expansion of the gas in the main cylinder causes the diaphragm to expand and this in turn oscillates. The oscillation, together with the engine vibration, causes the displacer to move vertically, thus displacing the working gas

(helium) from the hot end to the cold end of the engine. The cold end is kept at a low temperature by a closed cycle cooling system (Fig 2.12).

The flexible diaphragm, acting as a power piston, reciprocates the armature of a linear alternator, and as a result of the electrical loading by the alternator, lags 90° out of phase with the displacer. Since there are no sliding surfaces, the generator is efficient at power levels of a few tens of watts and because there is no static friction it is self-starting. Moreover there is no mechanical wear and no need for lubrication. All flexing components are tested and stressed to well below the fatigue limit, so there is no known limit to the operating life. Indeed a test diaphragm ran continuously for two and a half years. When compared to alternative sources of stored energy, the advantages of such a generator can be really assessed; for example, it would need a 1½ ton weight of batteries to give a 25 watt power output for one year, a job for which the TMG is admirably suited.

The FLUIDYNE engine also works on the principle of the Stirling- cycle. Heat is applied to one end of a cylinder, while the other end is kept cool; the working gas expands and work is performed. In this case however there are no metal parts (except two small non-return valves), no piston or displacer, con-rod, crank, flywheel etc. The working elements are gas (air) and a liquid (water). The operation of the basic Fluidyne is described by Dr. Colin West in his book with the aid of the accompanying illustration (Fig 2.13) and the following description:

"Suppose the water in the displacer is set to oscillate from one limb of the U-tube into the other limb and back; TDC in the cold end will correspond to the BDC in the hot end, as shown in the left-hand part of the illustration, in which most of the air trapped above the water in the displacer

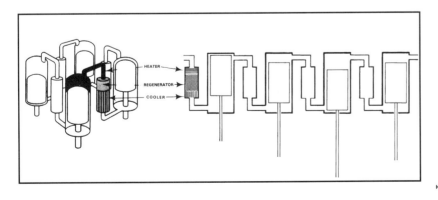

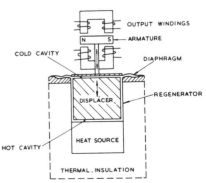

Fig 2.11 (Above) Double acting configuration.
Fig 2.12 (Right) AERE R-8036 TMG (AERE)

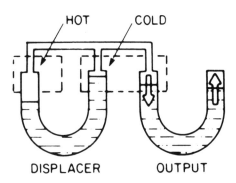

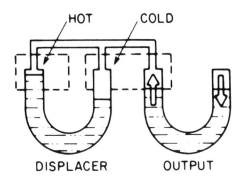

a) TOP DEAD CENTER IN
   THE COLD END OF
   THE DISPLACER

b) TOP DEAD CENTER IN
   THE HOT END OF
   THE DISPLACER

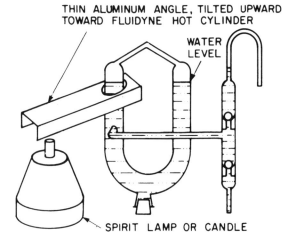

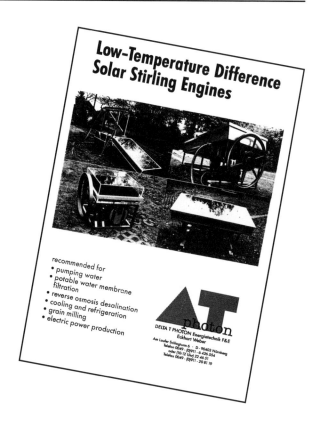

Fig 2.13 (Top) Basic operation of the Fluidyne
(courtesy: Dr Colin West).

Fig 2.14 (Above left) Small glass Fluidyne Pump
(courtesy: Dr Colin West).

Fig 2.15 (Right) Large scale development of Low Temperature
Differential engines for commercial use (courtesy: Eckhart
Weber, Delton Photon Energietecknik F & E, Nurnberg,
Germany).

is in the hot left-hand limb. Most of the air is therefore hot, so its pressure rises, tending to force the water in the outer tube to move from right to left, as the arrow indicates. Half a cycle later the displacer water will swing back into the other limb, so that the cold surface is at BDC; this is shown in the right-hand part of the illustration. Most of the air is now in the cold side of the machine, so its pressure will fall, pulling the water in the output column from left to right."

If the output tube is attached to a vertical tube with two one-way valves, such that water pushed out of the output tube flows upwards (without return), then on the swing of the displacer, water will return to the hot end and the vacuum created in the output tube will lift water from a tank to replace that pushed out of the output tube. Each cycle will, therefore, alternately push out water from the top and suck water from below. The FLUIDYNE possesses some other attractive features: low capital costs in manufacture even with small production volume; simplicity with ease of construction; durability and reliability; no solid moving parts; no lubrication required; use of low grade heat; starting on thermal-effects alone (self-starting); quietness of operation; long service life and high work output to cost ratio.

Great strides have been made in applying the Ringbom Stirling principle to large scale engine development working directly off solar energy. A company in Germany DELTA PHOTON ENERGIETECKNIK F&E of Nurnberg has produced quite large "Low-Temperature Difference Solar Stirling engines" (Fig 2.15), capable of pumping water, grain milling, electric power generation, cooling and refrigeration and other uses such as filtration water through membrane and reverse osmosis.

REASONS FOR LACK OF EFFICIENCY OF EARLIER HOT AIR ENGINES

1. Early hot air engines were very clumsy; they were equipped with heavy moving parts and mechanical drives which caused large friction loss.

2. The metal walls of the hot cylinder had to be thick, in order to withstand constant high temperature, and thus the heat conduction losses were tremendous.

3. The temperature of the hot chamber rarely exceeded 600°F.

4. Both the heater (furnace) and the cooler were primitive and rarely was the large temperature difference required maintained for long periods. Later engines which had a continuous flow of water by means of pumps (such as the Rider), were more efficient than earlier engines.

5. Many engines had a heavy transferer (displacer), often made from beaten iron sheets, the transferer served as a heat conductor rather than a regenerative displacer, thus lowering the temperature difference over a period of time.

SOME CHARACTERISTICS OF THE STIRLING-CYCLE ENGINE

1. STARTING: Stirling engines are generally not self-starting ; in fact it is one of the main disadvantages of these engines. Once the heated end of the cylinder(s) has reached the required temperature, force or push is applied to the flywheel which will then accelerate rapidly. In the case of small engines, a flick to the flywheel is sufficient; larger engines use a starter motor. (There are two notable developments, mentioned earlier, the TMG and the FLUIDYNE, that are self-starting.)

2. SPEED CONTROL: Some Stirling engines are designed to maintain a constant speed whatever the load - these include electric generators and water pumps. Other engines require speed variation - acceleration or deceleration. In early stages of development, engine operators relied on increasing or reducing heat; this method was cumbersome and inefficient. Later types relied on the use of valves to control speed. Modern engines are designed to respond rapidly to the power load

and various methods are used, but for the model engineer two methods give scope for experimentation - increase of gas pressure and variation in the stroke of the reciprocating elements which in turn alters the pressure. Both methods have scope for development, and it is known that a number of modellers have ongoing projects.

3. PRESSURISATION POTENTIAL. A Stirling engine that operates at normal air pressure has a limited potential for developing power. If an engine is pressurised, however, the power increases dramatically. An engine that works on helium or hydrogen, and is moreover pressurised, will develop such power that is easily comparable to petrol/diesel engines when power to weight ratios are taken into consideration.

4. FUEL VERSATILITY. The Stirling engine has been called "the future engine of the Third World". When the supply of mineral fuels is very much an open question for the future and when one considers that solar energy can provide an alternative fuel for this type of engine, one can see the attraction that the development of the Stirling-cycle holds for the next decade. It is also an area where the model engineer can contribute with his inherent resourcefulness.

A BRIEF OVERVIEW OF THE THERMODYNAMIC PRINCIPLES OF THE STIRLING CYCLE ENGINE

At the time that the Stirling Brothers invented and successfully used the Regenerator, the science of thermodynamics was still in its infancy. Some years had to elapse before a French scientist, Sadi Carnot, was to express a proposal that "a reversible heat engine is a perfect engine ...... all heat engines, working with whatever substance (gas), provided only that they can be reversible, convert into work all the amount of heat supplied to them."

Sadi Carnot went on to explain his theory of the perfect cycle by the following diagram:

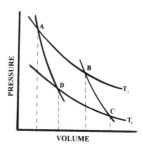

With this he illustrated that a perfect heat engine should regain almost all the heat expended, except that which is converted into useful work.

DIAGRAM OF THE THERMODYNAMIC CYCLE OF THE STIRING ENGINE

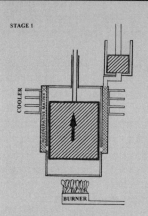 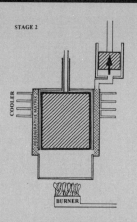 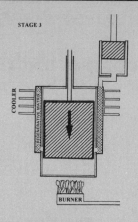 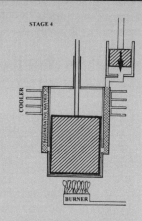

HEAT - TRANSFER PROCESS

P → Q = heat transfer to the gas from the regenerative matrix.	Q → R = heat transfer to the gas at (high) temperature supplied by an external source (burner).	R → S = heat transfer from the gas to the regenerative matrix.	S → P = heat transfer from the gas at (low) temperature to an external sink (cooler).

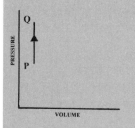 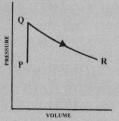 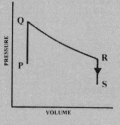 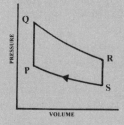

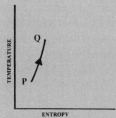 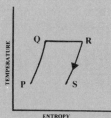 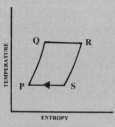

In **STAGE 1**, the displacer is on the way out and transferring gas from the cold end to the hot end, while the power piston is at TDC. The gas is passing through a regenerator which has stored heat (refer to Chapter 3 on Regenerators). Heat given up by the regenerator raises the temperature and pressure of the gas, at constant volume, from P to Q.

In **STAGE 2**, the gas is in the hot end and is expanding to pressure R, while a constant temperature (QR) is maintained applied at the hot end. The power piston at this stage is applying force to flywheel and this energy will be utilised throughout the remainder of the cycle.

In **STAGE 3**, the displacer is on the way in and is transferring gas to the cold end through the regenerator, causing a fall in temperature and pressure of the gas, at constant volume, from R to S. The power piston is at BDC and has exhausted its force in supplying energy to the flywheel.

In **STAGE 4**, the gas is in the cold end and is under compression by the power piston, which, acting under the energy of the flywheel, is approaching TDC, and compressing gas at constant temperature from S to P.

In this theoretical cycle an engine accepts heat energy from a high temperature source, converts part of the received energy into mechanical work, and rejects the remainder to a low temperature sink or cooler. The greater the temperature difference, the greater the efficiency of the engine. However good the theory is, there are serious practical difficulties in constructing Carnot's engine. The necessary high temperatures place a limit on the thermal efficiency that an actual engine can achieve.

The STIRLING CYCLE, on the other hand, accepts the limitations of high temperature but uses a regenerator to conserve energy to heat or cool the engine to the required temperature, adding on only that amount of heat that is used to convert into useful work, plus a certain amount lost to the surroundings.

The heat transfer process of the regenerator is quasi-reversible in that the temperature of the regenerator at each and every point should equal gas temperature at that point. It is this regenerator that gives the Stirling engine its high thermal efficiency.

It cannot be said that the Stirling engine is a perfect engine, but in practice it is closer to that state of efficiency than any other engine, whether steam or internal combustion. The Stirling engine offers the highest possible conversion rate of heat to work. This can be roughly calculated by taking the absolute temperature to which the hot part of the engine is subjected (T1), remove that amount which is required to convert (heat) into work output (T2) and reduce the difference between the two to a proportion of the original temperature:-

Thus

$$\frac{T_1 - T_2}{T_1} = \text{Thermal efficiency (effective)}$$

In order to reach the percentage of thermal efficiency, the working temperatures, the hot end and cold end, must be translated into absolute temperatures known as the Kelvin scale, and the final calculation made from these read-offs.

In the following example it is assumed that the engine has an efficient regenerator, that the temperatures at both ends of a displacer cylinder will be 400° C at the hot end and 100° C at the cold end, and it is assumed that the engine has a high capacity annular gas burner, and an efficient water cooler with running water. These two temperatures are equivalent to 673° K and 373°K (temperature for absolute 0° is -273° K; that is on the Kelvin scale 0° C = +273° K; therefore 100° C = 273 + 100 = 373° K and 400° C = 273 + 400 = 673°K.

Working on the above theoretical equation, the formula is:

$$\frac{673°K - 373°K}{673°K} = \frac{300}{673} \quad \text{or } 44.6\% \text{ *}$$

* (This is only a working example as this percentage of effective thermal efficiency is unduly high.)

The diagram (opposite) summarises the four stages of the Stirling Cycle,and explains the relative positions of the displacer and power piston,and the heat transfer process.

C H A P T E R   T H R E E

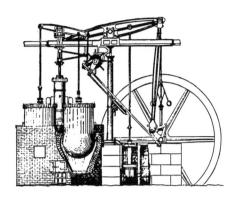

The Regenerator

The name originally given to what we now call the 'regenerator' was 'economiser' or 'heat economiser', which probably describes better the function of the device. It is certain that the inventor, Robert Stirling, had in mind economy of energy by using the device to store up to 95 per cent of the heat given by the furnace and re-using it continuously. The wasted 5 per cent of heat was made up by the furnace. Therefore, using this method ensured a saving of energy - an 'economiser' of heat.

For many generations the principle of the regenerator was not understood by successive manufacturers of hot air engines - indeed most of the engines they built had no regenerator. Other manufacturers, like Ericsson, Robinson, Lehmann etc., experimented with and without regenerators. Eventually the more successful engines incorporat-

ed some version or other of the regenerator. The regenerator is used with various modifications in all hot air engines under development today. It is now accepted that a regenerator is the most essential component in a hot air engine and that the efficiency of an engine is largely determined by the regenerator. Yet little is known about what actually happens inside the regenerator and in spite of the many detailed studies, the best designs for efficient regenerators depend on the results of actual experiments.

DESCRIPTION

The regenerator may be described as a 'sponge, alternately absorbing and releasing heat'. In its simplest form it can be a mass of metal between the two spaces of the hot air engine, the hot or expansion space and the cold or compression

Fig 3.1 (Above) Regenerator -a simple sketch.

Fig 3.2 (Middle right) Regenerator - temperature gradient zones.

Fig 3.3 (Far right) Regenerator - temperature gradient.

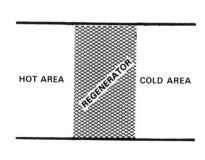

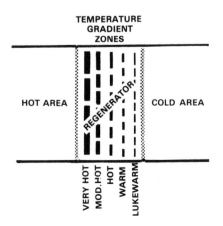

space. This 'sponge' of metal absorbs heat from the gas (which has been subjected to high temperature) on its way to the cold space where it is cooled, compressed and returned to the hot space (Fig 3.1). On its way to the cooling agent, the hot gas leaves behind in the 'sponge', a considerable amount of heat in a temperature gradient, with a high temperature on the side of the hot space, cooling progressively towards the cold space (Fig 3.2). In the compression stage the volume of gas which has been compressed, is cooled and then pushed back through the regenerator from where the stored heat is picked up (rather like the sponge being squeezed) prior to its entry into the heater.

In practice the regenerator works in the following manner. The heater brings up the temperature of the gas in the hot area to, say, 400°F while the cooler maintains a temperature of 40° in the cold space. The ideal regenerator will provide a temperature gradient of 300° on the hot side and 100° on the cold side. Gas entering the hot chamber from the regenerator is already at a temperature of around 300° - therefore the heater has that much less work to heat the incoming gas from 300° to 400°. Gas entering the cold chamber from the regenerator, is at a temperature of around 100°, having left much of its heat behind in the regenerator, and therefore to cool this gas to 40°, the cooler has relatively less work to perform.

Without the regenerator, both the heating and cooling elements have far greater work to do, heating gas from 40° to 400°, while the cooling agent cools the gas from 400° to 40°, all this as much as 1,000 times a minute if not more (Fig 3.3). Therefore the regenerator, apart from appreciably lessening the work of the heating and cooling elements and thus saving energy, also increases many times over the efficiency of the Stirling-cycle. The four types of regenerator: external, external annular, internal annular, and displacer, are discussed below.

EXTERNAL REGENERATORS: In this type of

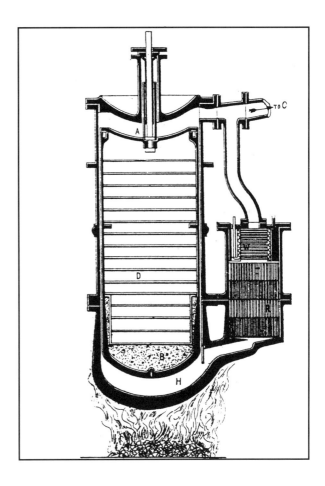

Fig 3.4 *Stirling's regenerator of 1840.*

regenerator the gas leaves the main body of the cylinder, passes through an external regenerator back into the main cylinder or to an adjoining cylinder which is connected to the same drive mechanism. This regenerator was first used by the Stirling brothers in an engine built around 1840. In this engine, the regenerator (and the cooler) were housed in a separate cylinder connected to the displacer cylinder and leading to the power cylinder. In this cycle, the hot air was forced out of the displacer cylinder by the displacer (or transferer) through the regenerator and cooler into the power cylinder, compressed and returned via the regenerator into the displacer cylinder.

The regenerator used in this particular engine needs to be described in order to understand the ingenuity of the inventor. The regenerator consisted of four separate stacks, each identical in shape and construction. Each stack contained a quantity of iron sheets 1/40in thick, standing upright and separated from each other by ridges with passages in between of about 1/50in width. The stacks themselves were separated in order to reduce longitudinal heat conduction. Dead space was reduced by filling the passages and gaps with pieces of broken glass, which also served as part of the regenerator. Altogether, considering the lack

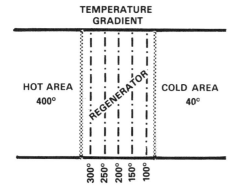

of suitable materials in those days, and working more on intuition than expertise, this type of regenerator was very far advanced in concept (Fig 3.4).

EXTERNAL ANNULAR REGENERATORS: In this type of regenerator the working gas leaves the displacer cylinder, passes through a regenerative matrix built between the cylinder and an outside cap or cover and is channeled into the power cylinder through a cooler. The regenerator matrix is totally enclosed within the outer cap to prevent loss of compression or escape of gas, and is built in such a way as to reduce dead space to a minimum. This type of regenerator was first used by Stirling in 1827. A description of the engine is worth reading as it explains the principle of the regenerator or 'economiser' as envisaged by the inventors (Fig 3.5).

'Displacer B moves vertically within the inner cylinder, fitting easily and without friction. The bottom of the inner cylinder X is drilled with several holes. Air is pushed to the outer cylinder YY which is under constant high temperature, through the regenerator C, through the cooler D, through the passage E to the power piston A. The annular space between the outer and inner cylinders contains the regenerator C which is a grating composed of thin vertical oblong strips of metal with narrow passages between them. The cooler D consists of a horizontal coil of fine copper tube through which a current of cold water is forced'.

The operation was further described as follows: 'The effect of the alternate motion of the plunger (displacer) B is to transfer a certain mass of air, which may be called 'working air' alternately to the upper and lower end of the (outer) cylinder, by making it pass up and down through the regenerator C.

The perforated hemispherical inner cylinder X causes a diffusion and rapid circulation of the air as it passes into the outer cylinder and thus facilitates the convection of heat to it, for the purpose of enabling it to undergo the expansion lifts (power) piston A. The descent of the plunger B causes the air to return through the regenerator to the upper end of the receiver. The greater part of the heat is stored in the plates of the regenerator; the remainder of that heat is abstracted by the refrigerator (cooler). The heat stored in the regenerator serves to raise the temperature of the air when this is returned to the lower end of the cylinder'.

The Philips air engine (Fig 3.6) was constructed with the same style of regenerator between displacer cylinder and the outer cylinder or cap. Philips, however, have used a much more efficient type, consisting of a porous coil of thin metal wire (Fig 3.7). It has been stated that this regenerator has over 95 per cent efficiency and is capable of raising the temperature of a quantity of air flowing through it from 100°C to 600° within 1/1000th second and the reverse, that is cooling from 600° C to 100° in the same fraction of time, while the temperature gradient in the direction of the air flow is maintained without appreciable loss of heat.

The construction of the award winning model engine 'Prova II' described in Chapter 13, involved the building, quite successfully as it turned out, of an external annular regenerator inserted between the regenerator cover and the engine cylinder. The first regenerator consisted of steel shim, 0.002 in thick, which was corrugated in shape and inserted to allow the working gas to pass on both sides. Further experiments with other regenerative material, such as fine steel mesh, slivers of ceramic and strands of fine steel wire, were also conducted.

Fig 3.5 (Right)
Stirling's regenerator
of 1827. A Power
Piston, B Displacer, C
Regenerator, D Cooler,
E Connecting Air
Passage, F Displacer
rod, X Inner displacer
cylinder, YY Outer
(and heated) cylinder.

Fig 3.6 (Far right)
Sectional view of the
Philips Air Engine
showing the position of
the annular
regenerator placed
between the burner
and the cooler.

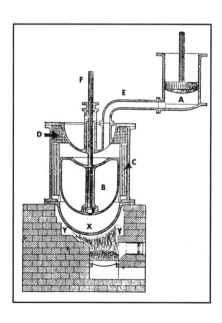

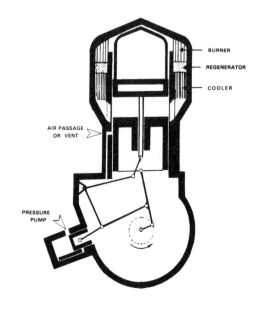

Steel shim was found to be the most effective, but required more surface area.

INTERNAL AND ANNULAR REGENERATORS: This type of regenerator is constructed or fitted in a narrow annular gap between the displacer and the cylinder wall or between two cylinders as in the Rider engine (Fig 3.8). The regenerator consists of thin steel sheet, steel mesh or coils of fine steel wire which allow heated gas to pass longitudinally, preferably on both sides, of the metal surface, depositing and withdrawing heat from the surface of the regenerative material. The steel sheet is usually hammered to raise dents or ridges on alternate sides, this method being used primarily to keep the sheet from surface contact with the cylinder wall and at the same time allowing gas to travel on both sides of the surface.

Occasional perforations permit airflow and create some turbulence, which is desirable. In the case of the steel mesh the only requirement is a minimal distance from the cylinder wall. This is by far the best type of regenerative material for internal regenerators since it has most of the important characteristics, low conduction, good airflow and turbulence and light weight.

Fine steel wire can be used for the purpose of regeneration as a coil inserted along the wall of the displacer cylinder or round a light-weight displacer. The first method was used successfully in the building of 'Dyna' (Chapter 17). The 1.5mm steel spring wire was used to narrow the annular gap. Excellent regeneration and low conduction of heat enabled this engine to develop power and to run for long periods. The second method was used by Stirling in 1818 in his first engine which had an elongated displacer with several layers of thin gauge wire around it. The author has not heard of any model engine with such a regenerator, but such a construction could be successful on a model. The only problem envisaged here is that of weight. Engines using this type of regenerator must of necessity have long displacers and cylinders in order that the regenerator may retain a temperature gradient. Ideally the construction of this type of regenerator should allow for airflow on both sides of the regenerator surface. As far as model engines are concerned, where weighty displacers are a determining factor, the perforated steel sheet or the fine steel mesh along the annular gap seems to be a more practical expedient.

MOVING REGENERATORS are constructed wholly or partly from a matrix capable of absorbing and releasing heat. These regenerators can broadly be classified under the following groups:

1. Displacers which enclose within a thin metal tube a matrix of fine wire mesh with perforated

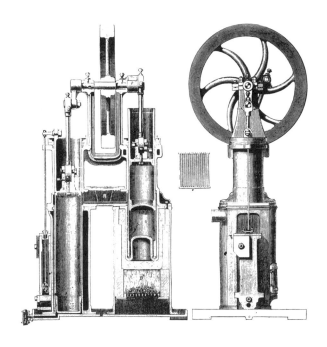

Fig 3.7 (Top) Philips regenerator coils (Philips).

Fig 3.8 (Above) Rider engine and regenerator.

Fig 3.9 (Right) Cut-away view of the Robinson Engine regenerator (Science Museum, London).

discs at both ends. A similar type of regenerative displacer was used as late as 1897 by A & H Robinson (Fig 3.9) who constructed several of these popular 'one-man' or 'two-man' engines, also called 'domestic motors'.

2. Displacers partly filled with regenerative matrix, normally alternating a layer of matrix with horizontal perforated discs, the layers reducing in thickness from the hot end to the cold end.

3. Displacers which are constructed of perforated metal discs or steel gauze discs, either supported by an outer cylinder of gauze, or the

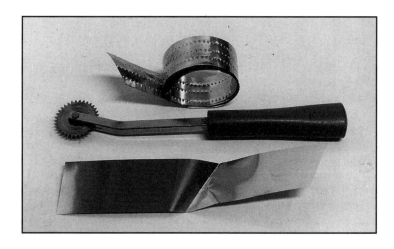

Fig 3.10 (Above) David Urwick's experimental regenerators.
Fig 3.11 (Right) Andy Ross' sleeve regenerator with the tracing wheel.

discs being mounted on a non-conductive metal or ceramic rod (Fig 3.10). In these cases the displacers fit the cylinder easily and without friction while allowing the gas to filter through the regenerators rather than along the cylinder wall.

4. Displacers, made of thin metal, along the outer circumference of which is wound a heat absorbing metal which acts as a regenerator when heated or cooled alternately. One of the finest examples is Stirling's first engine described earlier in this chapter . Displacers are constructed from two, three or four light-weight, air-tight cylinders, and are mechanically joined together. By this arrangement the various sections of the regenerator are separated and therefore the conduction of heat along the regenerator is interrupted.

The adaptability of any of the above regenerators to model Stirling engines is a matter for experimentation and research.

From time to time contributions on the Stirling-cycle/hot air engines appear in MODEL ENGINEER (published by Nexus Specialist Publications Ltd.) and in ENGINEERING in MINIATURE (TEE Publishing Ltd.). Usually these are written by model engineers who have become fascinated by the Stirling engine and who spend a great deal of their spare time developing increasingly efficient model engines.

One such contributor made an in-depth study of the moving regenerator. David Urwick has written and published a number of very informative articles on various aspects of the Stirling engine. One of the more detailed and time consuming studies was that on regenerators. David's experiment centered on the use of stainless steel wire gauze discs (30/40 mesh), enclosed within a wire gauze cylinder, the whole assembly being used as a regenerator/displacer. Careful note was taken of the number of discs in relation to the performance of the tested Stirling engine, any alteration to the position and number of discs being recorded. These articles appeared in MODEL ENGINEER of February 7 and 21 1975, and are highly recommended reading. Two other contributors, Robin S. Robbins and Andy Ross, in their contributions of June, July and August 1981 gave details of a 'sleeve' regenerator. In both cases steel shim/stainless foil, . 0001/.0002in was used, with dimples tapped or embossed with a tracing wheel. (Fig 3.11) Both contributions are worth reading. Quite apart from the relevant part on the regenerator, the description of the engines provides excellent know-how.

(In his recent book, "Making Stirling Engines", Andy Ross gives, in table 1, a comparative study of the regenerator material used, thickness, volume, fill factor etc.)

Another experiment involves an external regenerator of the first type mentioned earlier in this chapter. The engine consists of a two piston concentric arrangement (displacer and power pistons within one cylinder), with a heater, regenerator and cooler in an adjoining cylinder. The gas leaves the cylinder, goes into the regenerator assembly and re-enters between the power piston and the hot piston. The regenerator is made up of some 200 wafer-thin iron strips (1¼in long, ¼in wide and ¹⁄₆₄in thick), inserted in the direction of the airflow. The aims of these experiments are twofold: to prove that a model engine can perform satisfactorily with this type of external regenerator and secondly to find and test the best type of regenerative material for such small scale regenerator. The regenerator body in this experimental engine is constructed in such a way as to allow for changes of the matrix without too much trouble. In order to obtain accurate readings the heating and cooling elements are common to all experiments: heating by an electric element wound on the hot chamber, and cooling by water conduction in the cold chamber.

DESIRABLE CHARACTERISTICS OF THE REGENERATIVE MATRIX

The size and type of the regenerative matrix depends on the requirements of the regenerator vis-a-vis the total efficiency expected from the model engine or from a small hot air engine. It is therefore essential to remember the main characteristics of the regenerative matrix. Broadly, the types of matrix can be divided into four general classes.

1. The solid large matrix which allows maximum heat capacity. This improves the effectiveness of the regenerator while retaining the maximum ratio of heat compared to that of the gas which comes into contact with it.

2. The large finely-divided matrix which gives maximum heat transfer by allowing the gas to pass in contact with the largest surface area.

3. The small porous matrix which minimises flow losses, thus saving in energy expended.

4. The small dense matrix which minimises dead space and improves the ratio of maximum to minimum pressure.

The above characteristics tend to be conflicting and therefore the choice of the right type of matrix is to a large extent guesswork unless, by means of experiments with a removable regenerator casing or body, the various types of matrix can be alternated and the results plotted and compared. One factor that has a direct effect on the efficiency of the regenerator is gas turbulence. Empirical studies indicate that a turbulent gas flow, where the gas is made to flow in an uneven and irregular fashion in its passage through the matrix, gives a higher rate of heat transfer. In turn this releases and extracts greater efficiency from the regenerative matrix. Robert Stirling recognised this factor and in his 1816 patent application described the passages of the economiser as having "their sides jagged and rough by bodies projecting from them, as represented at Figure 4." which is reproduced here as Fig 3.12.

Computer-aided research has produced an extensive range of designs for engines and particularly for regenerators. Similar programmes

may even be undertaken with small home computers provided that the computer result is corroborated by actual practical design and construction and subject to the availability of the right materials.

In experimenting with regenerators the following basic factors should be borne in mind. We are dealing with 'model' engines and it may be found that the scaling down of regenerators used on larger engines will not produce the same or ratio-reduced efficient results. Secondly there are now more materials suitable for the construction of engine parts and regenerators than before. Therefore prior to designing and building a model engine, it is worthwhile testing interesting materials particularly with respect to their heat absorption and conduction characteristics. Materials that could be evaluated include: glass beads and glass rods; ceramic beads and ceramic rods; different types of wire wool/steel wool; fine bore narrow gauge steel or iron tubes; strips from transformer laminations; fine galvanised wire in short lengths or tight coils; successive thickness of wire used as above, and other materials. Various considerations are taken into account in the design of the regenerator, including the following: size of engine; volume of gas; estimated speed or speed required; regenerative materials available; type of heating available; amount and type of cooling available. Before these parameters are considered, two apparently conflicting requirements are to be kept in mind in the design of the regenerator, the problem of heat transfer and the problem of flow resistance. It is accepted that in order to obtain efficient heat transfer the gas must, in the shortest time possible pass in very close contact with the material of the matrix. In turn this produces flow resistance to the gas. It is therefore important that a balance be obtained between the absolute requirement of good heat transfer and the goal of minimising flow resistance, without impairing the regenerative effect.

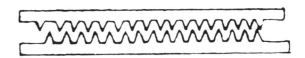

Fig 3.12 Stirling's first regenerator of 1818; simplified line drawing showing projections

CHAPTER   FOUR

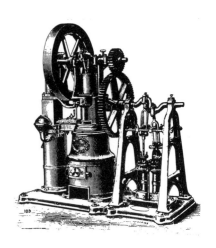

Heating & Cooling

Hot air engines require high external temperature at the hot end and efficient cooling at the other end of the displacer cylinder. Therefore careful consideration should be given to both the heating and cooling systems simultaneously. To obtain maximum efficiency from a model hot air engine at normal atmospheric pressure, one should aim to obtain a high difference factor, if possible to the power of 8; i.e. heating up to 640° F and cooling of around 80° F; possibly 800 - 100°. This may be difficult to achieve under normal home workshop conditions, but the nearer one gets to this difference factor the more efficient the engine becomes.

HEATING

Hot air engines are multifuel engines, that is they obtain heat from different fuels - oils, gas, coal, petrol, kerosene, wood etc. - any combustible material that gives intense and preferably concentrated heat. In the case of small model engines, where the size of the displacer cylinder determines the size of the flame, it is usual to turn to gas burners; methylated spirit burners are often used on the smaller model engine. These burners may be of the simple wick type, or the vaporised burner where the spirit is initially turned into combustible gas. Meth spirit pellets, cubes or bricks may also be used in the same manner as the wick type burner for horizontal cylinders. Obviously the heat generated by these burners is limited and so is the efficiency and the duration of the working power, although it is known and documented that as long ago as the turn of this century, a German toy manufacturer produced and

sold a spirit "vaporiser" which gave intense flames for over 5 hours. The humble candle has always had a minor role as a heating medium, in fact the night-light candle has also come into its own as a power-raiser, now popularly termed "gnat power". Heating with electric elements, whether from mains (with proper safeguards), or from transformers, or batteries, is sometimes used on demonstration models, particularly in exhibitions or under conditions where the naked flame is forbidden.

The gas burner is definitely a more efficient equipment to the model engineer, for several reasons: it heats a cylinder quickly, it produces far more heat, it is cleaner, gas is more readily available and a burner can be constructed for any size of cylinder in any position. An easy and readily available source of gas heating is by means of the BUNSEN BURNER, by far the most efficient method to test any kind of engine under work shop conditions, whether upright or horizontal displacer cylinders. Initially hand held, it is relatively easy to construct a holder, screw tightened, fixed to a workbench, a vice, or the engine base itself. The Bunsen burner is readily adaptable to fit into most kinds and shapes of burners, so long as the mixer tube fits tightly into the burner device to prevent gas leakage.

Any number of flame throwers, or combustion boxes can be made in different shapes and sizes to suit the cylinder being heated, always using the Bunsen burner as the main piece of equipment. It is surprising what can be done with various items of plumbing materials, particularly brass and

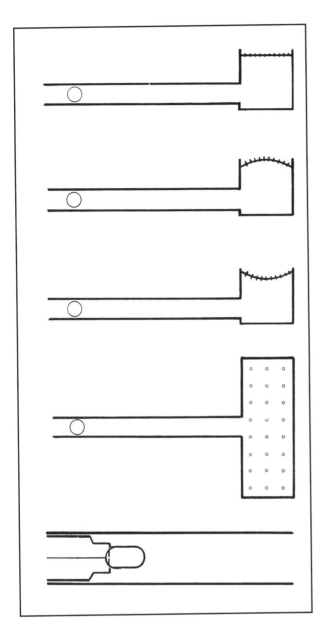

Fig 4.1 (Top) Various shapes of simple gas burners adapted to Bunsen burners, or for use with commercial gas canisters. Ceramic strips are now available for insertion as diffusers in the burner, giving a good flame.

Fig 4.2 (Above) Burners adapted from copper elbows.

copper connectors, bends, tees etc. Also useful are some of the burners used with paint strippers and scrapers; with a little bit of imagination and some alterations, fan-shaped, box-shaped, circular, convex, concave burners are possible (Fig 4.1). An alternative to the Bunsen burner is the jet tube which comes with each replaceable gas cylinder set, provided that adequate measures are taken to provide a proper oxygen to gas ratios.

The efficiency of these burners depends on the volume of gas to air mixture, on the type of gas jet/s, and on the number of holes which the burner has. As in the Bunsen burner, the mixer tube has in a position just opposite the gas jet, an oxygen vent hole, and a sliding ring which covers the oxygen vent and serves as a regulator. Any attempt at making a similar, longer or shorter, mixing tube should include both requirements, oxygen vent hole/s and slider ring. If the gas flame is yellow or yellowish, or if the flame is clinging, weak or without strength, the oxygen vent hole should be enlarged, or, if this is not possible, another hole drilled on the opposite side of the tube. The flame should be intense blue with a slight hissing noise. Care should be taken to ensure that the gas jet fitted to the mixer tube is suitable for the type of gas used: LPG, butane, propane and the butane/propane mix require different types of jets. Commercial gas jets can be purchased to fit mixer tubes of most sizes.

(A case in point happened to the Author when he bought from a scrap dealer two Bunsen burners which had been used in some school laboratory originally connected to the local town-gas supply, now long defunct. After many attempts at trying to secure a decent flame, alterations were made to the gas jet fitting, and a number of new commercial jets were tried until there is now a flame which would do credit to a brazing kit!).

Brass or copper elbows or easy bends, ⅜in to ½in ID. can easily be adapted to make a burner for a twin cylinder horizontal engine, by soldering at right angles an extension piece, one inch long, to fit over the mixer tube. A small quantity of coarse steel wool inserted in the U-shape will prevent blow-back (Fig 4.2).

Vertical displacer cylinders require different types of burners. A relatively easy and elementary type is one made from a ¼in of thin gauge copper or brass tube, bent to form a loop or ring round the displacer hot end leaving a gap or distance of about ¼in all round the circumference (Fig 4.3). The inner section is segmented by a fine saw or drilled by ¹⁄₁₆in holes; an average of 12 segments or holes may be sufficient. By way of calculation, a 1³⁄₁₆in cylinder requires a curved burner tube about 5½in long on the inside; a cut or hole every ½in

Fig 4.3 (Above) Copper Ring Burners.

Fig 4.4 (Below) Annular Burners.

will give good heating coverage. In addition to the loop an additional 3in for the mixer tube is required, with the oxygen vent hole some ¾in from the open end. The loop end of the tube should be flattened or crimped, or better still silver-soldered.

A far more efficient gas burner, suitable for horizontal or vertical cylinders, is the annular, box-like, burner which encloses a mass of gas, evenly distributed in its volume. This burner consists of a metal box structure, (fig 4.4) which fits, tailor-made, round the displacer; a number of holes are drilled in the internal wall of the box from which jets of intense blue flames are concentrated on the cylinder hot end. The box is constructed in such a way as to prevent the escape of gas from any source except the drilled holes. The inner ring is prepared first and drilled with two, three or four rows of ⅟₃₂in holes, depending on the length of stroke of the displacer; if the displacer stroke is, for

example 1 in long, three rows of jets should be sufficient. The outer ring or wall is then prepared leaving a space clearance of about ¼in all round. The third stage is to prepare two flat circular discs (washer type), with the inner and outer diameters equal to the two rings, or walls; the whole assembly is either silver soldered, brazed or welded. Finally the mixer tube is fitted on with the same method to the outer wall. For beginners to model engineering who will possess a lathe, but not brazing facility, the whole device can be machined and bolted tightly together; in this case the end discs should be fairly thick to withstand buckling. CARE SHOULD BE TAKEN AT ALL TIMES TO PREVENT GAS ESCAPE FROM ANY JOINT.

A fine mesh screen, tied with two rounds of wire strands, round the inside ring prevents blow-back and allows a better mix of air to gas, at the same time spreading the pressure of the mixture around the internal space, rather than having the gas finding its way out of the gas holes nearest the mixer tube. The mixer tube should be about 3in long, ⁵⁄₁₆in OD, with oxygen vent/s about ¾in from the end. 36 holes, in three rows, drilled in alternating, staggered or zigzag fashion, should give adequate heating cover. A twin burner version can be built on the same principle, and depending on the distance between the two cylinders, either two separate rings, or an oval-shaped box enclosing two burner rings will be sufficient for a moderately powerful model.

A canopy or flame guard (furnace) (Fig 4.5) may be an essential requirement for demonstration in a sensitive area where external flames are not allowed; moreover a nice looking flame guard or a canopy with a chimney effect lends grace to a mantle-piece model. However a canopy is also important to contain heat generated round the displacer cylinder hot end, particularly in small powered models. The construction of a canopy requires metal fabrication with brazing facilities, or a certain amount of tailoring with a tin-snip. The first type requires two round discs one of which has a hole cut in the centre, which only slightly larger than the diameter of the displacer cylinder. A flat plate, long enough to go round five sixths of the circumference is cut and brazed on. The remaining one-sixth is the bottom part of the canopy, which will be the base, and through which air is allowed to form a draught to the chimney. Two kinds of burners may be used inside the canopy, either an open-type flame, heating the bottom and sides of the cylinder, or a ring-type burner as described above. The mixer tube is either brazed or inserted into the back plate; finally two L-plates are brazed or screwed on to the canopy and the engine base giving sufficient clearance.

An alternative type of canopy is one similar to that used for LOLLY II, chapter 14. This is made from a single brass sheet, gauge 24, again tailor-made for the engine. The two basic measurements are the diameter of the cylinder and the height of the cylinder from the base. The design is simple and straight-forward, (Fig 4.6). Once the design has been drawn on paper, it is glued on to the brass sheet and the chimney hole punched out. The displacer position on the brass sheet is either punched out with a suitable large punch (+ ⅟₁₆in all round), or carefully cut with a tin-snip. In the case of the canopy for LOLLY II, this was trimmed out. The profile is then folded on the dotted lines, the seams are soldered, or the whole device screwed to the wooden base.

POWERFUL RING BURNERS AND OTHER HEATING SYSTEMS

Over the years a number of model engineers have experimented with and constructed some excellent burners, capable of producing intense heat for powerful Stirling engines. No doubt the protagonists were Philips of Eindhoven, but other engineers like Robin S. Robbins of Wales and Andy Ross of USA, to mention just two, have come up with types of burners which should interest those model engineers who have advanced beyond the initial beginners' stages! Robin Robbins, who in recent years has presented some interesting Stirling/Rider engines, such as ERGO I and ERGO II, constructed an excellent ring burner with a double mixing tube, a primary and a secondary tube arrangement fitted to a ring burner which has 4 rows of staggered holes, 6 per row. His detailed description of the burner (and ERGO II) in MODEL ENGINEER of June 5 and July 3, 1981, is followed closely by another elaborate and very powerful ring burner (Fig 4.7) this time by Andy Ross of USA for his 35cc Rider Stirling engine in his extremely interesting three-part article in MODEL ENGINEER of July 17, August 21 and September 18, 1981. This was followed by an update in the same magazine of September 6, 1985. These articles should be read closely as they contain a wealth of practical knowledge on advanced model building of Stirling and Rider engines. Andy Ross's latest book, "Making Stirling Engines", published in 1993 by Ross Experimental, Columbus, Ohio, USA, is a Stirling enthusiast's textbook which should serve as a mine of information and an encouragement to those engineers who have a belief in the future of the Stirling engine!

Another method of delivering intense heat to a cylinder head has also been derived from the early Philips engines - the use of heater tubes which supply direct heat inside the hot end of the cylinder. This involves a high degree of machining and brazing knowledge and facilities, and is somewhat beyond the scope of this book - an introduction to beginners. However for those modellers who would like to try their hand at this method, an article in two parts in MODEL ENGINEER of August 5 and 15, 1977 by Mr. E. Clapham, will serve as a guideline to the construction method and high performance achieved.

USE OF SOLAR ENERGY FOR HEATING

Direct solar energy, direct rays of the sun, is an alternative method of heating a displacer cylinder hot end. Although in northern latitudes the number of days when this energy is available is less than in southern regions, nevertheless this is a method of heating which bears experimentation; it can be quite surprising to discover the amount of power that can be generated by proper application of direct sun rays on a bright and sunny day.

There are basically two methods of focusing the rays on the cylinder hot end, by means of a

Fig 4.5 (Below left) Flame Guard. Fig 4.6. (Below right) Lolly II Canopy.

Fig 4.7 (Far right) 35cc Rider-Stirling showing Ring Burner (courtesy: Andy Ross).

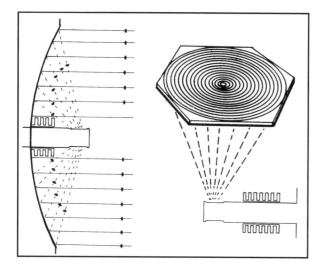

Fig 4.8 (Above left) Spread Focus of Parabolic Reflector.
Fig 4.9 (Above right) Fresnel Lens focusing on one point.

parabolic reflector, or by the use of a Fresnel lens. Chapter 16 describes a concentric single cylinder engine that works with either of these applications; the experiments that are described for SUNSPOT can be repeated on other engines.

Both the parabolic reflector and the Fresnel lens concentrate the rays on to a focal point. The reflector has the property of bringing the rays parallel to the axis to a point of focus, the focus being the circumference at the end of the cylinder, which is within the focal length of the reflector, (Fig 4.8), whereas the Fresnel lens direct the rays to one point or area of the cylinder (Fig 4.9). Another difference between the use of these two appliances is that with a parabolic reflector, the cylinder hot end is always pointing upwards the sun with the drive mechanism and the flywheel close to the base, whereas an engine heated by a Fresnel lens may be placed horizontally.

Parabolic reflectors are not easy to come by, and they can only be obtained from specialist suppliers. The size of the reflector is important, the greater the circumference of the reflector, the greater the concentration of the rays. In order to determine whether a reflector is truly parabolic, and at the same time find its focal point, the following formula, related to Fig 4.10 is used:

$$A = \frac{2D}{8d}$$

where "A" is the focal length. "D" is the diameter of the reflector and "d" is the depth of the reflector at its centre when a straight line is drawn across the diameter. It is not unusual to find a parabolic

reflector in a scrap yard - these were common surgery items in the past, in fact the author's first reflector was part of a dentist's clinic equipment, in very good condition, but needing re-chroming at the cost of a few pounds. This 12in reflector gave sufficient heat to turn the engine on which it was first used; however when it was replaced by an 18 in reflector, the concentration of heat was so much higher and the power output obviously greater.

With the above formula it is not beyond the capabilities of a good handyman to construct his own parabolic reflector to any size he requires and therefore suitable for longer and larger displacers. A framework of slats, filled with papier mâché or plaster with a layer of cardboard covered over with aluminised Mylar or simple kitchen foil, will make a more than adequate reflector. A Students' experiment on these lines at the University of Malta some years ago, was extremely successful in a similar project.

Fresnel lenses are also obtainable from specialist suppliers of school scientific equipment, mostly mail order, and these come in various sizes. The lenses are made of a type of plastic, relatively cheaper than the reflector, but requiring some woodwork to support the pliable lens stretched while making it possible for the whole device to tilt to the required angle in order to concentrate the rays on the hot end. As with the parabolic reflector, care is advised in handling the Fresnel lens as the temperature at the point of concentration is extremely high on a bright day and can burn a hole in wood or carpet in a matter of seconds.

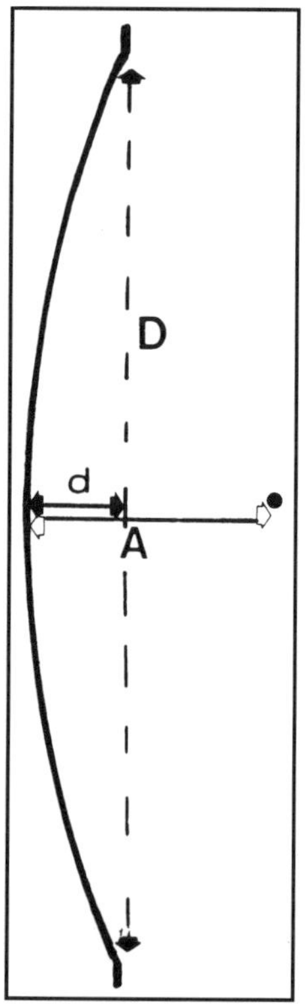

There is tremendous scope for experimenting with both or either of these methods for running Stirling engines.

COOLING

The two common methods used for cooling the displacer cylinder are AIR FIN and WATER cooling, or a combination of both. Further research may yet bring about alternative combinations of these methods and more efficient systems. The basic requirement is

Fig 4.10 Parabolic Reflector - Critical Measurements.

Fig 4.11 Types of fin coolers.
Fig 4.12 (Above) Fan cooler.

the efficient transfer of heat away from the cylinder to the surrounding atmosphere; therefore CLOSE SURFACE CONTACT BETWEEN THE COOLER AND THE CYLINDER is a prime requirement.

AIR FIN COOLING (Fig 4.11): Small desk-type model engines, used for demonstration purposes and normally run for a short duration, can be efficiently and sufficiently cooled by airfins. Fin coolers can be made in two ways - in order of efficiency these are:

(i) fin coolers machined from solid aluminum (dural) or brass, or

(ii) a quantity of squares or round discs, ¹⁄₁₆in dural or similar metal, drilled together and exactly to the outside diameter of the cylinder cool end.

Fin coolers machined from solid bar work best when they are tight-fitting; obviously the greater the contact, the more heat is quickly dissipated. Although both aluminum and brass make good dissipaters, aluminum or dural fins give a higher degree of heat transfer.

Machining from bar material normally follows this sequence:

1. The bar is drilled and bored in the chuck to the required diameter and length.

2. Parting tool is used to within a depth of ¹⁄₁₆in from the internal diameter of the bore.

3. Each fin should be thin, preferably ¹⁄₁₆in in thickness. However a great deal depends on the quality of the material.

4. The ideal space between each fin is the thickness of the parting tool plus a few microns to avoid stress on the fin, which otherwise tends to distort.

The outside diameter of the fins should ideally be in the proportion of 5:2, for example a 1in OD displacer cylinder would benefit greatly from a 2½in OD fin cooler; a larger diameter fin will not effect adversely, but neither would it be more efficient. Smaller fins, on the other hand, will absorb heat all over the surface area and thereafter the efficiency decreases enormously.

The second type of fin cooler, especially suitable for those modellers who do not have a medium sized lathe, is made from aluminum sheets or discs, ¹⁄₁₆in thick. There are some discs, used in computer and other electronic equipment, some 3½in OD, 1in ID, highly polished dural, which make excellent fins. These or other discs, squares etc. are drilled together to take four 4 BA bolts, with spacer washers in between. Alternatively another system that has been used in the past, is to cut a number of thin rings, brass or aluminum, slightly wider in diameter than the cylinder, and the fins or discs, spaced with these rings, epoxied together in place. Obviously this is a more permanent type of fixing, but surprisingly efficient.

Modellers can experiment further with fin coolers, particularly using an add-on mechanical device such as a fan (Fig 4.12). One can obtain a longer duration of the cooling effect of fins by fitting a small fan, belt driven from a pulley on the crankshaft or from the flywheel, sideways to the fins, thus helping with the dissipation of heat by air motion.

One novel idea by a fellow modeller Cristinu Vassallo of Malta, is an air duct device leading from the crankshaft to the cool end of the displacer, with an impeller with flat blades, fitted directly on the crankshaft, housed in the air duct supplying a fair amount of air to the whole circumference of the displacer cylinder, (Fig 4.13). This modeller has also used a slip-on pleated type of cooler/heat dissipater, suitable for short runs, and probably more elegant.

Fig 4.13 Cristinu Vassallo's integral fan cooled engine.

Fig 4.14 WATER COOLING: this system is generally more efficient since the temperature difference can be maintained for fairly long periods; it also allows for higher temperatures to the applied to the other end. With proper water flow and good close contact, the cold end may be kept at a reasonably low temperature for some time.

A simple, elementary type of cooler may be made from a soft lead or copper pipe carefully bent and wound round the displacer cold end; care taken during this operation and the use of an internal spring will eliminate distortion and therefore obstruction. The pipe is then connected to a tank or to a water tap.

Another simple, but more effective type of water cooler is the hopper type. This can be made from a tin box or container (such as Band-Aid, Durkee Pepper, Coleman Mustard etc.) (Fig 4.15). The tin is carefully drilled to fit the displacer cylinder tightly; once in place it is sweat-soldered carefully to make the tank water- tight. A better method is to solder a brass shim (.005in), in the form of a flat ring round the cylinder and then solder the tin container to the shim which is wider than the tank by about ⅛in each side. This method allows the water container to be slipped off, while at the same time giving excellent surface contact and heat dissipation through the brass shim.

Water tanks (Fig 4.16) may be made large enough to contain sufficient water for low temperature to be maintained for a reasonably long time. However, the water tower method described below allows for an even longer period of constant low temperature cooling. A water jacket (Fig 4.17) around the cylinder can be made from a small container, soldered on to a shim in the same manner as above, with inlet and outlet pipes on opposite sides of the jacket and connected by rubber tubing to a long and narrow container (approximately 12in x 3in), standing on legs, with its lower level preferably above the level of the water jacket. The container or water tower is filled with water to the level of the upper pipe. When the engine has been running for some time the hot water from the water jacket around the cylinder rises by thermo-syphon action to the top of the water tower and is replaced by cold water from the lower end.

Yet another method of cooling the water jacket of a

Fig 4.14 Examples of some of the various types of water tanks and fan coolers.

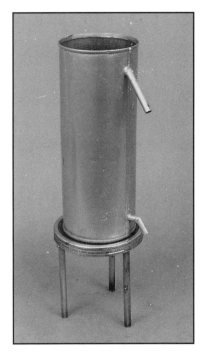

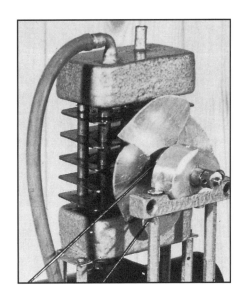

Fig 4.15 (Above left) Hopper and Jacket Type Water Coolers.

Fig 4.16 (Above right) Water Coolant Tank.

Fig 4.17 (Far left) Water Jacket attached to water tank.

Fig 4.18 (Left) Radiator and Engine Driven Fan.

larger, more powerful Stirling engine, is by using a radiator instead of a water tower, with the same thermo-syphon action as described above, the hot water rising into a piped radiator, adequately finned. The radiator may be cooled by a fan driven off the flywheel or crankshaft, (Fig 4.18). Such an engine may develop sufficient power to drive a vane-type water pump for a faster circulation of water, making it independent of the thermo-syphon action. A typical example of such an engine is the one described in Chapter 17, "DYNA", which has a radiator, fan and pump all driven by the engine crankshaft.

COOLING BY HIGHLY VOLATILE LIQUIDS: A cooling system using a highly volatile hydro-carbon liquid, Pentane, is a distinct possibility. Pentane has a boiling point of 97° F. As a cooling agent it is therefore admirably suitable, particularly in a closed-cycle device. If the device is made to consist of a radiator and a coiled tube filled with pentane, wound or placed round that part of the cylinder which requires cooling, the action that takes place is as follows: when the liquid heats up to 97°, the pentane surrounding the cylinder reaches its boiling point, vaporises and rises to the radiator where it cools, condenses and flows back to the cooling tube or coil. As long as the cycle is closed, the action is continuous in its movement. This method was used in the thermo-mechanical generators (TMG) under development at the AERE Harwell but was abandoned due to problems from leaking in flexible joints.

C H A P T E R   F I V E

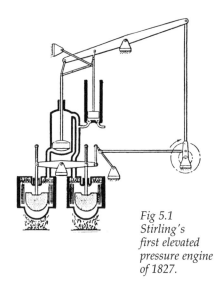

Fig 5.1
Stirling's
first elevated
pressure engine
of 1827.

Pressurisation

Robert Stirling was the first hot air engine developer to use elevated pressure as a means of obtaining greater engine power, but historians and writers on this subject do not agree which of the engines was the first to be run at 'elevated pressure'. An encyclopedia published before the end of that century gave the 1816 engine as being the first to work with an elevated pressure but there is no mention of this in the patent specifications. The specifications for the patent granted to the Stirling brothers in 1827 mention a 'vessel containing condensed air', which could be taken as a pressurised reservoir. However a more accurate description is given in the patent specification of 1840 which describes a pressure of air in the air vessels of 150 psi (Fig 5.1).

Some of the hot air engines built after Stirling's days employed a pump to replace loss by leakage rather than to elevate the working gas pressure, but information about this method is very scanty and cannot be relied upon to give any firm indication of how engine developers of those days felt about the pressurisation of engines. Some writers of those days do mention the fact that 'great energy was expended to supply air at an elevated pressure that very little power was left over for other work!'. As it happened the Stirling brothers were again several decades ahead of their time in perception, when in 1824 they converted a steam engine to run in as a double-acting hot air engine with a force pump to induce elevated pressure. The third engine, started in March 1843, also had this elevated pressure except that in this engine it was preplanned in the design state.

Sealing against losses from escaping gas was a great problem in those days, due mostly to lack of suitable materials. All glands near heated parts were generally sealed by wire, strips or rings of soft lead tightened firmly between two flat surfaces while leather washers soaked or immersed in oil were used around sliding surfaces or rods. Another problem which faced engineers was the lack of heat-resisting metals for the construction of the hot cylinder. It was therefore impossible to raise the temperature of the cylinder to a high degree or to subject it to any high pressure.

A brief mention should be made here about hot air engines which employed the open-cycle (as opposed to the Stirling engines which are of a closed-cycle). Most engines were made to work at atmospheric pressure. Inevitably these engines suffered loss of working gas through leakage which meant that the engines worked with a pressure which was alternately above and below atmospheric pressure. In order to compensate for the failing, many engines were designed to draw upon injections of air, by means of a one-way (or non-return) valve which allowed air to be drawn into the main cylinder when the pressure fell below atmospheric, or through a small pump working mechanically in conjunction with a spring-loaded valve and eccentric - or cam-driven from the engine crankshaft, injecting a small volume of air with every stroke. This latter pressure rarely exceeded 20 psi and can hardly be quoted as pressurisation.

The valve system used by these engineers, which for a time included Ericsson, placed these valves at the hot end, which is exactly where they should be so that the charge of air expands at constant temperature. However these valves burnt out with regular monotony due to the lack of heat-resisting metal available. Many modifications were tried, including water cooling jackets around the valves or valve areas. Other designers placed the valves away from the hot cylinder but this was not as successful as Ericsson's later and more advanced models, one of which is preserved in The Science Museum, London. The automatic valve system has come into use again in some model engines built in the last few years, sometimes called the 'snifter' valve. The Philips air engine, apart form having re-awakened the Stirling-cycle engine and given it a new life, embodied from the beginning of its development programme the concept of pure pressurisation.

THE CONCEPT OF PRESSURISATION

In hot air engines a small expansion ratio normally occurs, the maximum being twice, very rarely 2.5 times, the minimum pressure. This does not impart any great power to the crankshaft. Philips scientists realised this and quickly included a method of increasing power by inducing pressurised working gas into the working space. The availability of heat resisting metals (especially as a result of the gas turbine-related technology), made it possible for Philips to increase both heating and pressurised gas in their very first engine; in the case of heating, from 500° F to 1200° F, and the working pressure (mean effective pressure) from below 1 atmosphere to about 14 atmospheres.

The first Philips 'air motor' had two opposed pistons in a common cylinder with a complicated linkage drive which could not fit very well into a crankcase meant for pressurisation; this layout had another disadvantage, in that leakage could occur from both pistons unless they were extremely well fitting. On the other hand it had the advantage of having an arrangement whereby the cold and hot spaces within the cooler, regenerator and heater layout, were simply and efficiently laid out. In the end the mechanical problems of construction forced Philips to change the configuration to the V-type engine which had a drive totally enclosed in a crankcase. This design gave a simplified linkage to the crankcase allowing the engine to be balanced almost completely. The heater, regenerator and cooler were enclosed in a horizontal passage between the top of the two cylinders. This engine had two working pistons which meant that both had to have a good fit without friction or loss of air. The crankcase was pressurised and this helped to decrease air leakage from the working area to the crankcase, and also helped in avoiding friction.

After considerable research Philips scientists designed and constructed a vertical single cylinder concentric engine with the displacer (called transfer piston) on top of the working piston. The heater, regenerator and cooler were conveniently placed in the annular space around the cylinder which meant that the spaces could be kept reasonable small, avoiding dead space while allowing air flow with very little resistance. With this type of layout and construction and with high heat resistance steel and alloys, the Philips engine (Fig 5.2 and Fig 5.3) became a winner with a speed of around 2000 rpm and developing several horse-power.

The engine is constructed with a closed crankcase, with only one opening, for the engine shaft (flywheel end). Internally, on one side of the crankcase

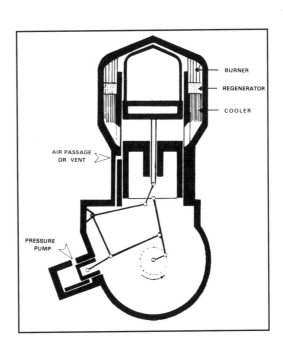

Fig 5.2 (Far left) Philips first pressurised single cylinder engine. (Philips).

Fig 5.3 (Left) Flow of gas from crankcase to power cylinder in Philips single cylinder engine.

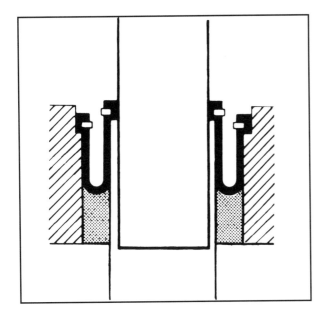

Fig 5.4 Rollsock seal.

a small pump directly connected to the crankshaft mechanism, provides air pressure as required, to the crankcase, by pumping air from outside. When the engine has been idle for a long time the pressure in the crankcase drops to atmospheric pressure due to slight leakage which is bound to occur from the engine shaft. When the engine is started there is initially very low power until the pump raises the pressure in the crankcase to the desired level. A connection between the crankcase and the lowest position of the power piston (BDC), allows the flow of pressurised gas from the crankcase to the space between the displacer and the power piston thus equating the minimum pressure of the cycle to that of the crankcase. Therefore the pressure of the latter (the crankcase) of 8 atmospheres brought about by the pump becomes equal to the engine minimum pressure (also of 8 atmospheres). This also means that the power of the engine can be regulated in a relatively simple way. The first engine designed in this manner had a top working pressure of 20 atmospheres (300 psi approximately), a minimum pressure of 8 atmospheres (120 psi approximately) and a crankcase pressure of 8 atmospheres.

The elevated pressure in the crankcase of a hot air engine offers these advantages:

1. Decrease of air leakage from the working space to the crankcase through the piston walls and piston rod (displacer rod);

2. Decrease in frictional losses and

3. Lighter load and stress on the bearings and the crankshaft.

These advantages are particularly useful in small engines of fractional horsepower and also for model engines of a single cylinder concentric configuration, although other engines with an enclosed and sealed crankcase can benefit from an elevated pressure.

SEALING PROBLEMS AND RELATED DEVELOPMENT

In large modern Stirling engines the working gas is usually helium or hydrogen; these gases are installed under very high pressure, in some cases as high as 200 atmospheres (almost 3000 psi). To contain this pressure there is a need for highly effective seals between the working space and the crankcase and around the engine shaft. These large engines also need shaft lubrication in view of the high speed and power output. The dangers of lubrication are the possibility of explosion or the contamination of the regenerative matrix which can also result in a burnt-out regenerator.

One development in the research for effective seals in the working area has been the 'rollsock' seal (Fig 5.4) which consists of a polyurethane tubular sleeve, very much like a sock, one end of which is attached to the piston rod and the other to the engine housing. This sleeve is very flexible and forms an effective barrier against escaping gas and oil contamination. Gas pressure on one side (the working side)) is counterbalanced by high pressure oil held in a reservoir under the seal. Although this is considered a breakthrough in sealing techniques, the high cost of installing a mechanism to provide the balancing oil pressure makes the rollsock seal a very expensive item in the engine construction. The crankcase/engine shaft is another problematic area although a number of different types of seals have been developed, including rotary seals, hydrodynamic seals and many others. The need for seal replacement usually arises when the engines have been running for some time and if the engine requires recharging with expensive gas, as opposed to free air the expense is compounded.

Small engines designed for electricity generating are designed with an inbuilt generator with only the power leads leaving the crankcase, making it relatively easy to provide effective sealing. Such engines usually have a small internal starter motor. This layout brings a Stirling engine/generator with crankcase pressurisation well within the bounds of mass production.

SIMPLE EXPERIMENTS WITH A MODEL ENGINE

The engine 'Sturdy' described in Chapter 15 has been the subject of some simple experiments in pressurisation. The configuration of the engine does not really lend itself to serious experiments since a co-axial single cylinder layout is a much better engine to pressurise. 'Sturdy' was fairly easily and readily adapted with minor construction work. In the first place the rear end of the engine was sealed off completely after the end part of the shaft had been removed. A ¼in dural plate was accurately cut to fit into the engine compartment, bonded in place with Super Epoxy and bolted by 6BA screws. The bonding was checked afterwards for cracks or pin holes. A bicycle tyre valve was fitted and bonded to the side of the engine compartment between the flywheel and the power cylinder on the left-hand side when looking at the flywheel from the front. The engine compartment required the drilling of a hole and some filing so that the valve could be accurately fitted from inside with fine rubber (ex-football bladder) washers on both sides of the engine compartment wall. Bonding is not really necessary, but since the engine was being completely and (hopefully) permanently sealed airtight, no chances were taken for minute leakage points in that assembly.

Two additional end plates or bulkheads were fitted to the engine. The crankshaft was reduced at the rear to fit the ball bearing without any protrusion. The end plate is well glued with super epoxy round the edges and screwed in place. The front end plate is drilled and tapped ⅜in BSF to take a new crankshaft guide bush, fitted in place, epoxied and screwed in. The engine should be air tight round the additional bulkheads.

A number of methods for sealing the engine shaft have been used, one superseding the other. The final attempt appeared to give the best result, internal pressure holding longer both with the engine static and running. This method involved sealing with two "O" rings. It was easier for the author to work on metric measurements as the local supply of "O" rings and ground shafts is

more readily available. In this method a ½in brass crankshaft guide bush was machined in two parts, threaded male/female ⅜in BSF. Two "O" rings, 5mm ID, 8mm OD, were placed between the two halves of the guide bush and with the engine running, the outer end of the bush slowly tightened, squeezing the rings very gently until the effect of friction was felt (Fig 5.5).

The next step was to test the engine for pressure loss over a number of hours; it could hold 30 PSI overnight. The engine was started up, remained sluggish for about 3 minutes, then picked up speed, however not exceeding 650 RPM. The shaft power was correspondingly much higher than without pressurisation. A curious thing emerged after a number of runs - the engine faltered and stalled when air pressure was induced while running, if on the other hand the engine was run after the crankcase had been pressurised, and preferably the internal pressure had been induced for some time before the run, the engine ran smoothly for about 10 minutes, before stalling. This behavior was apparently due to the internal crankcase pressure not being able to pass through to the top of the power cylinders through the displacer rods, while the engine was running. There is no provision in this engine for equalisation of pressure in the crankcase and the power cylinders.

The results obtained showed that elevated pressure of a few pounds in the crankcase made enough difference to warrant more investigations into the effects of pressurisation. It seemed that some of the pressure went through the displacer rod guide bush into the working area. This slightly elevated pressure increased speed by about 20 per cent, although the torque was appreciably higher. On the other hand this particular engine design and configuration were not conducive to either increased pressure or increased performance.

THE 'BRIAN THOMAS' SELF-PRESSURISING STIRLING ENGINE

The late Mr. F. Brian Thomas built a self-pressurising Stirling engine which he entered for the 1978 Hot Air Engine Competition, winning the award (Fig 5.6).

The engine is a rhombic drive, water-cooled single cylinder engine which was extended beneath the rhombic mechanism to take the pump body. The pump con-rod is directly linked to the rhombic drive, thus avoiding another link system to the crankshaft. The pump can bring the internal

Fig 5.5 Machined crankshaft housing in two parts, with "O" rings placed inside the housing.

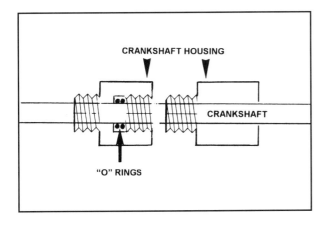

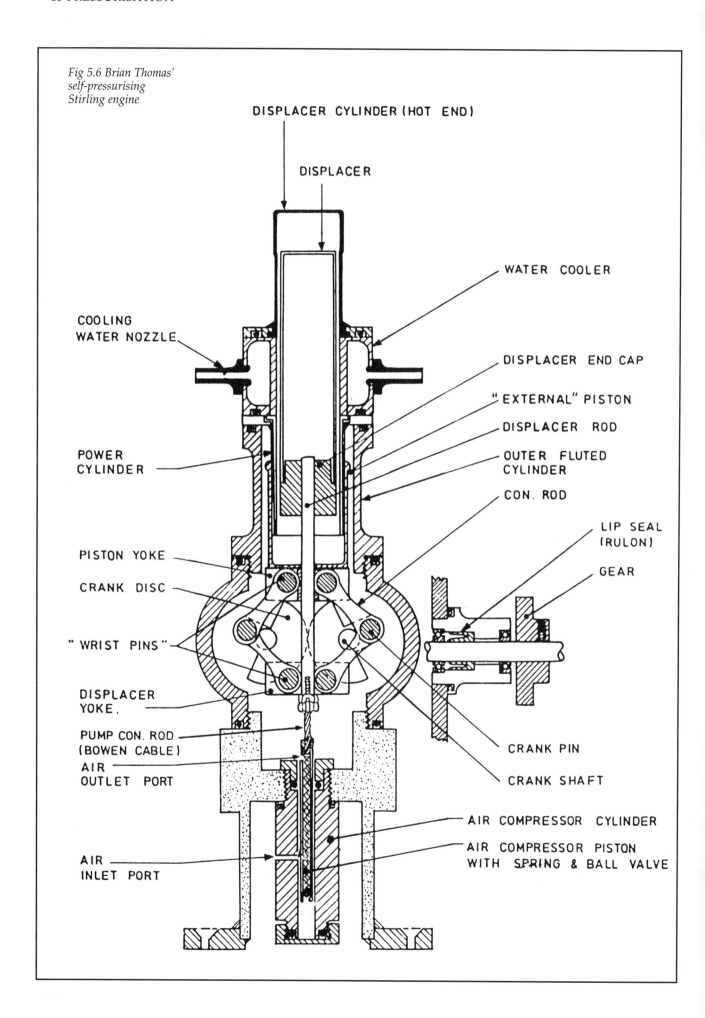

*Fig 5.6 Brian Thomas'
self-pressurising
Stirling engine*

DISPLACER CYLINDER (HOT END)

DISPLACER

WATER COOLER

COOLING
WATER NOZZLE

DISPLACER END CAP

"EXTERNAL" PISTON

DISPLACER ROD

OUTER FLUTED
CYLINDER

POWER
CYLINDER

CON. ROD

LIP SEAL
(RULON)

PISTON YOKE

GEAR

CRANK DISC

"WRIST PINS"

DISPLACER
YOKE.

CRANK PIN

PUMP CON. ROD
(BOWEN CABLE)

CRANK SHAFT

AIR
OUTLET PORT

AIR COMPRESSOR CYLINDER

AIR COMPRESSOR PISTON
WITH SPRING & BALL VALVE

AIR
INLET PORT

pressure up to 60 psi, but the engine operates best at 40 psi (just under 3 atmospheres). An adjustable safety valve and a pressure gauge are mounted on the engine cover. The description of the air pump (air compressor) construction as given by the late Mr. F. Brain Thomas is reproduced here by permission of Mrs. E. Thomas.

The pump body or cylinder was made from free-cutting mild steel hexagon rod, $\frac{5}{8}$in AF and the bore was drilled and reamed $\frac{1}{8}$in. The air inlet port is $\frac{1}{32}$in and is just cleared by the piston at TDC. The piston itself is of $\frac{1}{8}$in ground silver steel rod which is drilled as shown using a No 52 drill (0.0635in). This gives the right clearance for the $\frac{1}{16}$in (ball bearing) ball valve. Keep the $\frac{1}{32}$in hole at the lower end of the piston as short as possible to cut the clearance volume to the minimum. To get a good seal, the ball is hammered into its seal using a small punch. The very light compression spring (wound by Mr. Brian Thomas from the spring wire) is 0.010in diameter and the OD of the spring must be less than $\frac{1}{16}$in. The top end of the piston carries a 10 BA screw which is drilled to receive a short length of Bowden cable, which is soft soldered into the hole.

The outlet air port is drilled $\frac{1}{32}$ in, just below the lower end of the 10 BA screw. It must be clear of the 'O' ring near the upper end of the piston. The top end of the flexible pump piston connecting rod is soft-soldered into a hole drilled in the head of a 5 BA hexagon headed screw which screws into a threaded hole in the lower end of the displacer rod. The Bowden cable compressor rod is shown in the general arrangement drawing. It is about $\frac{1}{2}$in long and is adjustable for length at the 5 BA screw with its lock nut. The piston must be adjusted so that its

lower end is only about 0.002in from the pump cap at BDC.

The cap is machined from the same hexagon mild steel bar as the pump and is sealed with an 'O' ring. Probably the most vital part of the pump is the 'O' ring which seals the upper end of the piston. This is of white silicon rubber $\frac{1}{8}$in ID. Until this ring was fitted the pump never produced more than 25 psi. As soon as the ring was fitted 60 psi was obtained.

When the completed engine is finally assembled it must be tested for leaks as even the smallest leak will stop any worthwhile pressure building up. The adjustable safety valve carries a cycle tyre valve so that the engine can be pumped by hand; any major leak will show immediately by a rapidly falling pressure on the gauge, and when hand pumped the engine should hold its pressure for several hours. If it does not, the leak must be found. The only way to do this is to pump the engine up to 60 psi and then submerge it in paraffin. After curing all final leaks, the engine must be very carefully cleaned to remove all paraffin and the outer pair of ball races re-oiled.'

Mr. F. Brian Thomas' contribution in Model Engineer, May 19 1978, also includes a few notes on the construction of the engine in addition to some engine data.

Pressurising an engine is no doubt a fascinating development but it should not be the end-all of the humble Stirling-cycle engine. Much can be learnt from Andy Ross' experimental engines which develop tremendous power without pressurisation.

C H A P T E R   S I X

Designing & Building model Stirling Engines

"It is assumed that the reader is a modeller who has built at least one of the engines described in Chapters 10 and 12 and that he has grasped the principles of how the closed-cycle Stirling engine works before attempting to build an engine to his own design!"

A study made by R. SIER and published in MODEL ENGINEER of September 3, 1976 established that the design of the first Stirling engines followed broadly these parameters:

1. The length of the displacer chamber = 3 times its diameter.

2. The length of the heated chamber = ⅔ of the length of the displacer chamber (cylinder).

3. The length of the cooling chamber = ⅓ of the length of the displacer cylinder.

4. Swept volume of the displacer = 1½ times the swept volume of the power piston.

5. Length of the displacer = ⅔ of the length of the displacer cylinder.

6. Stroke of the displacer = ⅓ of the length of the displacer cylinder.

Indeed, from calculations made by the author of other engines by Lehmann, Bailey and many others, these parameters were almost always followed. This says much for Stirling's perception and grasp of the thermodynamic principles at that time.

Not all these parameters can however be followed in model engines. For example: to have a heated chamber or cylinder of that size requires a super cooling method not easily obtained in a small

engine. Also in Stirling's days, and for scores of years later, the metal used was poor in quality and massive in size, accounting for the need to heat a large area. With model engines constructed of bright mild steel, heating the rear end of the displacer cylinder is sufficient. Moreover if conduction of heat along the cylinder wall is reduced or avoided, better regeneration from the displacer is obtained and cooling is greatly facilitated. Stirling's displacer was two-thirds the length of the displacer cylinder. This method is used when the displacer itself is used as a regenerator, as in most model engines. When the regenerator is contained in a separate body, the displacer length can be shortened substantially, as in Philip's air motor. Some of the parameters are still generally followed in the construction of simple model engines. These are: compression ratio, phase angle, displacer cylinder length, displacer stroke and cooler area.

GENERAL NOTES ON ENGINE DESIGN

ENGINE CONFIGURATION: Three basic configurations are described in this book. The projects detailed in Part 2 of this book are based on these layouts, starting with a simple engine and working progressively towards more elaborate and interesting models. The three basic configurations are: 1. Twin cylinders (power and displacer) in parallel formation; 2. Twin cylinders in V-formation, or at 90° to each other; 3. Single-cylinder concentric with the power piston and displacer in the same cylinder.

A twin-cylinder engine, such as 'DOLLY' in Chapter 10 and 'DOLLY II' in Chapter 11 has the two cylinders parallel, but on opposite sides of the cylinder plate. Another version may have the parallel cylinders on the same side of the cylinder plate with an inter-connecting air passage from the front or side of the displacer cylinder to the top of the power cylinder. V-formation twin-cylinder engines, such as 'LOLLY I' and 'LOLLY II' in Chapters 13 & 14 and the marine engines in Chapters 15 & 16 have the power cylinders at right angle to the displacer cylinders, the con-rods working off the same crank pin or crankshaft. The concentric engines, the most efficient type of all, such as the 'ERICSSON' engine in Chapter 17, 'PROVA II' in Chapter 18, 'SUNSPOT' in Chapter 19, 'DYNA' in Chapter 20 and 'TUBA' in Chapter 22 have the displacer and power piston in the same cylinder. These engines have a single crankshaft but a double throw crank to give different strokes and the required phase angle. The only small difference between these engines is the method of regeneration. There are other engine configurations, some of which may be dealt with in a future publication.

THE TWIN-CYLINDER PARALLEL CONFIGU-RATION requires a simple and easy running mechanism capable of providing for alterations to phase and stroke without complications. Two types of drive, the flywheel/disc drive and the double crank mechanism, are readily adaptable for this configuration.

The flywheel/disc drive mechanism (Fig 6.1) is actually a combination of a flywheel and a disc or web, or two flywheels. The drive mechanism assembly is mounted on a pillar or brackets or a block, so that the flywheel on one side is connected to the power piston, while the other flywheel or disc on the opposite side is connected to the displacer. The block should be sufficiently wide to support the crankshaft from lateral stress. Alternatively two brackets are used with brass bushes or bearings at either end. The advantages of this type of drive are twofold. The phase angle can be varied or experimented on - simply by altering the positions of the flywheel and disc relative to each other, instead of the crankpins being at 90° to each other, these can be set at 85°, or 95° or 100°. Secondly the stroke of the pistons can be varied subject always to the repositioning of the respective cylinders.

The double-crank mechanism for a parallel cylinder engine is slightly more complex. The crankshaft passes through a housing placed to one side of the cylinder assembly, on the outer side of the housing the crankshaft supports the flywheel, on the inner side a crank disc about ¼in thick. The crank disc will take a crank pin, and is fitted offcentre to give the power piston the necessary length of stoke; for example if the model calls for a 1 in stroke, the crank pin is fitted ½in off centre. The crankpin should be sufficiently long to allow another disc or web to be fitted on; this crank disc also has another crankpin screwed in and this will give the displacer its length of stroke, once the two crankpins have been set at 90° to each other. Obviously the pins should be kept as short as possible to avoid stress on the crank discs. This mechanism requires that the power and displacer cylinders are close to each other, almost touching but it also helps in keeping the connecting air passage short, thus lessening dead space. "DOLLY II" has a similar mechanism.

The V-ENGINE is a fairly easy engine to design, requiring only some construction practice. It has the advantage of a compact and sturdy

Fig 6.1 (Far left) Combined double flywheel drive.

Fig 6.2 (Left) V-Type drive with single crankpin.

mechanism. V-type engines may be designed to have the displacer cylinder horizontal with the power cylinder vertical, or the other way round — the power cylinder lying horizontal or in a third formation, the actual "V" with both cylinders pointing upwards, at 45° from horizontal. As modellers progress with the hobby, they will realise that each of these positions has some advantages and disadvantages, the displacer may be too heavy in a horizontal position and therefore drags on the displacer rod guide bush, a horizontal displacer cylinder facilitates the choice of a burner, a burner for a vertical cylinder requires some practice, two cylinders "in-the-air" require counter balancing with a weighted crank web etc etc.

A single crankdisc and pin is used to drive both con-rods, and therefore both have the same throw (Fig 6.3). It is obvious therefore that to obtain the ratio of swept volumes of 1:1.5, two different sizes of cylinders are used, a wider diameter for the displacer cylinder, and a narrower diameter for the power cylinder. Any slight variation of the ratio will not necessarily affect engine performance.

The positioning of the cylinders in relation to the engine frame and the base is not critical, and for a beginner the burner and cooler availability has a more important role. Thus if a Bunsen burner or a disposable cylinder type burner is the only kind available to the modeller, probably the horizontal displacer configuration is the easiest; a water jacket or hopper works best in this position.

The V-type configuration works best when the weight of the power piston and the displacer are almost equal and counterbalanced by a bell-shaped crank disc or a weight on the crank disc. In designing this type of engine one has to keep in mind that the length of the connecting rod from the displacer to the crankpin is always longer than the power piston con-rod and therefore the displacer cylinder is placed further away from the engine frame, the cylinder being supported either by distant pieces or on body work; having said this, however, "LOLLY II" has a scotch yoke (see further on in this chapter) which actually brings the displacer cylinder right against the engine frame.

The SINGLE-CYLINDER CONCENTRIC OR CO-AXIAL ENGINE (Fig 6.3) is by far the most efficient type of engine both in design and performance. Almost most engines designed and constructed by more advanced modellers today are of this configuration. The main reason for the efficiency lies in the fact that in a compact engine of this type there is very little dead space or volume between the displacer and the power piston and the whole volume of gas is utilised to provide energy. The difficulty in building this engine lies mostly in the design and calculation stages, as it is

Fig 6.3 Double-throw crank for a concentric engine.

difficult to visualise the movement inside the cylinder when the engine is in motion. There are practical difficulties to be overcome in the construction of single-cylinder concentric engines - the displacer rod has to pass through the crown of the power piston to reach the crankshaft, creating a sealing problem of no small proportion, the outer cylinder wall tends to transmit heat along its length, causing the power piston area to expand and induce more friction. Lubrication of the power piston, always a sensitive point, becomes an additional problem. Therefore, in designing this type of engine the lower part of the cylinder and the power piston should be effectively cooled to avoid heat creep from the hot end of the cylinder.

DRIVE MECHANISMS

One of the more fascinating and challenging aspects of designing and constructing model Stirling engines is devising the mechanical drive of an engine. Variations of drive mechanisms are almost endless and scope for inventiveness is unlimited. Indeed many an efficient and interesting mechanism has evolved from the world of the model engineer and his ingenuity.

The drive mechanism has to transfer energy from the power cylinder to the flywheel, provide separate movements to the power piston and the displacer, provide different movements to the power piston and the displacer to create the 90° phase (if this is not provided by the natural position of the cylinders, such as the V-type assembly) and finally provide as near a friction-free movement of the crankshaft as possible.

The different types of drive mechanism may be divided as follows:

1. Crank and lever linkage mechanism.
2. Single-throw crank mechanism(V-type engine).
3. Multiple crank and disc mechanism.
4. Gear drive mechanism.
5. Scotch yoke mechanism.
6. Cam drive mechanism.
7. Swing-beam mechanism.
8. Siemans drive mechanism.
9. Swash-plate or wobble-plate mechanism.
10. Nutator drive mechanism.
11. Rhombic drive mechanism.
12. Ross linkage mechanism.
13. Diaphragm-power mechanism
14. Other novel drive mechanisms

This chapter can only give an overview of the above mechanisms - to go into details requires a separate publication; at the same time scope for research and experimentation must be retained. It is proposed to give a brief description of the mechanism, supported by a photo of an actual engine mechanism, or by a design.

1. The CRANK AND LEVER/LINKAGE MECHANISM is a complicated and cumbersome style of driving an engine, yet a fascination to those who prefer the delicate, intricate, waltz-like movement of links and levers. This system was widely used in olden days because no other means had been devised and partly also because the developers of that age followed too closely the design of the steam engine. This mechanism does not allow an engine to develop high speed, but it is delightful to watch. Power output ratio to energy used is very low (Fig 6.4).

2. The SINGLE-THROW CRANK MECHANISM used in the V-type engine, on the other hand is

Fig 6.4 Lever/link mechanism. (Photo: Courtesy John Wilkinson).

more efficient and capable of sustained stress and high speed (Fig 6.2). Modern engines, with 4 or 6 cylinders on line, on a single crankshaft, are capable of high speed and considerable power. This mechanism is ideal for beginners, for if all the other parameters are followed, it will give a modeller a trouble-free start to the hobby, with plenty of scope for improvement and experimentation.

3. The MULTIPLE CRANK AND DISCS MECHANISMS are variations of a theme - two flywheels, two discs, or a flywheel and a disc, a single crankshaft fabricated or machined to give two or more throws, in fact any combination one can think of whereby two or more cylinders in line are connected to a crankshaft. (Fig 6.5) illustrates one example, the crankshaft prepared for "DOPYU", in Chapter 12 is another. Where flywheels and/or discs are used to connect with pistons or displacers, a simple crankpin is used to give the necessary throw. These variations are mostly suitable for parallel configuration engines and ideal for desktop, mantle-piece or demonstration models.

4. The GEAR DRIVE MECHANISM is rarely used in model engines, although such engines if well constructed can develop high torque at low speed. The multiple gear assembly in Fig 6.6 was used by

Fig 6.5 Twin-flywheel and single throw crankshaft combination.

Fig 6.6 (Above) Gear drive mechanism with two spur gears and two bevel gears.
Fig 6.7 (Right) Gear drive mechanism with two spur gears. (Courtesy: Model Engineer).

the author in a marine engine to drive two diametrically opposed power pistons via the lower spur gear and two parallel horizontal displacers by means of a shaft driven by the bevel gears- quite successfully too! Fig 6.8 is the drive mechanism of "PROVA II" which was entered for the 1986 MODEL ENGINEER EXHIBITION, F. Brian Thomas Memorial Trophy Competition at which it was placed second, soundly beaten by an Australian entry. The advantage of this drive mechanism is its capability for minute alterations of the phase angle in experimenting for higher pressure build-up. "PROVA II" was a concentric single-cylinder engine with an annular foil regenerator (see Chapter 3) of which the author does not have any adequate photographs and had to borrow the picture in Fig 6.7 above from MODEL ENGINEER by kind permission of the Editor, Ted Jolliffe. (Incidentally this engine was donated to a church bazaar to be auctioned for fund raising).

5. The SCOTCH YOKE MECHANISM has been used quite successfully on model engines where space or design do not allow for long connecting rods. Displacers in particular require a long con-rod fitting; the use of the scotch yoke can shorten a con-rod substantially. "LOLLY II" in Chapter 12 has the displacer cylinder right against the engine frame as a result of this yoke; however a clearer example of an all round use of the yoke is in Fig 6.8 a neat little engine by Cristinu Vassallo of Malta, in which all four con-rods, two for the power pistons and two for the displacers operate by means of the yoke.

An interesting engine design (Fig 6.9) by the late David Urwick employs a scotch yoke within a piston which is double acting; the crankshaft also has two similar yokes to move two displacers,

moving regenerators, at each end. The regenerators move at 180 degrees to each other. This engine with a 7 in bore and a 3 in stroke could give an output of 500 watts at a speed of 500 RPM, and would be ideal for third world countries where it can be operated for long periods by an unskilled person.

6. The CAM-DRIVE MECHANISM, is rarely used in model engines as it requires precision machining and perfect alignment, but once the matching operation is successful, an engine can be quite powerful, with fairly moderate speeds of around 1000 RPM. The cam drive is normally used on the displacer cylinder con-rod; its potential

Fig 6.8 Double scotch yoke mechanism on a single crankshaft.

success is in fact due to its design which moves the displacer during 120° of crankshaft rotation, dwells at one end (cold or hot end) for 60°, moves again during the next 120°, dwelling again at the opposite end for another 60°. The dwell of the displacer at the cold end allows considerable pressure to build up due to the fact that the gas contained at the hot end has time to absorb much of the heat applied. The late F. Brian Thomas used the cam-drive with great effect in his engine which attained 1500RPM and is described in MODEL ENGINEER of October 3, l975. The only known old engine to have the cam-drive mechanism was produced by Schwartzkopff in Berlin around 1860, but very little is known about its efficiency.

7. The SWING-BEAM MECHANISM is a rarity if not an oddity; by right it should be included under Other Novel Drives, however having seen two in operation, and having corresponded with the late F. Brian Thomas, FRCS, on his own swing-beam project, it was felt appropriate to give this mechanism its own standing. As a driving mechanism, it may not be one of the more efficient ones, and indeed when the engine is going at speed, little more than a blur is seen of levers, but as Mr Brian Thomas wrote, ".... it certainly does create an interest!" His model reached a speed at 1150 RPM, giving a very good performance.

The engine has two displacers and two power pistons working in the same cylinder, Fig 6.10 shows Brian Thomas' own sketch of the layout. The model takes up a fairly large area, with a two-throw crankshaft connecting two rocking levers and two short con-rods. Altogether, a slow motion version would probably create even more interest.

Another example of a swing-beam mechanism (Fig 6.11) comes from the stable of Cristinu Vassallo of Malta, whose model is far more compact than the one above, pleasing in appearance and apparently more powerful.

8. The SIEMANS DRIVE MECHANISM (Fig 6.12) is very often confused with the swash-plate or the wobble-plate because of the similarity of movement of the drive plate or disc, a similarity that is apparent on paper but not in action. This mechanism is best described in David Urwick's own writing for MODEL ENGINEER: "The Siemans drive plate rocks on a fulcrum and serves as a bell crank, or a series of bell cranks, transferring the piston rod thrusts to a single crank pin driving a flywheel or disc. The Siemans pin drive is a positive direct linkage and the throw can be as large or small as desired, like a normal crankshaft. This pin is headed by a ball entering freely into a hole in the crank-disc, drilled at a radius to give any desired throw. There is no end thrust at all on the main shaft, reducing vibration and friction."

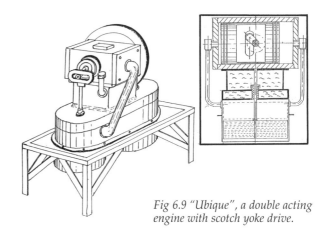

Fig 6.9 "Ubique", a double acting engine with scotch yoke drive.

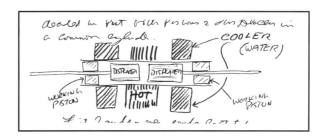

Fig 6.10 F. Brian Thomas' own design for a swing-beam engine.

Fig 6.11 Swing beam engine by Cristinu Vassallo.

Fig 6.12 Siemans drive mechanism by David Urwick.

Fig 6.13 (Top) Swash-plate mechanism by Albert Debono.

Fig 6.14 (Middle) Nutator mechanical drive by David Urwick.

Fig 6.15 (Below) Horizontal Rhombic Drive mechanism by Charles Camilleri.

This drive was later modified by David, replacing the ball fulcrum on which the rocking plate rocks by a Carden-style universal joint.

David described the drive mechanism in detail in MODEL ENGINEER of December 1980, January 1981 and June 1982. The author had the opportunity to see this lovely engine in action while David still lived in Malta. It was a very beautiful and precise piece of engineering and while running it was perfectly quiet, smooth and vibration-free. A sample test run brought the speed in excess of 1400 RPM in a relatively short time. The original four-cylinder double-acting engine is thought to have been invented, on paper, by a celebrated British scientist, Sir William Siemans in 1863, but no contemporary working engine with this type of mechanism is known to have existed.

9. The SWASH-PLATE or WOBBLE-PLATE MECHANISM is a fairly recent innovation to the model engine field and is really a modification of the SIEMANS drive. The swash-plate is a rotating inclined disc on a crankshaft which cause piston/s and/or displacer/s to move backwards and forwards as the disc rotates. This mechanism is suitable for single and multiple cylinder engines. The swash-plate mechanism in Fig 6.13 was incorporated in an engine built by Albert Debono of Malta and described in MODEL ENGINEER of September 19, 1975. The swash-plate is fixed to the crankshaft with a 'follower on top to pull and push the displacer rod. The 'follower' holds revolving steel balls to reduce friction. Altogether it is a lively mechanism, delightful to watch and relatively easy to experiment with.

10. The NUTATOR MECHANISM is another modification of the SIEMANS or SWASH-PLATE drives, which is best described as a multiple ball and socket arrangement, the effect of which is a 'nodding' action - hence the word 'nutator'. The mechanism works extremely smoothly when a brief flick of the flywheel starts the swivelling and nodding action of the drive, balanced on the various balls and sockets, pushing and pulling the power piston and displacer alternately through the crank half-plate. It is one of those mechanisms with which one experiments for the sake of knowledge rather than researching for efficiency (Fig 6.14).

11. The RHOMBIC DRIVE MECHANISM, invented by Philips of Eindhoven, Holland in the early days of their development of the Stirling engine (the Philips Air Motor), is a magnificent piece of engineering based on the knowledge of geometry. This mechanism gives a single-cylinder engine several advantages over similar size engines with other kinds of drive mechanisms - the engine can attain and hold high speeds without

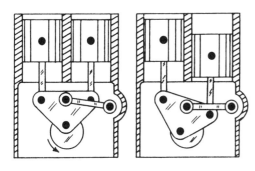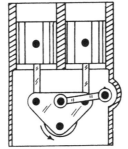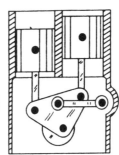

*Fig 6.16
Andy Ross'
original
version of the
yoke drive/Ross
linkage.*

any lateral or side thrust on the power piston or displacer rod, and is, above all, totally vibration free. As a result of its particular mechanism, wear and tear normally minimal in hot air engines, is negligible with this drive. It is also relatively easy to contain this mechanism in an enclosed crankcase with only one outlet, the crankshaft bearing.

It takes an experienced modeller with good workshop equipment to machine the parts with great accuracy, and a good mathematical approach to design the right stroke, phase and ratio while maintaining the efficiency this engine calls for. The RHOMBIC DRIVE MECHANISM shown in Fig 6.15 was constructed by Professor Charles Camilleri of the University of Malta, and during a trial run in the presence of the author achieved a speed well in excess of 1000 RPM in a few seconds.

12. The ROSS LINKAGE MECHANISM, (Fig 6.16), is one of the latest to be devised in the model or small engine field. This mechanism consists of a balanced crankshaft with a triangular yoke drive or linkage (called the ROSS LINKAGE after its inventor, Andy Ross of USA, Patent No 4,138,897). The yoke is held captive to one side of the crankcase, secured in the centre to a revolving bell crank, and linked at one end to a power piston (cold side) and linked at the other end (hot end) to another piston with an extension. The engine is in fact a RIDER, on which Mr Ross has become an authority. This type of mechanism is slightly complex for the beginner to model hot air engines but it has scope for experimentation and research as one becomes more experienced.

The 35cc Rider Stirling engine which first made use of this linkage is fully described in MODEL ENGINEER of July/September 1981, while the development of Stirling engines by Mr Ross himself is discussed in a detailed article in LIVE STEAM (USA) of January 1983, and in MODEL ENGINEER of 6 September, 1985. In 1993, Andy Ross published an excellent book "MAKING STIRLING ENGINES", wherein he sets out in great detail his development of various Rider/Stirling engines in his search for power.

13. DIAPHRAGM POWER MECHANISM
Diaphragm-powered Stirling engines have had very few followers, yet Geoff Bartlett of Selly Oak, Birmingham, has demonstrated that his unusual and effective method of replacing a conventional power piston by a sealed diaphragm component is a viable and altogether successful alternative mechanical drive to power small Stirling engines (Fig 6.17).

The diaphragm is usually made from rubber or silicon rubber and has some obvious advantages over the common piston, such as low friction, good sealing and the elimnation of one swivel joint (the little end) of the connecting or push rod. These advantages balance against the extra dead space contained within the diaphragm. Obviously low scale pressurisation compensates for this additional working volume.

Geoff Bartlett has written a highly informative and well illustrated article in two parts on "WHY PISTONS" which appeared in MODEL

Fig 6.17 Diaphragm powered Stirling engine by Geoff Bartlett.

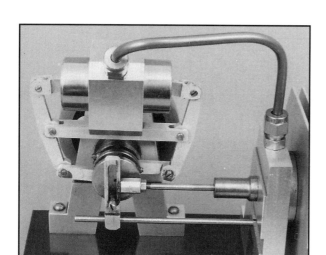

Fig 6.18 Novel mechanical drive employing two rocker arms and scotch-yoke by Charles Camilleri.

ENGINEER of November 6th and December 4th, 1992. In this article Geoff describes how to construct a high speed, medium pressure, Stirling engine with turbulent flow, as a result of a swirling displacer.

A recent innovative use of the diaphragm mechanism has been made in two Low Temperature Differential engines built by Geoff.

It is interesting to note that among the large scale applications of diaphragm power, the TMG mentioned in Chapters 1 and 2 uses a metal flexible diaphragm acting as a power piston to reciprocate the armature of a linear alternator.

OTHER NOVEL DRIVE MECHANISMS

In the course of corresponding and meeting with fellow enthusiasts, also while visiting various Exhibitions, the author has come across some novel mechanical drives for which there is no known 'name'.

One of these engines, Fig 6.18, was constructed by Professor Charles Camilleri of Malta, for which there seems to be no short descriptive title. The mechanism consists of a double crank machined from a 1in solid mild steel bar on a crankshaft, the integral crankpins being machined on opposite sides of the webs to give the necessary simultaneous throw to two con-rods. Two rocker arms on either side of the assembly join the lower con-rods from the crank and the upper con-rods from the power pistons, the two power pistons being contained in a single cylinder. When the drive mechanism is activated, the cranks push the lower con-rods outwards, forcing the rocker arms to push the upper con-rods inwards to perform the compression stage. Meanwhile a crankpin on the

outer web carries a Scotch Yoke at the end of a displacer rod, the action of which is at 90 degrees to the crank throw/rocker arm movement. This is a beautifully machined mechanism delightful to watch. It has a no-load speed well in excess of 1000 RPM, picking up revolutions very quickly.

Another type of engine that has been appearing in greater frequency is one based on the Ringbom principle. In this engine the displacer con-rod is replaced by a largish short displacer rod in a precisely machined fitted guide.

Professor J.R. Senft of the University of Wisconsin, USA in his excellent three-part article in ENGINEERING IN MINIATURE of September, October and November 1992 described an engine he built on this principle and which he called "Tapper" (after the noise the displacer makes), introducing it as a 'hybrid' Stirling engine, that is an engine which is a mix of the original Stirling principle and the invention of Professor William Beale of the Ohio University, USA, the free piston/free displacer flywheel-less "space" engine.

"Tapper" (Fig 6.19) is an engine for the more advanced engineer with substantial workshop facilities. This device was followed by other experiments in the field of Ringbom technology, a configuration which was found to be suitable for

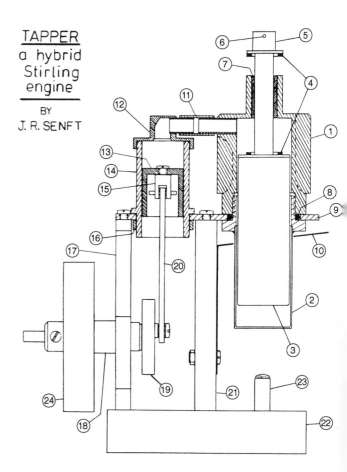

TAPPER
a hybrid
Stirling
engine

BY
J. R. SENFT

development of low temperature differential (L.T.D.) engines, that is engines that need very few degrees of temperature difference between the hot and cold ends in order for them to function. L.T.D. engines are extremely suitable to operate everywhere and practically under all conditions, including direct sunlight without concentrators.

L.T.D. engines may be of two designs, single-crank operation where only the power piston is connected to the flywheel, and the other design where both the displacer and the power piston are connected to the flywheel with the normal 90° phase.

A new mechanical drive (Fig 6.20) has been recently developed for single cylinder concentric engines, called the "inclined yoke" drive. This development appears in Prof. James R. Senft's book, published in 1993 by Moriya Press, USA, "AN INTRODUCTION TO STIRLING ENGINES", and is described in Prof. Senft's words as follows: "A scotch yoke with an angled slot connects the piston to the crankpin, and another angled the other way links the displacer to the same crankpin. Each oscillates as the crankshaft rotates, and the angles make a phase difference between the two. This is a simple and compact arrangement."

This new development appears to have all the advantages of the rhombic drive, however with

less moving parts, and should make an ideal experimental subject for the advanced modeller.

THE DESIGN STAGE

> "THE SECRET OF A GOOD MECHANICAL DRIVE SYSTEM IS FOR THE ENGINE TO DEVELOP, AND LEAVE OVER, POWER AT THE SHAFT AFTER HAVING OVERCOME ALL FRICTIONAL AND HEAT LOSSES."

At some stage a hot air engine enthusiast will attempt to design his own engine. Almost all modellers of Stirling engines known to the author have constructed one engine to their own design, while others have taken this hobby even more seriously and experimented with many configurations and mechanisms. The following notes are pointers to the requirements of the initial design stages. As in everything else, the first attempt is bound to encounter problems and difficulties - worse still if the completed engine fails to go after the first few attempts. The reaction may well extend to throwing it and the designs out of the nearest window!

Generally speaking there are two types of designers: those who first design an engine and then get down to the task of finding materials to use and to machine; the others design an engine on or around the materials available, obtaining the rest as they go along. The author belongs to the latter class, with one proviso. Over the years a fair number of boxes have been stacked in odd corners of the workshop and garage, containing bits and pieces of materials which one day may prove useful! The difference between these two approaches to design is evident, the first can go more by the book while the latter has to improvise and possibly experiment more with the parameters. Anyway it is a worthwhile stage to reach, and when the model is to one's own design works, there is the added pride of a double achievement.

Usually the design stage follows this pattern:

1. Decide on the configuration of the engine;
2. Draw the layout roughly to see whether it is feasible and to find out if dead space or dead volume can be avoided or at least reduced;
3. Draw the layout to scale;
4. Cut cardboard templates to the original size and scale, pin to a board where appropriate (e.g. con-rods, links, levers etc.) and check for free uninterrupted movement;

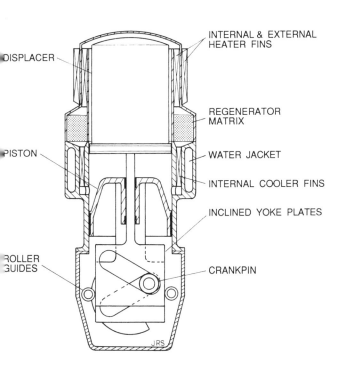

DISPLACER

INTERNAL & EXTERNAL HEATER FINS

REGENERATOR MATRIX

PISTON

WATER JACKET

INTERNAL COOLER FINS

INCLINED YOKE PLATES

ROLLER GUIDES

CRANKPIN

Fig 6.19 (Left) "TAPPER", a hybrid Stirling engine by James R. Senft.

Fig 6.20 (Above) Inclined yoke mechanical drive by James R. Senft.

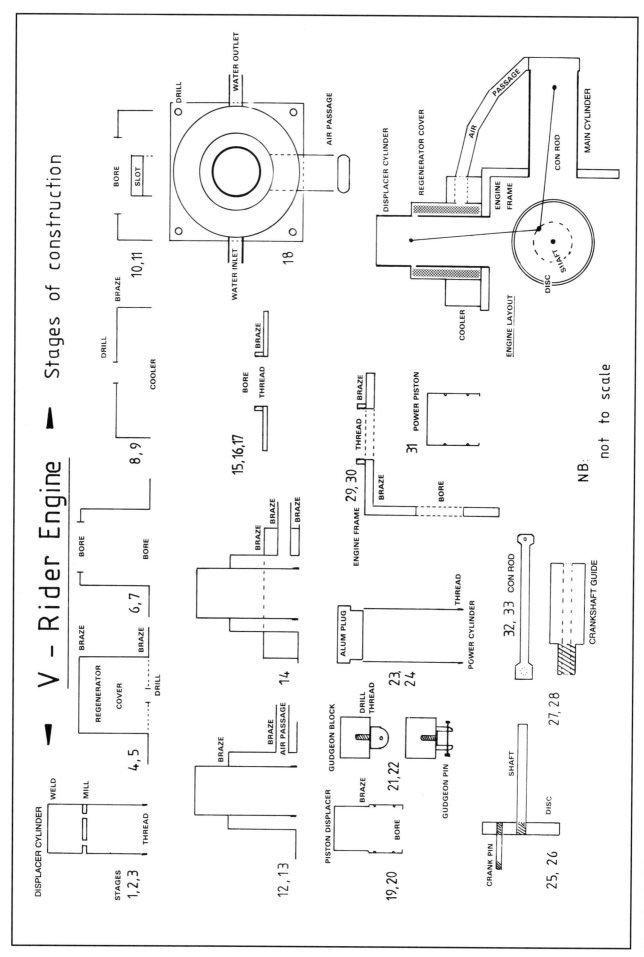

Fig 6.21 Workshop "working plan" for a Stirling Rider engine under construction.

5. Make working drawings, top view, side elevation, front elevation;
6. Draw the drive mechanism to an enlarged scale to obtain precise measurements.

The next stage is the construction stage. Here again experience has taught that planning the stages of construction carefully, not necessarily in great detail, helps to avoid mistakes. All the more so when the model is complicated and involves different machining and bench fitting processes. The drawing for the construction stages should be sufficiently large, (board size) to be followed at a glance, each stage being crossed out when completed. The illustration in Fig 6.21 is an actual construction plan of a V-Rider Stirling engine. In putting the stages of construction on paper before commencing operations, the modeller is creating a system or method of approach, making an inventory of materials required, planning bench fitting and machining operations in correct order, avoiding repetition and re-use of equipment and finally ensuring that no construction or machining stage is overlooked.

DESIGNING A CONCENTRIC ENGINE

The concentric engine requires a slightly different approach in the design stages in view of the positions of the power piston and the displacer within the same cylinder, and the problem of mentally following the movement of these two components during the various stages of motion. In this case the design stages follow this pattern:

1. Decide on the following parameters: ratio and length of strokes of the power piston and displacer; the length of the power piston; the distance from the centre of the crankshaft to the engine frame/cylinder plate, keeping in mind that short connecting rods tend to cause friction and lateral thrust.
2. Decide on the scale of the first layout drawing of the engine, i.e. x2, x3 etc.
3. Draw on the diagram the position of the main cylinder and locate the centre-point of the crankshaft.
4. With the same scale, draw two circles from the crankshaft centre, the inner circle representing the power crank stroke and the outer circle representing the displacer crank stroke.
5. Mark the position of the displacer at TDC, i.e. fully pushed in. Measure the distance between the displacer front-end and a point on the outer circle nearest the cylinder plate (step 7 of Fig 6.23). That distance represents the combined length of the displacer rod coupled to the con-rod.
6. With the above con-rod/displacer rod length,

(and the known length of the displacer), draw the displacer at the position of 10 past 11 o'clock on a clock dial (step 2). Place the power piston with a 1/32in gap from the displacer, and draw a line which represents the power con-rod, from the piston crown to the power crank-pin represented by the 11 o'clock hand of Step 2. Obviously the power con-rod includes the gudgeon block.

7. Fill in the other steps and check that the various measurements and phases are correct.

> THE MOST IMPORTANT POINT TO REMEMBER DURING THE DESIGN STAGES IS THAT DEAD SPACE OR CUSHION AIR DIMINISHES THE COMPRESSION RATIO AND THEREFORE THE POWER OUTPUT, THUS AFFECTING ADVERSELY THE ENGINE PERFORMANCE.

Fig 6.22 gives the more important stages in the movement of the piston and displacer and the relationship between these two components during certain movements of the crank. Unlike the internal combustion engine, where each cycle of operation consists of four distinct phases: induction, compression, ignition (or power) and exhaust, the hot air engine phases are not so distinct and one phase leads into the other. In designing such an engine one must therefore look at all the various stages of movement to obtain a complete picture of the mechanical action inside the cylinder. The construction of a concentric engine follows the pattern set out in Chapter 15, "PROVA II", Chapter 18 and, in Chapter 20, "DYNA".

SOME PRACTICAL HINTS ON ENGINE DESIGN

There is a relationship between the power cylinder bore diameter and power piston stroke, not unlike that of an internal combustion engine. Generally the relationship follows one of the following three applications. In a SQUARE engine, the power piston has an almost equal bore to stroke ratio (e.g. 1in diameter x 1in stroke); in an OVER-SQUARE engine, the stroke is shorter than the diameter (e.g. 1/2in stroke x 1in diameter), while in an UNDER-SQUARE engine the stroke is longer than the diameter (e.g. 1in stroke x 1/2in diameter).

In a small model Stirling engine built for experiments or demonstrations, the SQUARE

*Fig 6.22
Stirling cycle co-axial
engine displacer
and power piston
movement plan.*

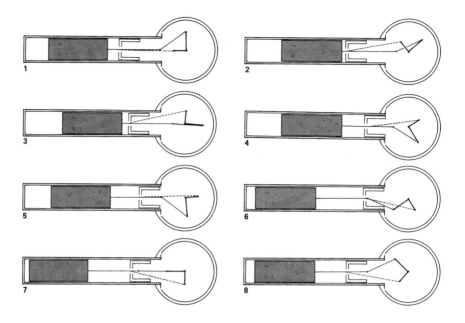

arrangement is the most suitable: side or lateral thrust on the piston wall is roughly equal to the load on the crank and bushes. For high revolution engines, the OVER-SQUARE arrangement is more suitable, since there is reduced friction in the piston movement due to the shorter stroke; the disadvantage is a higher load on the crankpin and main bearing. For higher torque engines, the UNDER-SQUARE engine is more efficient, particularly if a long con-rod is used.

Where possible long con-rods should be used with power pistons; the longer the con-rod, the less there is lateral thrust due to reduced angular displacement. The same applies with the con-rod fitting from the displacer rod to the crankpin.

'Compression ratio' in Stirling engines is something of a misnomer and really signifies the volume of air swept by the displacer piston and the volume of air swept by the power piston. Stirling must have found that the ratio of 1.5 : 1 was the ideal one by trial and error, in fact in one of his early engines, the mechanical drive that he used allowed him to change the ratio to 2 : 1 and 3 : 1 after the engine had been in operation for some time. As regards model engines this 'compression' ratio is by no means to be taken as dogmatic. Different engine designs may require different ratios - indeed engines of the same configuration sometimes also vary; while one engine may require a 2 : 1 ratio, another is quite happy a with 1.25 : 1. There are other types of engines, such as the Rider/Stirling, that have a 'compression' ratio nearer to unity, i.e. 1 : 1, yet the power obtained from such models is amazing (Andy Ross' Rider

engines are typical examples).

Engines should be constructed in such a way as to dismantle quickly if and when the need arises. There is nothing more infuriating than to have to take to pieces a whole engine for a minor fault or adjustment. This applies particularly to the concentric engine where the displacer and power piston are in the same cylinder.

The variable factors determining the success or otherwise of a Stirling engine are so numerous that the scope for invention or mechanical experiments has by no means been exhausted. Many an experimental or test-bed engine has been built in school laboratories and workshops, with a view to testing some of these variables.

In the first place the test-bed engine frame should be easily dismantled, with all main parts quickly removable. This should be done in such a manner that any one part under study can be removed or changed without disturbing the rest. If it is decided, for example, to experiment on displacers or moving regenerators, as David Urwick has done (see Chapter 3), the test-bed engine should have a common drive mechanism, proven to be reliable and efficient, and all experiments undertaken by the simple removal of the main cylinder, either by unscrewing it or removing the bolts from the flange.

Designing a test-bed engine is a most interesting exercise, worthy of consideration by any enthusiast who wants to learn more about the application of the thermodynamic principles of the Stirling-cycle.

C H A P T E R   S E V E N

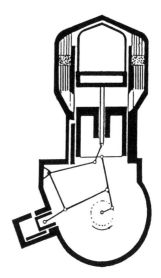

Workshop Practice

Building the simple model engine does not call for sophisticated tools or special skills. Building a hot air engine can be fun even with a few basic workshop tools. Rarely, however, does the story end there. Many modellers have gone on to building more advanced engines, to researching on the principle, and to designing their own models. The author built his first working model from a school textbook with nothing more elaborate than an electric drill on a stand in the workshop. Progress in building more model engines brought about better equipment and tools. Every engine is a challenge not only in its performance but in building it with what equipment and materials are readily available. Since cost and availability of materials may be limiting factors, ways and means of obtaining good working materials from alternative sources with least cost to the hobbyist are discussed in this chapter. The construction of 'Dyna' , described in Chapter 17 , is an example of how to design and construct an engine with minimum of tools and purchased material.

WORKSHOP FACILITIES

Basic tools are : Bench drill or drill press; set of HSS drills; set of taps and dies; conecut or fly cutter (or similar adjustable hole boring tool); set of spanners - open-ended, ring and tubular; 3in to 4in bench vice; drill vice; reamers - hand; normal workshop hand tools - pliers, mole wrench, cutter, hack saws, screwdrivers, steel rule, hammer etc, etc,; miscellaneous files; small G-clamps; vernier calipers, scriber, centre punch.

Expenditure on a number of workshop small tools can be reduced with some planning. For example,

the more common size screws, bolts and nuts are used in these models, mostly, 6BA and 4BA although sometimes 8BA or 2BA are required. Similarly, silver steel rods (for connecting rods and crankshafts) of ⅛in and ³⁄₁₆in are more commonly used since they are easier sizes to handle and to find. It follows therefore that HSS drills, reamers, taps & dies, spanners to be used with the above sizes will be quite sufficient to begin with, before decisions are taken on how and when to expand workshop facilities. One way of cutting down on costs is shopping by post from the many excellent mail-order firms that specialize in surplus engineers' supplies, materials and redundant stocks.

At some stage a beginner to model engineering will think about setting up his own workshop, however small, however modest, and invariably the first acquisition will be the lathe; not surprising since the model engineer's workshop revolves round a lathe. A great deal of thought should go into the choice. Type, size and economics - all have their considerations and generally some bearing on the choice. The first question, which only the hobbyist can answer, is 'how far is my hobby likely to go'? Far too many beginners invest in expensive tools only to find that they really have little aptitude, or no time, or have had to move to smaller living premises. One should also consider whether by joining the local model engineering club, some of the heavier pieces of lathe work can be done in the club workshop and the minor work done on a small model engineer's lathe at home. Work on model Stirling engines mostly involves the use of the smaller lathe with only the occasional use of a larger chuck if cylinders exceed the 2in

*Fig 7.1
Dismantled
shock absorbers.*

OD. The 1in to 1¼in OD cylinder gives ample scope for experimenting. In addition, the size of the engine remains relatively small while material for cylinders, displacers and pistons is more readily available.

A model engineer's lathe should meet all his immediate and long term requirements. In looking for one among the many kinds available on the market one should compare the different features, centre height, distance between centres, range of speeds, ruggedness of headstock and tailstock, screw cutting (with capability to change from imperial to metric threads) and the possibility of adding attachments for extra tooling, such as milling and drilling, as well as other optional extras such as change of tool holders, or a bored spindle. One should look for bargains available during reduced stock sales and national exhibitions. Many a good bargain can be had from advertisements in popular engineering periodicals where used lathes and other equipment in very good condition, made by reputable firms with household names are advertised for quick sale at greatly reduced prices. In the case of used equipment, a beginner should always seek the advice and assistance of the older members of the local club or others with engineering experience.

Except for the odd job in the workshop, there is not much call for the electric arc welding set, certainly not at the beginning. But the same cannot be said about oxyacetylene or oxygen-propane/butane-brazing sets. Although one can build the first few engines with the occasional help of a friend's kit, the need for this equipment gradually increases with workshop practice and usage. If the need is for the odd job around the house, some model engine work and such like jobs, then a small portable oxyacetylene or oxy-propane/butane set

with rechargeable or exchangeable cylinders will be just the right type of equipment, available nowadays at very reasonable prices.

There are a number of engineering supply firms that specialise in selling workshop accessories in kit and castings which make valuable additions to the workshop equipment. Among the useful sets of castings one can find; bench and drill vices, power hacksaws, bench grinders, grinding jigs and angle plates. The advice here is to choose the more important and less complicated casting kit and work upwards with expertise.

SOURCES OF SUITABLE WORKSHOP MATERIAL

Shock absorbers (dampers) are a good source of material which can be used in the building of model engines (Fig 7.1). Most shock absorbers have an internal cylinder or tube through which a plunger operates on hydraulic oil (and sometimes gas). A shock absorber that has not been grossly overworked or damaged can provide a number of materials that can be utilised. The internal cylinder can be used for displacer cylinders or even power cylinders. The metal, usually bright mild steel, is readily machinable giving an extremely fine finish. Most of these (internal) tubes from medium sized absorbers have an internal diameter of approximately ⅞in which is ideal for most engines. Some of the larger shock absorbers have a heavy solid and single drawn outer cover which, with very little work, can be used for single cylinder concentric engines of moderate size. Other shock absorbers have as plungers a piston with one or more compression rings. These pistons can be used with minor modifications, changing to low compression rings or using 'O' rings, as power pistons, provided that friction can be avoided. Other parts that can be salvaged from the smaller shock absorbers are piston rods, narrow-bore thin gauge pipes and chromed spindle rods.

A word of caution on opening shock absorbers; invariably these are sealed under pressure and should the absorber being dismantled still contain either gas or fluid under pressure, the sudden release can cause havoc to clothes, workbench and, very often, the ceiling. Always cut an opening with a very fine hacksaw blade some ¼in from the top end, keeping a cloth handy to cover the opening in the event of fluid escaping under pressure. Continue to cut around the circumference taking care not to go too deep and damage the internal cylinder. Ensure that the plunger is completely extended out of the absorber so that any remaining fluid is contained at the bottom end of the absorber body.

Odd cuts of different diameter silencer pipes as well as the outer casings of the larger shock absorbers make excellent ring burners (see Chapter 4).

Another source of material is from scrapped or surplus ex-services electrical equipment which can still be found or purchased for very little money. The amount of material that can be salvaged from some of this equipment is amazing, from high quality 2, 4, 6 BA bolts and nuts, to brass and dural rods and other bits and pieces that can prove useful. Some component chassis make ideal bases for the model Stirling engine.

THE MATERIAL COMPONENTS OF MODEL HOT AIR MACHINES

Displacer cylinders or working cylinders of single cylinder engines are best made out of stainless steel. When this is not available, bright mild steel tubes are a good close second. Ideally stainless steel cylinders should have their closed ends TIG-welded or MIG-welded and therefore capable of withstanding very high heat. TIG welding facilities are not readily available to all model engineers. The alternative is bright mild steel, brazed with iron fillings rods or arc-welded. This type of welding also withstands considerable heat. Silver soldering, although suitable for most small hot air engines, does not stand as much direct heat, especially from powerful gas burners.

A novel way of closing a stainless steel cylinder end without any kind of welding has been evolved by Cristinu Vassallo of Malta and used for his Stirling engines (Fig 7.2). This method involves delicate lathe work and bench fitting. The rear internal end of the stainless steel cylinder has a V-groove recessed, by machining in the lathe, to

0.045in , 0.030in inside from the end. A stainless steel disc, only very slightly smaller in diameter than the total internal diameter of the recessed part (i.e., the diameter of the cylinder + 0.045in + 0.045in), is prepared on a grinder so that the edge is ground all round the circumference into a V-shape. The disc is placed inside the V-groove, and the overlay very, very gently hammered by small taps of a light hammer into a folded seam over the disc. A salt solution is then prepared, one tablespoon of kitchen salt just liquefied with water, poured inside the cylinder and left standing overnight. On the following day the cylinder is cleaned internally and light oil applied until the cylinder is ready for use. The chemical action together with the fine machining gives a completely airtight cylinder capable of withstanding gas heat.

Another novel method of closing displacer cylinder hot ends is used by Professor Charles Camilleri of Malta. This method also requires high precision work and involves the cutting of an internal thread (about 40 tpi) in the displacer cylinder hot end and an external thread of the same size in a ³⁄₁₆in brass disc which then fits snugly and exactly in the cylinder. The brass disc is additionally machined on the internal face to reduce the thickness of material and on the external face to take a slot for a screwdriver. No bonding or other sealing is necessary. When screwed tight and heat is applied the expansion of the brass disc is sufficient to prevent any escape of the working gas.

After welding, brazing or otherwise closing the hot end, the cylinder is thinned down by machining to 0.015in, certainly not exceeding 0.030in, to cut down on heat conduction along the cylinder wall.

Fig 7.2 Sealing a stainless steel cylinder without welding (C. Vassallo).

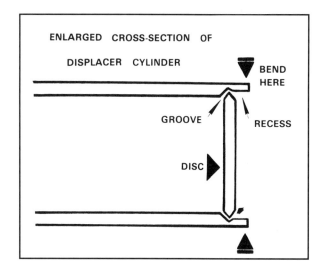

Displacer lengths (except for single cylinder engines) may be broadly calculated at three to four times the diameter; single cylinder engine lengths depend on the layout and the drive mechanism employed.

Power cylinders can be made from different materials, stainless steel, bright mild steel, brass or even pyrex. The most important requirement is the fine internal finish, first through machining, honing and then lapping. The length of power cylinders depends on the engine layout, the piston length and the stroke. In single cylinder concentric engines where the front end serves as the power cylinder, the internal finish should be just as fine as with any other power cylinder. Lapping is essential to give a mirror finish (see Chapter 8 for lapping).

Displacer and power cylinders are generally fitted to the engine frame in one of two ways. Flange fitting requires the brazing of a plate to the cylinder, drilling the bore before or after fitting (Fig 7.3). The flange plate, usually of bright mild steel should be at least ⅛in thick, preferably ³⁄₃₂in. Care should be taken during the heat application stage to avoid distortion of the cylinder. Thread fitting requires the cutting of a fine thread on two components, an external thread on the cylinder and an internal thread on the receiving engine frame or cylinder plate. In this part of the operation if the cylinder plate is of bright mild steel or of brass, another method can be used; a brass ring (⅛in thick), is threaded and brazed (silver soldering is sufficient) to the engine frame or cylinder plate. If dural plate is used (³⁄₁₆in to ¼in), this can be threaded internally by placing the plate in a four-jaw chuck.

The 'heat and freeze' method described below can be used quite successfully in the fitting of flanges and power piston 'closed-ends'. 'Sturdy', described in Chapter 15, has four flanges, two for displacer cylinders and two for power cylinders, fitted with this method, while the two power cylinder closed ends are similarly fitted on. This system is particularly useful for those modellers who have no brazing facilities. The fitting of flanges by brazing or welding invariably causes cylinder warping and distortion by the application of high heat, therefore all bores must be refreshed and re-lapped.

Basically the method involves freezing one component, heating the other and putting the two together with some bonding agent. Usually the metals used are different, dural and bright mild steel, for example. Dural has a high coefficient of expansion while mild steel has a low coefficient of expansion. The dural flange has a hole bored which does not quite take the mild steel cylinder.

Cooling the cylinder in a freezer for one hour to -20°C. and heating the flange by gas flame gives sufficient contraction and expansion difference to obtain a good, sliding fit. A smear of bonding agent to the lip of the cylinder before insertion ensures secure fitting against pressures. The dural plate should be ³⁄₁₆in to ¼in thick to prevent warping and provide a strong flange.

Displacers are light in weight and airtight, unless a displacer of the mesh kind described in Chapter 3 is used. Normally they are three and a half to four times the diameter in length. Thus a 1in OD displacer is about 3½in to 4in long. The fitting of displacers in the displacer cylinder is critical. Too narrow a gap between the cylinder wall and the displacer will cause a damping effect; too wide a gap will give too much dead space and no regenerative effect. The same applies if the gap at the top and bottom of the stroke of the displacer is too big. Clearance around the displacer is normally of 0.015in on radius or 0.030in on diameter, with the same gap at both ends.

In very small models, where it is not possible to make very light-in-weight displacers, the use of aluminium containers such as used for cosmetics or medicine, is an acceptable alternative. However the regenerative effect of aluminium displacers is limited. Once the displacer becomes hot throughout its length, the regenerative effect is lost, the difference in temperature between the hot and cold ends narrows and the engine efficiency falls drastically.

Where possible, displacers are made of bright mild steel, brazed at one end and plugged at the other by a lightweight plug and made airtight. The outer wall of the displacer is slowly thinned down by facing it with a number of fine cuts while in the lathe. The result is well worth the effort and time spent on the job. Displacers are checked for airtightness by placing in hot water and looking for tell-tale bubbles.

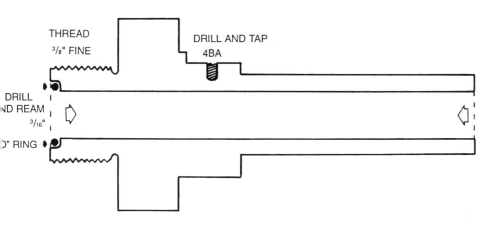

THREAD
³/₈" FINE

DRILL AND TAP
4BA

DRILL
AND REAM
³/₁₆"

"O" RING

Fig 7.3 (Far left) Displacer cylinder with brazed flange and flange to fit displacer rod guide bush and air-vent connection.

Fig 7.4 (Left) Displacer rod guide bush.

Displacer con-rods are normally made up in two parts, the part that fits into the displacer and the con-rod. In between there is usually a gudgeon block arrangement. The top part of the displacer rod is screwed tightly into the displacer plug end. In the course of running, it slides in the guide bush several hundred times a minute. This part is usually made from high quality silver steel, ground steel or polished (chromed) spindle steel, depending on the size of the model and the power output expected from it. An ordinary small model engine built for pleasure or minor experiments works well with a silver steel rod. On the other hand a competition engine would do better with a ground, polished or chromed rod.

The con-rod attachment is made from bright mild steel or brass; at one end the con-rod fits into a gudgeon block fitted to the displacer rod, while at the other end of the con-rod fits into a crankpin or similar arrangement. The con-rod can also be a combination of a small-end and a big-end with a threaded connecting rod between the two. This arrangement is quite handy for minor adjustments which may be required in the final fitting of an engine. The small-end of the con-rod fits into the gudgeon block while the big-end usually has a bush or a ball bearing fitting to the crank pin. This type of con-rod is suitable for the larger type of model engine. In the case of small engines with a short stroke to the displacer, a Scotch yoke fitting can be made to the displacer rod.

Guides or guide bushes (Fig 7.4) are made of brass or bright mild steel. The guide is made fairly long and is accurately machined in the lathe.

It is centre drilled and drilled in two stages (in the first stage by a drill slightly smaller than the final cut) and then finished off by a reamer. The length of the guide varies according to the size of the engine and the weight of the displacers. A long guide tends to create friction while a short guide has a double negative effect, possibility of easier

escape of gas and faster wear on the displacer rod, particularly if the displacer is slightly heavy.

The displacer rod and guide assembly is a frequent area of failure and a reason why engines refuse to work or work sluggishly. Normally the two extremes are the cause. Too tight a fit creates friction or too loose a fit allows the escape of gas and consequent loss of pressure. The latter can be detected by the application of lubricating oil in the rod and listening for the hiss of escaping gas. Sometimes an engine which has refused to work, will do so on the application of a few drops of medium oil, but only until the sealing effect diminishes.

Guides of concentric engines are machined somewhat differently although the drilling and reaming operation is common. These guides are either inserted in or are part of the power piston and are used at the same time as gudgeon blocks or yokes to the power con-rods.

Gudgeon blocks (also known as the coupling) and gudgeon pins are the names given to a connecting point between two moving levers, one of which usually moves in a fixed direction, such as a piston or a displacer and rod, while the other is a lever that can turn through 360 deg. This arrangement can take different shapes. Whether a round or square bar is used depends on the engine requirements. All the engines described in Part 2 have one or other type of gudgeon block fitting. Gudgeon blocks are machined so that the displacer rod is either screwed into or slides into one end of the block. In the latter case a set screw is used to retain the displacer rod. The other end of the gudgeon block has a slot cut into it for some length into which fits a con-rod without binding or loose action (Fig 7.5). The retaining pin is called a gudgeon pin (or sometimes a wrist pin). Gudgeon blocks are machined from brass or bright mild steel, although any other material such as nylon, or PTFE may be used. The pin can be a bolt,

Fig 7.5 (Right) Gudgeon or coupling block.

Fig 7.6 (Middle right) PTFE power piston used by Mick Collins for his award winning "Whippet".

Fig 7.7 (Far right) A machined power piston.

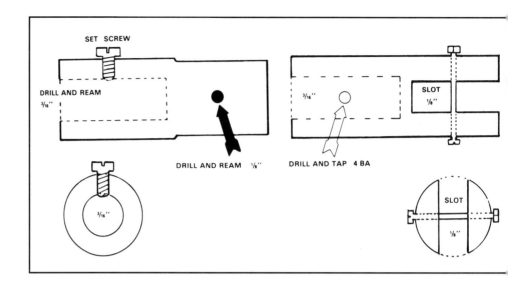

preferably with a straight shank or a cotter (split) pin.

Power pistons are best made from cast iron or from an alloy which has a relatively low coefficient of expansion. Modellers have experimented with other materials such as PTFE and Rulon and have had highly successful results. One particular modeller, F.M. Collins of Elstead, Surrey, has described and illustrated his method of machining PTFE power pistons (MODEL ENGINEER, June 20 1980, page 757) for his award winning engine 'Whippet' (Fig 7.6) and also for 'Phoelix' described in the issue of August 3 1979. Brass is sometimes used in model engines and has been found quite suitable. Bright mild steel bars or pipes brazed at the closed end are also used. A piston made from old cast iron conduit water pipe, brazed and machined (Fig 7.7) has given long and valuable service in one of the engines ('Dyna') described in this book.

The length of the power piston is a matter of calculation and depends on the diameter of the piston as well as on the stroke being used; generally speaking a length of ¾in to 1in for the smaller engine and 1in to 1.25in for the larger models is suitable. Power pistons are usually grooved with fine cuts to serve as oil grooves and an aid to compression. Some modellers prefer to give one of the grooves a deeper cut and to fill this with a PTFE twisted strand. Excellent compression can be obtained with this method. Yet another compression aid is the use of 'O' rings. The fitting of these is critical and requires good machining techniques and calculations. An 'O' ring can make a power piston stick and create a substantial amount of friction. If too loose there is no benefit accruing. Even in the best fitting 'O'-ringed piston there may be no bounce or reaction from a power piston when heat is applied to an engine - simply because of the 'sticking' effect.

The power piston usually employs a gudgeon block or yoke to take the con-rod which will connect the piston to the crank pin, disc or web. The construction of the gudgeon block is not very different from that described earlier. It is only the fitting to the power piston which differs. There are two principal methods for this fitting - either using a screw from the piston crown to the gudgeon block, or reducing and threading the end of the gudgeon block to fit into the similarly tapped crown of the piston. Either way requires that no gas will escape through this fitting. In concentric engines the con-rod is assembled directly into or to the power piston (see displacer guide bush note above).

The use of steel shims as regenerative material is gradually gaining ground for two reasons. Steel is not a good heat conductor and heat deposited along a steel shim regenerator does not dissipate along the surface. It is readily picked up again by the working gas on its return. This is particularly useful in high speed engines. The second reason is that fine steel shim, 0.002in occupies very little space while providing a large surface area particularly if the surface on both sides is used. Moreover if the regenerative gap is sufficiently wide and each layer is kept apart from the cylinder wall and from the next layer, more than one layer of shim can be inserted. This can be done by raising dimples (as with a seamstress tracing wheel - Andy Ross, Model Engineer, August 21 1981) or ruling it with a scriber along its length and pleated (as used in 'Prova II' in Chapter 15). Steel shim stock can be obtained in various thickness from 0.002in upwards. A few odd pieces of this material and some brass shim are always useful in the workshop.

Flywheels (Fig 7.8) for model hot air engines should not be heavy. Depending on the size of the engine a flywheel of three inches diameter,

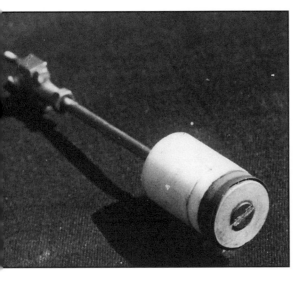

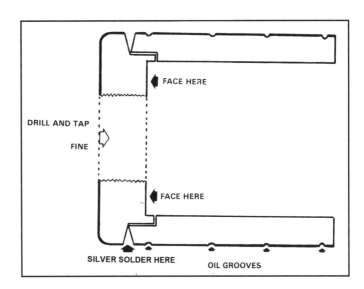

weighing between 8 to 12oz is quite sufficient. Larger models, such as 'Dyna' described in Chapter 15 and the Ericsson engine described in Chapter 12, require a larger diameter flywheel, weighing about 14-16oz. Hardwood flywheels, with a fairly thick rim, are an excellent alternative if metal ones are not readily available.

The flywheel is a component that is sometimes not fully understood. At best, some modellers think of the flywheel as a store of mechanical energy, carrying the energy delivered by the power piston by means of rotation. One often reads of an engine that will not run until a larger or heavier flywheel has been put on. Some engines require a mass of stored energy in the flywheel, which is already in motion through a push or flick, to carry it over the 'hump', which is the compression stage of the engine. Once the 'hump' has been overcome by two or three revolutions, the expanded volume of gas takes over and the excess of energy will continue to turn over the flywheel.

Fig 7.8 A selection of flywheels used by the Author on various models

At this stage one should differentiate between two types of flywheels, the heavy rimmed type and the thin rimmed disc-like type. A heavy rimmed flywheel stores more energy, reaches its limit of energy quicker, but will not go beyond its inherent rotation speed due to centrifugal stress. On the other hand, a lightweight thin rimmed flywheel in the shape of a disc which is THICKENED TOWARDS THE HUB, will gain higher speeds before it reaches its limit of centrifugal stress. With this in mind a modeller should choose the right type of flywheel to suit best the engine under construction.

BUILDING ENGINES FROM KITS OR TO PLANS

It is possible nowadays to buy the models in kit-form or castings and to complete it by machining and bench fitting at home or in the school laboratory. This method of building an engine has much to recommend it particularly when it is not possible or practicable to obtain the right materials or castings. The beginner to model engineering may have successfully completed one or two basic and simple engines and yet finds difficulty in going ahead with serious development because of such materials problems or the lack of proven advanced engine designs. This is where kits of castings for engines become useful alternatives.

At one time Andy Ross of Ross Experimental Inc, of Columbus, OHIO, USA, produced a small number of kits of his B-20 Stirling Rider engine for the serious and advanced modeller keen on obtaining substantial power from a small hot air engine, while at the same time experimenting with the Ross Linkage. Unfortunately there was not enough interest to encourage Andy Ross to continue this service which demands time and attention. In the States other engines in kit form, or as finished models are produced by various

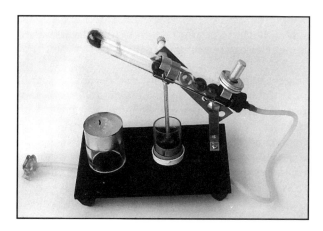

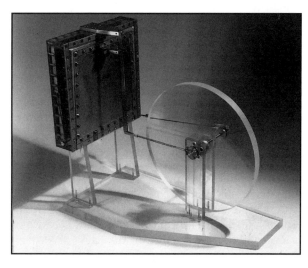

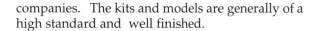

Fig 7.9 (Top left) "Stirlingmotor" by Dieter Viebach of Kolbermoor, Germany.

Fig 7.10 (Left) Sun motor designed by Prof I. Kolin, sent to the author by Bernhart Scharl of Munich, Germany.

Fig 7.11 (Top right) "Handwarmer" Stirlingmotor by Dieter Schager; a low temperature differential Ringbom engine.

Fig 7.12 (Above) Stirling engine devised by David J. Gingery and marketed by Ginsberg Scientific Inc, of Macks Creek, Missouri, USA.

companies. The kits and models are generally of a high standard and well finished.

Werner Wiggers of Kempen, Germany advertises a beautifully designed "two-cylinder Hot Air Engine" of 'olde-world' design, available as drawings, castings or as a finished working model. Dieter Viebach of Kolbermoor, Germany, produces castings for a fair-size "STIRLING MOTOR", a V-type design which can be pressurised (Fig 7.9). Plans and instructions for this motor are also

available. "Stirlingmotor" is obviously an engine for the more advanced model engineer with a medium size lathe; it is also a good introduction to pressurisation.

Modellers interested in Sun Motors (on the Stirling principle), will do well to contact:-

Arbeitskreis Arche "Stirlingmotor" (AK-Arche) der Evangelischen StudentInnengemeinde an der Fachhochschule Munchen Lorisstrasse I/I8000

Munchen 2; they have produced a detailed study (in German) and plans for an ingenious sun motor designed by Professor I. Kolin, (Fig 7.10).

From Offenbach/M, Germany comes a hand-warmed Low Temperature Differential Ringbom Stirling engine produced and marketed by Dieter Schager. The Schager Handwarmer Stirlingmotor (Fig 7.11) requires a 3 Kelvin temperature difference to start running, reaching a substantial speed at 6 to 8 Kelvin temperature difference.

Dieter Schager has produced other types of LTD Ringbom Stirling engines, one particularly deserving special mention, constructed in a horizontal quartz glass single cylinder configuration, and running very well on a low spirit flame.

THE GINSBERG/GINGERY STIRLING ENGINE:
An unusual and delightful Stirling Cycle demonstration engine has been devised by David J. Gingery and is being marketed by Ginsberg Scientific Inc. of Macks Creek, Missouri, U.S.A. (Fig. 7.12) This unorthodox engine is an educational model in so far as it demonstrates the principles of the Stirling cycle very clearly and visibly. Its glass tube displacer cylinder and the glass marbles, standing for the displacer, is a very effective method of transferring gas from the hot end to the cold side while allowing for compression to transfer to a cut-away rubber balloon which acts as a power piston. The engine, complete including candle, comes in kit form with very precise instructions and recommendations for further experiments and developments.

B. & R. Tite of Colwall, Malvern, Worcs produce and sell a delightful small Stirling engine "HENRY" (Fig 7.13) which is particularly suitable for beginners with little or no workshop equipment, but who would like to have a mantle-piece model that runs well, quite attractive to look at. This model is a Heinrici type engine and requires only some bench fitting and finishing to one's particular colour preference. Detailed drawings and instructions come with the kit.

(The author carried out a few modifications to this model, as a result of which the engine starts up more quickly and runs at higher speed on a gas flame; it can even run on a night candle flame (gnat-power). A bell shaped fitting was made to contain the heat from such a candle . The displacer cylinder was reduced internally to obtain a cylinder wall 50% of its original thickness, and further reduced externally in the lower (heated) end. The kit displacer was replaced by a BMS thin-walled home-made displacer, with greatly reduced annular space. The stroke of the power piston was lengthened to obtain a 1.5 : 1 ratio; this involved changing the crankdisc to permit a 1in throw.

Such modifications can be carried out on a small lathe by a modeller who has reached a certain proficiency.)

STERLING STIRLING (Fig 7.14) of Newport, Gwent, has a number of Stirling engine models of various makes and configurations, from a beam/scotch yoke drive to a Ross linkage drive model, from a horizontal Ringbom to a Low Temperature Differential engine based on James Senft's design.

(Sterling Stirling also supplies some materials for the Stirling Engine modeller, including solid drawn stainless steel hot cap sets for displacers/cylinders, and stainless steel tubing of various diameters of use in the production of tubular heaters for pressurised engines. Of

Fig 7.13 (Left) "Henry", a Heinrici type model produced by B & R Tite of Colwall, Malvern, Worcs.

Fig 7.14 (Below) One of the models produced and marketed by Sterling Stirling of Newport, Gwent.

particular interest to the hobbyist is a strobe lamp used to measure engine speed (see Chapter 20) from approximately 60 to 2400 RPM.

Another delightful model is "Eva", first exhibited at the 1995 Model Engineering Exhibition. This well finished V-Type model (Fig 7.15) is made by Axiom of Edgar Street, Hereford, and is one of a series of models which the Company is currently producing for enthusiasts and for research.

Bruce Engineering of Shepperton, Middlesex, are marketing an interesting concept for model engineers, two different engines based on the same casting (Fig. 7.16). One is a Scott Vacuum engine (a type of hot air engine) and the other is a Stirling Engine designed by Richard White (see Chapter 19) called ARIEL. This latter engine has a concentric configuration with a 1⅝₆in. bore, developing 5.3 watts at 720 RPM, and a free running speed of at least 1200 RPM. Both engines come in kit form and can be machined on a lathe with a 2⅝in. centre or over.

A number of firms in the UK supply engine castings for specific models; among these are A.J. Reeves & Co of Marston Green, Birmingham (HEINRICI MOTOR); Maidstone Engineering Services of Maidstone, Kent (ROBINSON HOT AIR ENGINE); Camden Miniature Steam Services of Rode, Bath (RIDER-ERICSSON HOT AIR PUMPING ENGINE).

(The author has only managed to obtain the castings for the Robinson Hot Air Engine, Fig 7.17, and the Rider-Ericsson Hot Air Pumping engine, Fig 7.18, so far. The modifications made by the author to the Ericsson engine are explained in detail in Chapter 14).

Maidstone Engineering Services have plans to introduce a set of castings for a

Fig 7.15 (Above left) "Eva" produced by Axiom of Hereford (Courtesy: Keith James).

Fig 7.16 (Right) Concentric Stirling engine from Bruce Engineering of Shepperton, Middlesex, designed by Richard White.

Fig 7.17 (Above right) Robinson Hot Air Engine castings from Maidstone Engineering Services.

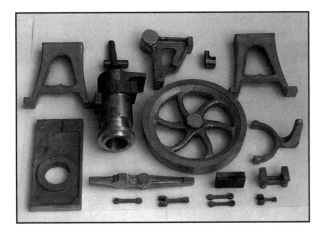

Fig 7.18 (Above left) Rider-Ericsson Hot Air Pumping Engine castings supplied by the Publishers' model engineering section.

Fig 7.19 (Above right) Gunmetal castings for Stirling engines produced for the Author by John C. Tipton of Hollywood, Birmingham.

"DraegerVentilator" hot air engine fan. This will be a scaled down version of a German fan produced in the early 1900s for the East African market. The recently discovered original co-axial fan, about 2' high, is an excellent example of technical efficiency in a classic design of outstanding appearance.

Modellers who prefer working to a design have some choice from the Plans Service of Nexus Specialist Interests Ltd., who publish Edgar T. Westbury's HEINRICI engine and Robin S. Robbins' ERGO II, a 19cc V2 Marine Rider Engine working plan in remarkable detail, covering not only the construction of the engine, but also the gas burner.

HOME-MADE CASTINGS or CASTINGS MADE TO ONE'S OWN PATTERN

Many modellers reach a stage where they want to experiment with their own castings; some may even attempt to cast their own components either with equipment built to directions from a number of articles found in engineering magazines or with equipment purchased from specialist suppliers. There is a sense of adventure in these kinds of experiments!

The author has only gone as far as making his own

patterns and having two engine frames and a crankshaft bearing, first cast locally by students with a rudimentary knowledge of foundry-work and metallurgy; later the patterns were sent to John C. Tipton of Hollywood, Birmingham, who in his normal efficient manner, produced some high quality castings in gunmetal (Fig 7.19). The same arrangement has been made for flywheels - either John Tipton is asked to supply a number of cast flywheels to a pattern made by himself to the author's specifications (Fig 7.20), or to a pattern sent by the author; whichever way the result is superb quality at reasonable prices and good delivery dates.

Fig 7.20 Cast flywheels by John C. Tipton.

C H A P T E R   E I G H T

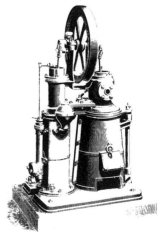

Starting & Running an Engine

The author's very first engine started at the first attempt; it was constructed as faithfully as workshop facilities allowed at the time, from T.E.Haynes' HOT AIR ENGINE, Book 2 of " Model Engineering for Schools" published by John Murray. It cannot be said that all other engines were so cooperative. Indeed some of those built with tender and loving care were quite frustrating, until they eventually started running, but once they did, they ran sweetly afterwards. Even the best designed and well constructed model hot air engines take some time to settle down. Some are even like exasperating prima donnas; a couple have simply refused to run for no apparent reason at all!!

Perhaps even more than an internal combustion engine or a steam engine, a hot air engine requires a period of running-in, both during the various stages of assembly as well as in the initial period of its working life. Whereas the internal combustion engine has explosive power to counter the effect of friction during the running-in stages, a hot air engine has only the pressure of heated gas to make it turn. The running-in involves four stages:

Fig 8.1
A wood-lap device.

Stage 1: Preparatory work prior to assembly;
Stage 2: Running-in the assembled parts without
compression;
Stage 3: Running-in the engine under
compression but without heating;
Stage 4: Running-in the engine under its own
power.

STAGE 1: PRE-ASSEMBLY

The power piston/power cylinder assembly is that part of the engine, irrespective of the type of engine, that is most sensitive and liable to friction, and this assembly requires the greatest attention during construction and the running-in process. No matter how fine a cut and how good a machine finish is given to the two components, the final stages of finishing off this particular assembly should be treated meticulously.

LAPPING may be done in the following manner: a wooden dowel of the same diameter as the piston is dipped in paraffin (kerosene) until well soaked, smeared very lightly with extra-fine valve grinding paste and inserted into the cylinder. The dowel is rotated slowly and evenly while at the same time moved in and out. Dipping in paraffin and smearing with extra-fine grinding paste continues until a silver mirror finish is achieved. The longer the job takes, the better the finish to the bore. Apart from a silver mirror finish, perfect roundness is obtained by constantly turning the lap until there is no binding.

A wooden lap may be prepared in such a way as to allow for its expansion should there be excessive wear of the dowel. One way to do this effectively is to make a cut along the length of the dowel and insert either a thin wedge, or better still a long fine wood screw. The author has assembled a turning device for just this purpose, which is extremely useful, practical, labour-saving and efficient. The device (Fig 8.1), has a 3in lathe chuck mounted on a shaft with ball bearings and a 5in three-step pulley at the other end, the whole assembly fitted on a piece of scrap equipment made of cast iron; the shaft is driven by a second-hand geared motor with a 1½in pulley. The wood lap, lightly smeared, is held in the chuck and is made to revolve at the slowest speed possible. The cylinder is pushed in along its length and then reversed until lapping is completed. If the cylinder is open-ended, any adjustment to the wood lap as above may be made with the cylinder completely in and the tip of the lap showing. The cylinder is thoroughly cleaned with liberal application of paraffin, and finished off with a polishing compound.

The power piston is best finished off while still in the lathe. Once it has been ascertained that the fit is near perfect, the chuck is turned at the slowest speed possible and an extremely fine wet and dry emery paper is applied along the piston length at one go. Only the slightest pressure is required to obtain a smooth and shiny finish. All traces of grit are removed by liberal use of paraffin; application of a polishing compound is recommended at this stage. If at all possible and the material allows, a length equal to the proposed piston stroke plus ⅛in. between the chuck and the piston may be undercut by about 3 thou. so that the cylinder can be tried in place. Any snagging or binding is removed with fine paper or, if very slight, with a polishing compound. Binding spots are easily discernible on the piston and in the cylinder wall; the cylinder and piston are thoroughly cleaned once more and extra-fine oil VERY lightly smeared on the components.

Another part of the engine assembly that requires particular attention during pre-assembly stage is the displacer rod/guide bush fitting; it is a problem area because of the ease with which gas can escape through the fitting of these components when the displacer cylinder is under internal pressure. Although some remedial action can be taken if the leakage is slight, by means of "O" rings or lipped PTFE washers, the precision taken during the machining, fitting and running-in stages outlasts any corrective action taken later. Many beginners use silver steel for displacer rods - unfortunately some of this material is not as perfectly round as one wishes. If one's techniques extends to machining and lapping this rod to a high degree of finish better results from the final assembly may be expected. Whereas a guide bush can be reamed and a good bore achieved, the displacer rod is a more difficult component. At this stage the rod is run-in gently with a smear of light oil throughout its length in the guide bush.

Other moving parts of the engine, such as the crankshaft, connecting rods and crankpins should be tried and turned by hand several times, and any binding, however slight, removed before final assembly.

STAGE 2: THE ASSEMBLED ENGINE

Once the engine has been assembled the second stage of running-in may begin. In order to avoid any unnecessary strain on the crankpins and connecting rods, provision should be made (at the design stage), for the working gas to escape at will. In separate or parallel twin-cylinder with an air connection, the loosening of this part is sufficient. For single-cylinder engines, the author has devised an escape vent drilled in the power piston crown tapped to take a plug bolt.

During this second stage the engine is worked by hand - turning the flywheel several times to check

Fig 8.2
Slow-turning
running-in
device.

again for any binding spots. Once all snags have been ironed out, the engine is turned over at low speed by mechanical means. Any number of methods may be used - the author has a small electro-mechanical device that he has used on almost all the engines constructed, made up of a slow-running electric mains synchronous geared motor that turns a mere 5 RPM (Fig 8.2), fitted with a 2½in pulley, and bolted to a base. The assembled engine, fitted with a pulley, 2in or thereabouts, is also mounted on the base, with the pulleys aligned and a rubber belt as a drive. With this equipment the author has left an engine running-in for a couple of hours, with an occasional drop of light lubricating oil on the moving parts.

STAGE 3: RUNNING-IN UNDER COMPRESSION

So far the engine has been turned without the benefit of internal compression; by now the moving parts have bedded and the engine should be turning easily and freely. Any binding has been removed, the crankshaft, crank and con-rods are smooth in their movements. In Stage 3 compression is reintroduced by reversing the method used in Stage 2. The engine should immediately stiffen in its movements and back pressure felt as the flywheel is turned by hand.

This stage of running-in requires only a relatively SHORT work-out, if sufficient servicing has been

done in the first two stages. However patience is now required as the natural impulse is to skip any further time-consuming exercise and to start the engine. Experience has taught the author that this and the next stage not only ensure the successful completion of the running-in process but also a long trouble-free work-out. The few hundred revolutions required in this Stage can be performed with the aid of a simple device, consisting of a lever about 12 in long (x ½in x ¼in), in the centre of which is drilled a hole of the same diameter as the crankshaft. A grub screw is used to tighten this lever to the shaft. A freely revolving knob at one end will help in turning over the engine by hand against compression.

STAGE 4: RUNNING-IN THE ENGINE UNDER ITS OWN POWER

Heat is applied and the flywheel flicked in the direction the engine has been designed to go. Here speaks the voice of experience - and no engine is like another! With some the flywheel may complete one or two turns, the revolutions increasing as sufficient pressure builds up to over-come the 'hump'. With other engines, they will just run on after the first two flicks as if they have been running for ages!

An engine that refuses to go or will not run beyond a few revolutions, should be allowed to cool down completely before heat is re-applied. Very often this can go on for hours, but perseverance means success. If, on the other hand, the engine still does not run, reference to the four trouble-shooting charts in this chapter is advised. One further word of advice - if the engine continues to be troublesome, either put in on the shelf for the next few months and get on with another design, or use some of the components on other designs. The author knows a number of half-hearted enthusiasts who built an engine that refused to go, and promptly gave up! When they turn up at exhibitions they gape and gulp!!

One word of warning: there is a natural tendency to increase heat in order to increase the speed of a newly developed engine. This should be avoided in the first few runs. The cooling system has be checked carefully as it should be at its most efficient in these early stages. When an engine has reached its efficiency peak, the amount of heating required levels off considerably, whereas cooling efficiency should remain constant.

ENGINE TUNING

An engine may appear to be giving its best performance, yet the odd adjustment may bring about even better results. In engines where the phase angle may be varied, tuning can be attempted by altering the angle first one way, then another, with certain safeguards. In the first place it is assumed that the engine has bedded down and the running-in completed. Secondly the engine revolutions have been read over and over again by a mechanical revolution counter or by stroboscope or by tachometer. A clear indication that engine tuning is successful can only be obtained by reading off and comparing readings between one tune-up and another. The variations can be so slight that they will not be picked up by the naked eye.

The original position of the mechanism is very clearly marked so that it can be resumed in the event that further tuning is not positive. The phase angle is then increased, a few degrees at a time, certainly not more than 5°, preferably 1 or 2. The engine is run a few times and readings are taken. The engine should be allowed to cool off between runs. If the readings are consistent, that is fine; if there is some minor variation, an average over a number of runs is taken. The angle is again advanced by one or two degrees, and readings retaken. This should go on until no further speed improvement is registered or the engine will not run.

The original angle is resumed and further tests are taken below the 90 degree phase, again by small

changes in the settings, again the smaller the difference, the better. The readings are noted down and comparisons made.

EXAMPLE:	
Original runs	600 RPM
93 ° phase	610 RPM
96 ° phase	615 RPM
100 ° phase	620 RPM
103 ° phase	580 RPM
106 ° phase	no run
87 ° phase	600 RPM
84 ° phase	410 RPM
80 ° phase	no run

Obviously the engine's speed efficiency in this example is best at the phase angle of 100 °, giving 620 RPM.

With a twin-cylinder engine it is possible to change the compression ratio by altering one or both strokes of the con-rods, power piston and displacer, WITH APPROPRIATE CHANGES TO THE FITTINGS AND COMPONENTS. These experiments are both useful and instructive. There are so many variables that influence the efficiency of a hot air engine that any experiments conducted on these lines will bring about greater understanding of the thermo-dynamic principles on which the Stirling engine is based.

MAINTENANCE AND TROUBLE-SHOOTING

As with all engines, once the running-in has been completed, a hot air engine should be cleaned of grime and used oil, the power piston wiped and very light lubricating oil smeared on the piston and the displacer rod, while other working parts, crankshaft, con-rods, bushes etc. given a drop of the same lubricant. All bolts and nuts are checked and tightened, and any gasket examined for cracks or tears; worn parts are replaced and the engine prepared for demonstration.

The accompanying charts have been prepared as an easy reference to the more common defects which can prevent the model from working or working efficiently. The illustrations (Figs 8.3 to 8.6) are set out by particular problem areas so that the modeller can locate the defect or defects, cross-checking first against the general area which is suspect and then the particular trouble spot.

POTENTIAL FRICTION POINTS

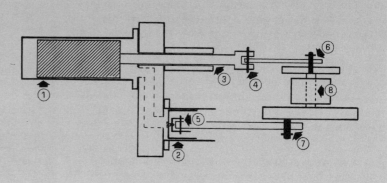

Fig 8.3 Friction diagram showing points of potential friction.

Point 1: Displacer scraping along the cylinder wall;
Point 2: Power piston fit - too tight;
Point 3: Displacer rod fit - too tight;
Points 4 & 5: Gudgeon block/pin fitting of con-rods - too tight;
Points 6 & 7: Crankpin fitting of con-rods - too tight;
Point 8: Crankshaft fitting in the bearing block - too tight.

FRICTION is the greatest 'killer' of hot air engines - any of the points illustrated in fig 8.3, or worse still any combination of points will prevent an engine from running. It is therefore important to check thoroughly all potential problem points or areas during the early stages of running-in and before the final run. Friction points are the first suspect areas in any engine that will simply refuse to go, and not one of these can be disregarded.

Some defects leave tell-tale marks, others indicate binding during the free running period of Stage 2 above. A scratching displacer can be heard, and if taken out of the cylinder can be checked for scratches along the surface. The power piston can be tested by a very simple method of blowing and sucking through the power cylinder end - the sliding fit should just permit the movement of the piston but not the escape of air. Another method is to block by finger or palm of hand one end of the cylinder and hold it down in such a way that it will fall freely if the finger or palm is removed, otherwise it will resist even a tug of the con-rod. The displacer rod can be tested by inverting the displacer cylinder (or engine) and checking whether the weight of the displacer acting on the rod allows easy sliding movement without any lubrication. The other points may be tested and checked visually for binding; the combined friction of the con-rod/crankpin fitting is enough to prevent an engine from running efficiently.

A point of potential friction which is often ignored is the expansion of metal under heat, in this case applying to the power cylinder and the power piston. It should be remembered that different metals react differently when subjected to heat over a long period. Aluminium expands more than brass, which expands more than cast iron or bright mild steel. If a model whose power piston is close to the heat output, such as in a concentric cylinder (which may even be insufficiently or inefficiently cooled), the expansion of the power piston metal may cause some friction if the engine has been running for a long time, causing the engine to slow down, or even stop.

POTENTIAL COMPRESSION-LOSS POINTS

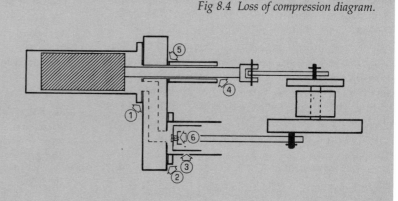

Fig 8.4 Loss of compression diagram.

Point 1: Displacer cylinder flange;
Point 2: Power cylinder flange;
Point 3: Power piston fitting;
Point 4: Displacer rod fitting in guide bush;
Point 5: Guide bush fitting in cylinder plate;
Point 6: Power piston gudgeon block fitting.

LOSS OF COMPRESSION is the second major trouble area. Hot air engines are low pressure machines and therefore the escape of a proportion of the working gas will prevent an engine from running. The major problem points are shown in the above illustration, Fig 8.4. Leaking flanges and cylinder plate fittings can be corrected quickly and without bother, while other components may require additional machining. A loose displacer rod fitting in the guide bush is best corrected by redrilling and reaming the bush to the next size of displacer rod available (e.g. from ⅛in to ⁵⁄₃₂in), while the gudgeon block fitting in the power piston crown can be corrected by a fibre washer or a thick bonding agent.

The major problem point is the power piston fitting in its cylinder - if the fitting is only very slightly loose a minor corrective operation may suffice, although frankly this is not good workmanship. A deep groove in the piston skirt is packed with a finely twisted strand of PTFE tape, or a very precisely fitted "O" ring. The only real solution lies in machining a new piston with greater precision.

A quick and reliable test for the power piston is the following: place the power cylinder open end up on a piece of blotting paper with a few drops of water about the circumference. Place the power piston attached to the con-rod, without any lubrication, just inside the cylinder. If the piston falls through the cylinder quickly, the fitting is too loose or there is a leak in the gudgeon block fitting; if the piston does not budge with finger pressure, the fitting is too tight; if the piston sinks very, very slowly, the fitting is just right!

Compression losses are nearly always detectable by faint hissing noise at any of the points if a very light oil is applied; better still if the engine is placed in a shallow tray with sufficient paraffin to cover the engine, tell tale bubbles will show the location of the trouble spot as soon as the flywheel is turned by hand.

DEAD SPACE or DEAD VOLUME (also known as CUSHION AIR) may not prevent an engine from running, but it will not work efficiently as it should. If dead space is excessive the engine will probably run for a few seconds at a time, but not for long. Dead volume is completely unproductive, allowing heated gas to expand into the unoccupied space without any return for the energy expended in heating it. The major points of dead space are indicated in the above diagram (fig 8.5) and are found usually within the displacer cylinder where the greatest volume of gas is contained. The displacer fitting is critical and the clearance between it and the displacer cylinder wall reduced to bare minimum; for example an engine with a displacer cylinder of 1¼in ID should ideally have a gap not exceeding ¹⁄₆₄in on the radius and ¹⁄₃₂in on the diameter; a ¹⁄₃₂in gap at the top and bottom of the stoke is maximum allowable. Displacers made of aluminium containers expand on the application of high heat, some may even form a dome at the closed (heated) end. This will cause a 'clacking' sound increasing in severity as the hot end is heated up. An engine may 'seize' if the increase in expansion exceeds the gap mentioned above. For engines with a lightweight aluminium container, the author generally allows slightly more than ¹⁄₃₂ in gap; if in the course of running the 'clacking' noise is heard, a slightly thicker gasket material is used between the flange and the cylinder plate, when appropriate.

The connecting air passage in twin-cylinder engines should be the shortest route between them, the bore not exceeding ³⁄₁₆in. The power piston at TDC should just about touch the closed end of the power cylinder; a tiny scrap of thick paper, e.g. 80 gsm, between the top of the piston crown and the cylinder top is sufficient.

DEAD SPACE OR DEAD VOLUME

Fig 8.5 Dead space diagram.

Points 1 & 2: Dead space at the top and bottom of the displacer stroke;
Point 3: Dead space between the displacer and the cylinder wall;
Point 4: Dead space in the connecting air passage;
Point 5: Dead space at the top of the power stroke.

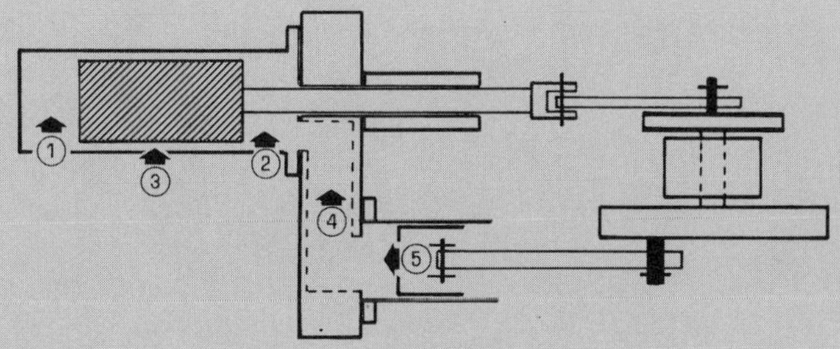

OTHER PROBLEM AREAS

Fig 8.6 Diagram showing other problem areas.

Point 1: Too narrow a gap between the displacer and the cylinder wall - damping effect;
Point 2: Displacer not air-tight;
Point 3: Displacer too heavy;
Point 4: Displacer too short;
Point 5: Compression ratio needs revising;
Point 6: Insufficient cooling.

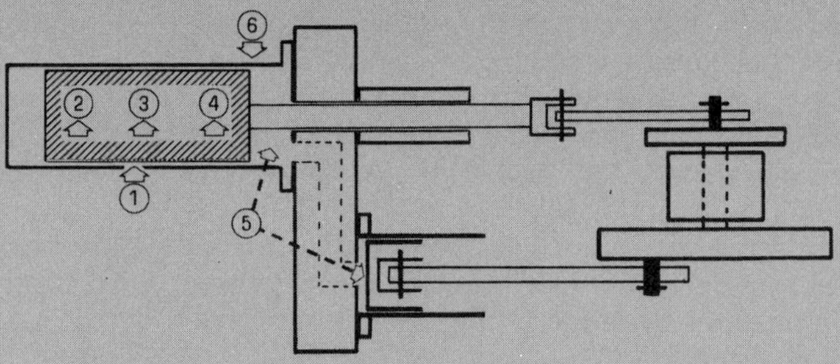

OTHER FACTORS will also effect the working of an engine. If the displacer fitting is too tight and the clearance is not sufficient for the working gas to push through with relative ease, the displacer will act as a damper. This fitting may be roughly tested by the amount of air resistance met during quick movements of the displacer pushed through the cylinder. The displacer should be completely air-tight - the slightest hole will prevent the engine from running due to the expansion of the working gas into the displacer - in effect it will be just dead volume. A heavy displacer is a drag on engine power causing severe friction and sluggishness, while a short displacer and cylinder will not allow for the difference in temperature between the hot end and the cold end to be maintained for long.

Another common failing point is an incorrectly calculated compression ratio. Although an engine may work on a ratio of 1:1 or 1:2, a smaller or larger ratio will probably prevent an engine from running at all. Last, but definitely not least, insufficient cooling will stop an engine dead within a few minutes and should be considered as a failing point. There may be other problems areas that can occur; the above are the more common ones.

The most reliable engine test is the engine "bounce". With the engine cold, if the flywheel is flicked lightly, it should not complete its revolution, but bounce back, more or less to its original position. If it is flicked sharply, it will turn a couple of revolutions and again bounce backwards and forwards a few times. An engine that has little compression or too much friction will not bounce; instead the flywheel may stop anywhere in its revolutions. Another indication of the efficiency of the power piston assembly is the immediate reaction of the flywheel as soon as heat is applied - the flywheel will turn slightly one way or the other.

One other indication of a "good" engine is the length of time it will take to stop once heat is removed; if the engine stops dead or quickly there is in all probability some friction in the engine; if the engine continues to run over for as long as 30 to 60 seconds, that is a sign that the engine is smooth and that there is good regeneration of heat.

A Stirling Selection

1. (Previous page) V type engine (courtesy: Keith James). **2**. Original "Rider Ericsson" Hot Air Pumping engine under restoration by A.C. Spooner. **3**. Rhombic 100cc Stirling engine by Andy Ross.
4. A diaphragm powered Stirling engine by Geoff Bartlett. **5**. Roy Darlington's schematic diagram of the Stirling Cycle. **6**. Dietr Schager's Beta-Ringbom engine.

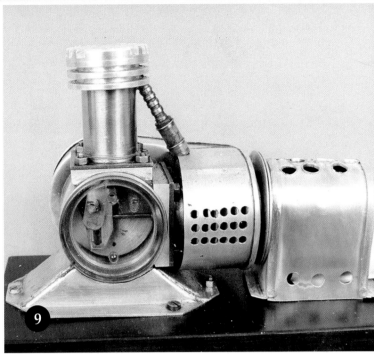

7. and **8.** Two more of the many impressive Stirling engines built by Andy Ross. **9.** Air cooled Stirling engine by Cristinu Vassallo. **10.** Ross Linkage drive Stirling engine by Roy Darlington. **11.** Swash plate drive Stirling engine by Albert Debono.

C H A P T E R   N I N E

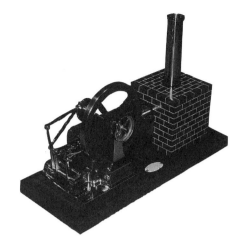

...Of Models & Modelling

Fig 9.1 BAILEY model engine (ca 1895) from M.P. Symes, Ashford, Kent.

Models of Stirling engines and other hot air engines have been around far longer than one imagines, some for over a century! A few are still in existence, in Museums and in private hands, some capable of turning at the slightest touch of a flame. Occasionally one hears of a small cob-webbed model found in a box of disused toys in an attic - many years ago the author, well before he knew what a hot air engine was, saw a now fairly common Carette toy model in Portobello Road for which an American tourist haggled and paid five pounds!

AN OVERVIEW OF OLD MODELS

The earliest factory-produced models appear to be scaled model versions of the BAILEY (also read LEHMANN) horizontal engine, complete with

Fig 9.2 Models from GEORGES CARETTE (1890 - 1910) Courtesy: New Cavendish Books, "The Great Toys of Georges Carette".

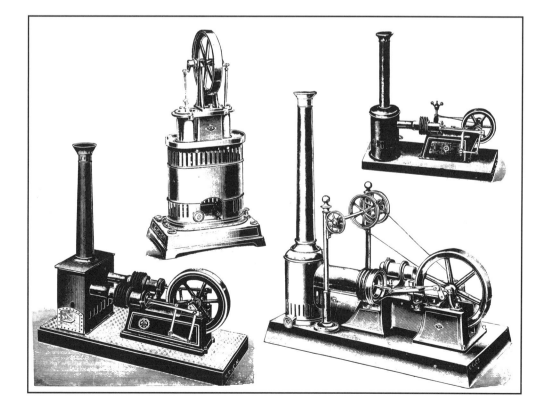

simulated brickwork and highly accurate lever mechanism. The model in Fig 1.10 is found in the Science Museum, Kensington, apparently donated in 1894; the model in Fig 9.1 belongs to Mr M.P. Symes of Ashford, Kent who inherited this model from his late father; he stripped it, cleaned and rebuilt parts of it and is now a showpiece model. A similar LEHMANN model, without trimmings, is found in the Deutsches Museum, Munich.

Of great interest to serious modellers is a catalogue of engines and components which was accidentally discovered fairly recently by the author in Foyles of London. This encyclopedia of toy engines was originally published in 1911, re-published in 1976 by NEW CAVENDISH Books and is called "The Great Toys of Georges Carette (of Nuremberg)". It is in effect a trade catalogue of mechanical toys and a comprehensive survey of the products of Carette, "manufacturers of mechanical, optical and electrical toys and working models". Hot Air engines (BETA and GAMMA configurations) take five pages of the catalogue, with many more pages devoted to steam engines and useful accessories such as shafts, pulleys, flywheels and hundreds of other items (Fig 9.2).

The model engines sold by Carette were beautifully finished, the components and fittings being japanned or nickelled, the bases were either cast iron or tin plated with ornamental tiled patterns and the whole mounted on highly polished wooden bases. The horizontal engines sported a tall ornamental chimney with fluted or bell-shaped tops made of brass. The furnace was very elaborate and pleasing to the eye; invariably these furnaces had a grate opening or door of a different metal, usually brass, standing out significantly against the black japanned metal. Most of the engines had finned cooling, (called "ribs" in the English version of the catalogue).

Some of the Carette models had shafting carried on ornamental pillars with belts between the flywheel pulley and the shafting pulley; additional pulleys on the shaft were presumably meant to drive other components - all very elaborate and highly decorative. Different sizes of each model were produced and sold.

It is interesting to note that Carette introduced the concentric BETA models in the year 1903, a design which was "protected" in Germany. The description of this particular design as being "extra powerful Hot Air Engines, the displacer and the working cylinder are arranged the one inside the other", meant, allowing for a free translation, that the displacer and power piston were arranged within one cylinder.

Another interesting feature was the use and types of burners - gas burners, spirit lamps and "spirit vapour generators" were used on the models, the customers having the right of choice. One presumes, and this is confirmed by the drawings, that the spirit vapour generator was a contrivance that produced gas from methylated spirit under pressure. One such burner was described as giving five hours of heat between refilling!

Other Carette models were vertical in design, not unlike the Rider Hot air pump, and two of them employed a fan to create a breeze. A vertical pump model was described as being capable of drawing water from 20 inches and delivered to a height of 10 yards - no mean feat for a small model standing in all 19 inches.

Immediately after WW1, a number of models appeared on the market as "boys' toys", but there was little sustained interest, mainly because the steam had a particular fascination, the engine was more powerful and more versatile, with attractive

Fig 9.3
Various experimental engines by David Urwick.

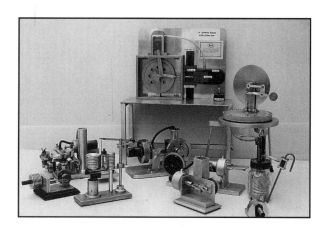

Fig 9.4 A collection of Stirling engines by Roy Darlington, Worthing, Sussex.

alternatives as generating stations, steam rollers, steam boats - the varieties were far more interesting. In fact the general impression one gets was that the hot air engine "could be given to little Tommy" because it was not considered as a dangerous toy! This situation prevailed for several years, with the odd article describing the construction of another basic model in magazines for boys or model mechanics.

THE PRESENT....

The period from the 1940s to the 1970s is signposted by three important studies and 'papers', not all directly related to model engineering, but their contents have in some way or other prompted more research and influenced "home engineers" to turn their attention to the Stirling engine. These studies are still consulted and referred to just like readings from the gospel!

In 1940, during the early war years, a series of articles "Practical Notes on Hot Air Engines", written by 'Artificer", was published in MODEL ENGINEER, the first article appearing in September 1940. In 1946-47, a series of articles appeared in the PHILIPS TECHNICAL REVIEW, which revealed in great detail the experimental work done behind the scenes by Philips of Eindhoven, in their development of the Philips Air Motor. Then, in 1959, a three-part study by Dr T. Finkelstein, Ph.D., A.M.MechE, appeared in THE ENGINEER under the heading "AIR ENGINES". These three contributions did more to kindle interest in the hot air engine than any other publications, up to that period. The turning point appears to be the early 1970s when a number of well written and researched articles started to appear fairly regularly in MODEL ENGINEER. Contributions by stalwarts of the hobby, such as Edgar T. Westbury, David Urwick, F.M.Collins, Stan Bray, F.Brian Thomas, Andy Ross,

Robin S. Robbins and others did much to create and sustain an interest. At the same time more models appeared at the MODEL ENGINEERING Exhibitions in Wembley, Crystal Palace and lately in Olympia, both on Club Stands as well as participants in the Edgar T. Westbury, A.N.Clarke and later F. Brian Thomas Memorial Trophy Competitions.

Professor D. H. Chaddock was especially instrumental in promoting the hot air engine and his articles were meant to encourage the beginners and the falterers. The two most important articles were "Hot Air Wrinkles" and "Why a Hot Air Engine?" both of which appeared in MODEL ENGINEER (see Appendix 4 for Bibliography).

One Engineer who was dedicated in his research on model Stirling engines, and who was a prolific writer, was the late David Urwick. David retired to Malta on selling up his engineering business, set up a well equipped workshop overlooking a 300-year old garden, and devoted all his spare time to this hobby, encouraged by his devoted wife, Jane. His experiments with regenerators and later with special mechanical drives (SIEMANS, SWASH-PLATE and NUTATOR), were masterpieces of experimentation and writing (Fig 9.3).

(The author got to know David Urwick in the last few years he lived in Malta before he decided to return to England where he died two years later at the age of 82. Up to the end he was still advising on the construction of his design UBIQUE - see Chapter 6. The author and David spent long hours, David the mentor and the author the learner, going through the various experiments.)

Model engineers belong to different categories, sometimes overlapping all the way - there are those who enjoy building a model, then advance to more demanding designs; those that aim for demonstration and exhibition by their standards; those who aim for power and those who start from the first category and go through the lot! The common elements are enthusiasm and the sense of sharing, almost unequaled in any other hobby.

THE FOLLOWING IS A DEDICATION TO SOME MODEL ENGINEERS WHOM THE AUTHOR GOT TO KNOW, EITHER THROUGH MEETING AT ENGINEERING EXHIBITIONS OR BY CORRESPONDENCE. THERE IS NO ORDER OR PREFERENCE IN THE WAY THEY ARE MENTIONED, NOR IS ANY ONE ENGINE MORE WORTHY OF MENTION THAN ANOTHER. THE WHOLE AIM OF THIS EXERCISE IS TO ENCOURAGE BEGINNERS AND TO SHOW THE WAY AHEAD.

Some engineers have made their mark in one way or another. A fellow modeller, Roy Darlington of

Fig 9.5 (Below left) Low Temperature Diferential engine by Roy Darlington.
Fig 9.6 (Above right) Free Piston, flywheel-less engine by Roy Darlington.
Fig 9.7 (Below right) Independent Displacer MARTINI-design Engine by Roy Darlington.

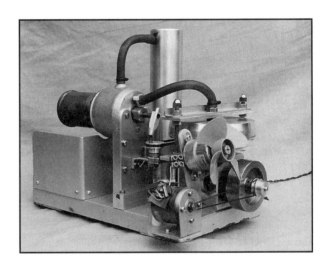

Worthing, Sussex built an amazing amount of different Stirling engines (Fig 9.4) within four years of his retirement, all high quality exhibition-standard, which have provoked interest and enthusiasm in many beginners during visits to Exhibitions where he not only placed the models on show, but demonstrated their capability. His Low Temperature Differential engine built around a piece of gas mains pipe (Fig 9.5) runs for long hours on a bowl of hot water, or solar power, a small night candle or even a spotlight. The other components are a polystyrene displacer, a balanced power piston, an 8in aluminium disc and a finely tuned mechanism. This engine was well described by Richard White in MODEL ENGINEER of February 4, 1994. His Ringbom style engine (Fig 9.6) has an underslung displacer assembly and a counter-balanced power piston which can be adjusted according to the tuning required for running the engine, the counter-weights being moved or removed to give the right harmonic speed.   Roy's most advanced and complicated project to date is an engine that has a displacer working independently of the engine mechanism; in fact it is run by pulleys and a belt off a small variable speed electric motor (Fig 9.7).

One of the pulleys drives the displacer by means of a ball-joint/crank mechanism, the speed of the motor controlling the strokes of the displacer, and the volumetric fluctuations in turn controlling the power piston strokes and thereby the engine speed - at a certain speed however the power piston loses phase with the displacer and the engine stalls.

Roy's 'buddy', John Wilkinson of Steyning, W. Sussex has a collection of "oldies" that are rarely seen in such a variety; among these are a KYKO fan (Fig 9.8), two JOST floor standing fans , a hot-air engine-driven MAESTRO-PHONE gramo-phone (Fig 9.9) and a number of old toy models similar to the Carette mentioned earlier (Figs 9.10 and 9.11). John also exhibits this collection with pride as well as other Stirling engines he has built.

At the other end of the scale and on the other side of the ocean, Andy Ross of Columbus, Ohio, USA has developed a number of very powerful Stirling Rider engines that for volume and size develop sheer power beyond the expectations of any modeller. Possibly no engineer has managed to reach such peaks before. In his semi-technical and fascinating book, "MAKING STIRLING

Fig 9.8 (Far left) "KYKO" FAN (ca 1910).

Fig 9.9 (Left) "MAESTRO-PHONE" gramaphone (ca 1910) Stirling engine driven.

Fig 9.10 (Below left) Concentric Stirling model toy engine (ca 1920.

Fig 9.11 (Below right) A popular early model toy engine (ca 1920).

Fig 9.12 (Bottom left) 60cc STIRLING RIDER engine.

Fig 9.13 (Bottom right) The D-60cc, an upgraded STIRLING RIDER engine.

Figs 9.8 -9.11 from John Wilkinson, Steyning, W. Sussex. 9.12-9.13 by Andy Ross, Ohio, USA.

ENGINES", published in 1993 (see Bibliography), he mapped out his experiences in developing the Stirling Rider engine from 1971 to date. He describes the various engines he has built, his experiments, his successes and the occasional bugs. This book shows not only his dedication but also the great craftsmanship with which he designed and machined the engines and their components. These Stirling engines vary in size from an 11cc Rhombic drive to a 15cc alpha yoke drive, then on to a 35cc, a 60cc (Fig 9.12), an upgraded D-60cc (Fig 9.13) and now under test a 90cc engine seen here mounted on a bicycle (Fig 9.14).

At one time Andy Ross decided to invest some of his energy into producing engines in kit form with which other model engineers could experiment. One of these, the B-20 was a small compact engine with a Ross linkage yoke drive; however lack of interest on the part of modellers and considerable effort required to service this venture, made him channel his attention back to further development.

A mechanical drive system he has invented, the Ross Linkage, and the later version, the compact

inverted Yoke Drive, will remain one of his greatest contributions to the development of the Stirling Rider engine (Fig 6.16).

Another modeller, from the States, (San Francisco, California) Alphonse Vassallo, originally from Malta, whose brother also appears in various sections of this book, has experimented with solar-powered Stirling engines; his latest engine however being this unusual reverse-hot-cylinder-to-power engine to his own design, (Fig 9.15). In this engine Alphonse has transferred the burner next to the power cylinder thereby applying volumetric expansion directly to power. Compressed air on the return stroke of the power piston is diverted to the cool side of the displacer cylinder through two valves, a reed valve placed at the top of the power cylinder to divert air to the crankshaft, and a rotary valve on the crankshaft. The crankshaft, which is sealed at both ends, has a flat part milled opposite the pipe input/output sockets and this serves as a rotating port. This engine has an amazing turn of speed and torque unexpected of a configuration that apparently goes against all the parameters of the Stirling principle.

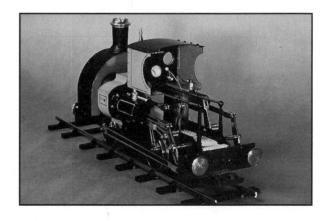

Fig 9.14 (Top left) 90cc STIRLING RIDER engine mounted on a bicycle, by Andy Ross.
Fig 9.15 (Above left) A Stirling engine of unusual design by Alphonse Vassallo of California, USA.
Fig 9.16 (Above right) Stationary Mill Stirling engine.
Fig 9.17 (Right) "CALORIC No.1" Hot Air engine Locomotive. Figs 9.16 and 9.17 by Roy Key, Stoke-on-Trent.

The power cylinder has a 1in bore and a 1in stroke, the displacer cylinder a 1¼in bore and a 1½in stroke, giving a ratio of almost 1.85 : 1.

Some of the most beautifully finished working models, demonstration and display standard, are the handwork of Roy Key of Stoke-on-Trent, Staffs, His ERICSSON Hot Air Engine, featured also in Chapter 14, is a masterpiece of high caliber bench fitting, machining and paint work. Four other models from Roy Key which are featured in this Chapter are of the same high class presentation, which gives tremendous standing to the humble Stirling engine. The first engine built by Roy Key, in 1951, was a stationary hot air mill engine (Fig 9.16), based on a design which appeared in MODEL ENGINEER of April 14, 1949, under the name "Intruders". From the beginning Roy insisted on a high standard of finish, which earned him the third place in the 'Stationary Section' of the first MIDLANDS MODEL ENGINEERING EXHIBITION, Granby Halls, Leicester.

The "CALORIC No 1", a hot air engine-locomotive was the subject of a two-part article written by Roy Key himself for MODEL ENGINEER of July 3 and August 7, 1992. The photograph of this locomotive, taken by John Atkinson, (Fig 9.17) shows in detail the intricate and exciting mechanism of the engine. Roy then followed this model with a traction engine, (Fig 9.18), which has a power-operated crane. The engine in Fig 9.19 which is also Roy Key's design, employs a rocking beam, U-shaped at one end, to lift the hooped displacer yoke; the power piston at the top of the displacer cylinder is at right angles, giving the engine a single-throw crank, driving both the power piston and the displacer through the under-beam at the same time. Not only is the mechanism pleasing and efficient, the whole engine layout with the working platform, ascending staircase, supporting columns and chimney lends a very elegant look to the model.

The 'piece de resistance' is of course the elegant ERICSSON engine (Fig 9.20), which is described in MODEL ENGINEER of February 18, 1994. No wonder that this superb model fetched a selling price of £2,420 at Christie's Auction!

The Maltese engineering community were fortunate to have had among them a Stirling personality like David Urwick; he shared his enthusiasm with a number of local model engineers, among whom is Cristinu Vassallo, brother of Alphonse mentioned earlier. Cristinu's principal hobby is small model engine development, steam, internal combustion, aircraft or marine, Stirling engines, photographic camera mechanisms; his specialty is miniature engines. His collection of hot air engines, all different and mostly to his own design, makes him one of the

Fig 9.18 (above) Traction Stirling engine with power-operated crane.

Fig 9.19 Stationary rocking-beam Stirling engine.

Fig 9.20 (below) An elegant ERICSSON engine. (Courtesy: Christies Images).

Figs 9.18 to 9.20 by Roy Key.

most prolific modellers. Some of his engines are featured in one way or another through the components; his latest, a four-cylinder Scotch yoke drive Stirling (Fig 9.21), is a compact, powerful model suitable for marine or traction application.

Another Maltese model engineer, Professor Charles Camilleri of the University of Malta, has entered into the model world with two beautifully finished and unusual engines based on different mechanical drives. His horizontal rhombic (Fig 9.22) has a fast turn of speed, it is however at low speed that one can appreciate the delightful frog's legs motion; at speed the mechanism becomes a blur, however it is very smooth and whisper silent. The compact swing-beam engine (Fig 9.23) is a magnificent piece of precision engineering, embodying a number of mechanisms that only a craftsman can assemble in such a small model. The turn of speed and torque is quite surprising.

Mr E. Woods of Thornton, Cleveleys, Lancs, discovered an unusual model hot air engine of which no details as to date of manufacture or maker are available (Fig 9.24). It is a twin cylinder engine with a fairly substantial cooling jacket and a pump, driven by a ball joint in the flywheel, which pushes the cooling water into the water jacket, the hot water flowing back into the top of a nearby tank. The power cylinder on the opposite side of the engine employs a rocker arm, as does the displacer, to give the 90 degree phase from the flywheel. The use of some castings in its construction could indicate that this was not a "one-off" model; whether any other will eventually surface remains to be seen.

Mr F.M.Collins' famous models, the "PHOELIX", (Fig 9.25) and "WHIPPET", (Fig 9.26) are reproduced here as examples of great precision small models with tremendous performance. The construction of "WHIPPET", a competition winning 12 ozs total weight, 5cc and delivering 4.5 watts, is well described by Mick Collins in his five-part article in MODEL ENGINEER between May 16 and August 15, 1980.

Mike Symes, of Ashford, Middlesex, has a beautifully restored horizontal Bailey model (LEHMANN type) made in the 1890s (ca.). On the same principle and with similar configuration, Mike has constructed two other model engines, one is a self-propelled traction engine, and the other a 3 watt stationary engine (Fig 9.27) with an

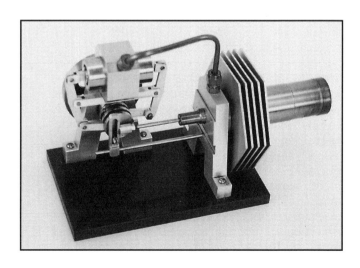

Fig 9.21 (above left) Four cylinder Scotch-yoke drive engine by Cristinu Vassallo, Malta.

Fig 9.22 (above right) Horizontal Rhombic drive Stirling engine by Charles Camilleri, Malta.

Fig 9.23 (right) Compact swing twin-rocker Stirling engine by Charles Camilleri, Malta.

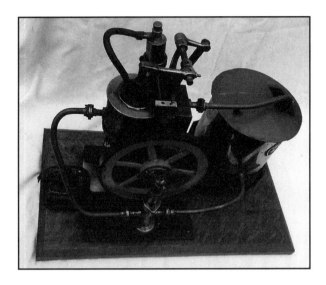

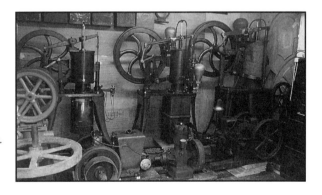

Fig 9.24 (top left) Unusual early hot air engine from Eric Woods, Thornton Cleveleys, Staffs.
Fig 9.25 (above) "PHOELIX" high performance Stirling engine by Mick Collins, Elstead, Surrey.
Fig 9.26 (top right) "WHIPPET", award-winning Stirling engine by Mick Collins.
Fig 9.27 (above right) Stationary Stirling engine based on the LEHMANN/BAILEY design, by Mike Symes of Ashford, Middlesex.
Fig 9.28 (right) Some ERICSSON RIDER engine pumps, part of a collection of vintage engines from A.C. Spooner of Hailsham, East Sussex.

improved linkage system and an ingenious double-roller arrangement for supporting the long displacer.

Mike considers the early Lehmann engine as basically a well designed and constructed piece of machinery which should translate well in small scale engineering, giving scope for an attractive bench or mantelpiece model with a concentric piston configuration and an interesting linkage system which shows up well at the relatively low speed of these engines.

There are a number of Stirling enthusiasts whose hobby extends to collecting vintage engines which are now becoming increasingly rare. One such enthusiast, Mr. A.C. Spooner of Hailsham, East Sussex, has an impressive set (Fig 9.28) of Ericsson, Heinrici, Robinson and Kyko engines, as well as scaled down models of some of the above, and some small size original engines which could have been engineering colleges' projects.

C H A P T E R   T E N

How to Construct "Dolly" I

(Since the first project, "DOLLY", appeared in the original publication, MODELLING STIRLING AND HOT AIR ENGINES, it has become accepted as a remarkably simple but effective introduction to model hot air engine construction and quite a number of beginners used this model as their first step. In the course of time the author was asked if he could design a simple engine made from castings - the result is "DOLLY II", described in Chapter 11.)

'DOLLY', (Fig 10.1) is a basic model specially designed for beginners to the hobby. It is a compact engine and if well finished makes an ideal demonstration or desk-top model. The engine can easily attain a speed of 1000RPM and will continue to run steadily as long as a flame is applied. Heat from a spirit burner or solid fuel is sufficient. The construction allows for some minor but nevertheless interesting experiments; an up-scaled version of the engine can serve as a basis for research into

Fig 10.1
Completed engine.

Fig 10.2 General engine layout.

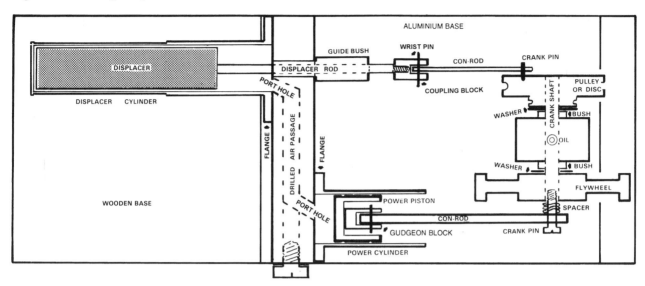

the various parameters of engine construction and the basic principles of thermodynamics.

The design is pleasing to the eye, has clean lines and is uncomplicated in construction; it should pose no problems to the modeller or to anyone interested to learn how the Stirling engine works. Only basic workshop tools are required but access to a small lathe and to soldering and brazing equipment will ensure trouble-free working and a good finish.

GENERAL ENGINE LAYOUT

The engine consists of two cylinders placed parallel to each other and bolted on opposite sides of a cylinder plate; one of the cylinders houses the displacer, while the other is the power cylinder. The displacer rod and power piston con-rod run parallel to a central drive mechanism consisting of a flywheel on the power side and a disc or narrow pulley on the displacer side. The expansion of gas, increased pressure and compression are transmitted from one cylinder to the other through a 'hidden' connecting passage drilled through the cylinder plate in such a way that the working gas (air) is well contained between the two cylinders. Heating is by methylated spirit (solid or liquid) while cooling is by the fin method (see Chapter 4). A larger scale model can be heated by gas and cooled by a water jacket. The design and construction allows for two parameters to be changed and experimented upon: phase angle and the ratio of volumes.

METHOD OF CONSTRUCTION

The CYLINDER PLATE is made from ⅜in or ½in dural, polished, marked and drilled. On the power side the plate is drilled to take the displacer rod

guide bush, the power cylinder (flange), and at an angle shown in Fig 10.2, the power side of the inter-connecting port hole. On the reverse, the displacer cylinder side, the plate is drilled to take the displacer cylinder flange and again at the angle shown, the displacer port. The cylinder plate is then drilled crosswise from the power side to connect with the two angled ports from the displacer and power cylinders (Fig 10.2). The hole is tapped to take a ¼in bolt and fibre washer as an airtight plug. The displacer rod guide bush hole is drilled and tapped 0 BA, the holes for the two flanges are tapped 4 BA, the interconnecting air passage is drilled ³⁄₁₆in. The cylinder plate is also drilled and tapped (2 BA) underneath for bolting to the dural base.

The POWER CYLINDER is open at both ends with a flange soldered on, or bonded (heat and freeze method - see Chapter 7). The cylinder is made from solid drawn thin walled bright mild steel, honed and lapped to take the power piston.

The POWER PISTON is machined from a suitable piece of cast iron, (BMS is a good alternative). The piston is finished smooth, however one or two oil grooves may aid compression since a smear of light oil retained in these grooves will provide internal lubrication. A precision gas-tight fit is essential for the engine to run and to run at a good speed; it should be friction free, sliding freely without binding. Time consumed in preparing this component is never wasted. The piston crown is drilled and countersunk to take a 2 BA bolt which will screw into the gudgeon block made from ⅝in brass, drilled and tapped 2 BA at one end and slotted at the other end to take the con-rod. A ¹⁄₁₆in hole is drilled crosswise in the slotted part of the gudgeon block to take the gudgeon or wrist pin. The con-rod is shaped from ⅛in x ¼in or ⅜in BMS flat bar, shaped and then drilled at one end to take the gudgeon pin and at the other end the crankpin.

The DISPLACER CYLINDER is made from bright mild steel tube, silver soldered, brazed or welded at the closed end and fitted to a flange at the other (cold) end. Before fitting to the flange it is recommended that the displacer cylinder is reduced in wall thickness as much as possible, preferably between 50% to 75%. This will give better heat transfer from the burner and lessen conduction of heat along the length of the displacer.

The DISPLACER is made or cut from a suitable aluminium container; in this engine it is from a felt pen body. A dural plug is machined to fit in tightly into the displacer, then drilled and tapped 6 BA. The length of the displacer should be approximately $\frac{1}{16}$in less that the internal length of the cylinder; there is a good possibility that the aluminium displacer will expand very slightly by forming a dome on the sustained application of heat and a 'clacking' noise will be heard while the engine is running. A very thin fibre gasket between the flange and the cylinder plate will cure this defect. A lightweight thin gauge BMS displacer, greatly reduced in wall thickness will make an even better displacer, since this metal is not as good a heat conductor as aluminium.

The most important requirements in the displacer are two: the annular gap between the displacer and the cylinder wall should not exceed $\frac{1}{64}$in on the radius or $\frac{1}{32}$in on the diameter and that it is absolutely air tight.

The DISPLACER ROD GUIDE BUSH is best machined from $\frac{3}{8}$in brass rod, reduced at one end and threaded 0 BA. The bush is centre - drilled, drilled and reamed $\frac{1}{8}$in to take the displacer rod.

The DRIVE MECHANISM consists of a central dural block, $\frac{5}{8}$in thick, x 1in wide x $1\frac{3}{8}$ in high. A $\frac{5}{16}$in hole is drilled laterally (see Fig 10.5) to take two brass bushes, or if desired two ball bearings,

OD $\frac{3}{8}$in., ID $\frac{1}{8}$in. An oil lubricating hole is drilled from the top if brass bushes are used. The block is also drilled underneath to take two 2 BA screws. The flywheel is either cast or machined from 2 $\frac{1}{2}$in brass, $\frac{1}{2}$in thick and drilled $\frac{1}{8}$in to take the crankshaft; the inner flywheel boss is drilled and tapped 6 BA to take a grub screw. The outside boss of the flywheel should be at least $1\frac{1}{8}$in in diameter to allow for various crankpin fittings in the event of making further experiments and alterations to the stroke. At this stage the crankpin is fitted $\frac{1}{4}$in off-centre to give the power piston a $\frac{1}{2}$in stroke.

The other part of the drive mechanism is a disc or a narrow pulley, depending on whether or not the modeller intends to attempt driving another accessory. The diameter of this disc can vary between $1\frac{1}{2}$in to $2\frac{1}{2}$in provided it is finished flush, the boss being on the inner side. A 6 BA grub screw is used to bolt the disc to the crankshaft. The crankpin for the displacer con-rod is inserted $\frac{7}{16}$in offcentre to give the displacer a $\frac{7}{8}$in stroke.

There are various ways of making the crankpin/con-rod fitting: using 4 BA bolts screwed into the flywheel and disc with corresponding drilled holes in the con-rods; using $\frac{1}{8}$in silver steel dowels threaded 4 BA to fit in the flywheel/disc, again with corresponding holes if using brass bushes in the con - rods; using miniature ball bearings in the con-rods (by far the most efficient way), with dowels or pins to fit in the bearings and screwed into the flywheel/disc, etc.

A polished DURAL BASE completes the engine frame; once the cylinder plate and the drive mechanism block are measured, marked and fitted in place, the finished engine is mounted on a wooden base with a rubber disc at each corner.

FINAL STAGES OF ASSEMBLY

The cylinder plate is prepared with the interconnecting air passage, with the plug bolt lightly screwed in. The power cylinder is screwed in place

Fig 10.3 (Left) Side elevation - power side.

Fig 10.4 (Middle) Side elevation - displacer side.

Fig 10.5 (Right) Front elevation.

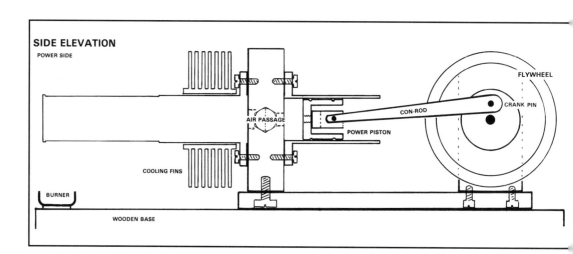

ensuring that the air-vent connection is completely clear. The displacer rod guide bush is finger-tightened with a smear of Loctite Screwlock 222, the displacer rod and displacer are inserted from the reverse side, and checked for alignment and straight fitting.

To ensure that the displacer cylinder is correctly positioned so as to avoid friction between it and the displacer, a piece of electrical tape is wound twice round the displacer hot end, and another piece at the front end. The cylinder plate is held face down in a vice and the displacer cylinder slipped on to the displacer; the cylinder should fit just right - if it is too loose, another turn or two is made with the tape. Finally the position of the flange is marked on the cylinder plate, holes drilled and tapped accordingly. The tape is removed, a light gasket placed between the displacer cylinder flange and the cylinder plate, the whole assembly screwed in and the displacer is tried for friction. Any adjustments required are made at this stage. The main problem normally is friction of the displacer against the cylinder wall sometimes as a result of an unaligned fitting of the displacer rod into the displacer; the method used by the author is to place the displacer rod in the chuck of a bench drill (or lathe chuck), revolving it by hand and using a surface gauge or a suitable piece of makeshift equipment, such a long canvas needle fitted to an upright stand, to check whether the displacer is running true.

The next stage involves the assembly of the drive mechanism - the flywheel and disc are fitted onto the crankshaft with washers and spacers as required for the correct alignment of the con-rods which must not too far out on the crankpins or too tight against the flywheel/disc. The drive mechanism and the cylinder plate are then bolted to the metal base.

CON-ROD LENGTH CALCULATIONS: the following method may be used to ensure the correct lengths of the two con-rods, assuming that these have been drilled at one end only, and the other end is still unmarked.

The power piston is inserted all the way into its cylinder with a scrap of paper at the top to allow for minute expansion. The flywheel is then turned so that the crankpin is in its nearest position to the power cylinder. A scriber is used to mark the position of the crankpin, which incidentally is known as Top Dead Centre, TDC. With the power piston in this position, the disc on the displacer side is turned so that the crankpin is nearest to the base, and therefore at right angles to the first crankpin. The displacer is pushed almost right in (less $\frac{1}{32}$in), the disc is turned so that its crankpin is now closest to the displacer cylinder (or cylinder plate), and crankpin position is marked on the displacer con-rod. The con-rods are then fitted in place; there should be no need for any alterations if the above exercise and the right measurements have been taken. However the displacer assembly may need the odd adjustment: such measures could include a thicker gasket or reducing the stroke very very slightly by placing the crankpin closer to the crankshaft centre. Care is recommended not to disturb too much the ratio of the two volumes.

TIMING THE DRIVE MECHANISM

The displacer is set 90° (a quarter of a turn) in advance of the power piston. Therefore if the engine is designed to turn clockwise, the setting of the drive mechanism should be done in this manner:

(a) the flywheel (power piston side) is turned so that the crankpin is at its highest position above the base (Fig 10.6a);

(b) the disc (attached to the displacer con-rod) is turned so that the crankpin is furthest away from the cylinder plate/displacer cylinder (Fig 10.6b); in this position the displacer is in the cold side of

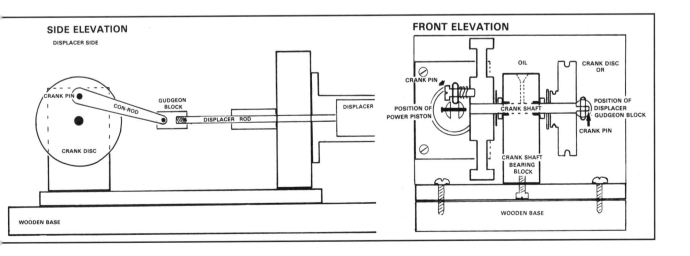

DOLLY I: ENGINE SPECIFICATIONS

	IMPERIAL SIZES	NEAREST "WORKING" METRIC EQUIVALENTS
Dural base	5in x 3½in x ¼in	125mm x 90m x 6mm
Dl. cylinder plate	3½in x 2¼in x ⅝in	90mm x 60mm x 15mm
Displacer cylinder	3⁹⁄₁₆in external length 3½in internal length ¾in OD ²¹⁄₃₂in ID	90mm 89mm 19mm 16.5mm
Displacer cylinder flange	1½in x 1½in	40mm x 40mm
Displacer	⅝in OD 2¹⁹⁄₃₂in length	15.5mm 66mm
Displacer rod	⅛in silver steel 2⅞in to coupling block centre	3mm 73mm
Displacer con- rod	1⁹⁄₁₆in between centres	40mm
Power cylinder	1½in length ¾in OD ¹¹⁄₁₆in ID	40mm 19mm 17.5mm
Power cylinder flange	1⅛in x 1½in	30mm x 40mm
Power piston	⅞in length ¹¹⁄₁₆in OD	22mm 17.5mm
Power piston con-rod	2⅝in between centres	66.5mm
Guide bush	1⅜in length ⅜in OD	35mm 10mm
Flywheel	2⅜in OD ⅜in rim	60mm 10mm
Displacer disc/pulley drive	1½in OD ⅜in thickness, including boss	40mm 10mm
Central drive dural block	⅝in thickness 1in length 1⅜in height	15mm-16mm 25mm 35mm
Cooling fins	1in total cover 2in - 2¼in OD	25mm 50mm - 60mm
Power piston stroke	½in	12.5mm
Displacer stroke	⅞in	22mm.

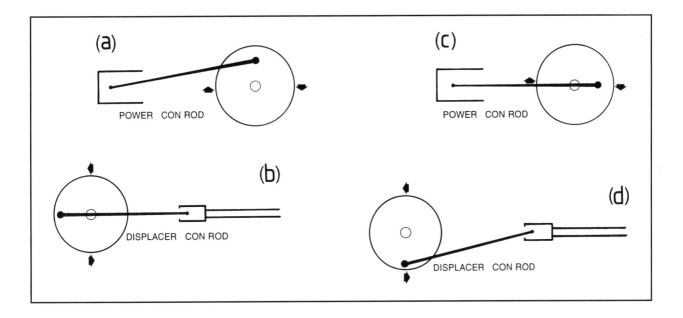

the cylinder and the air in the hot space;

(c) if the flywheel is turned from position (a) clockwise for a quarter of a turn (Fig 10.6c), the power piston is at BDC while ......

(d) the displacer crankpin is in its lowest position relative to the base and the displacer is half way into the hot space (Fig 10.6d).

If it is desired that the flywheel turns anti-clockwise, all that is required is to reverse the position of the displacer by 180° while leaving the power piston crankpin in its highest position relative to the base.

It may happen that an engine works better if the phase angle varies slightly above or below 90°.

PERFORMANCE & MODIFICATIONS

The first prototype made its first full run after about 15 minutes - the flywheel had been flicked forward a number of times. However the engine bounce and increasing flywheel response indicated from the beginning that there was sufficient 'feel' in the engine to show promise. The first run lasted for about two minutes but the engine would not run again until it had cooled down completely; at

Fig 10.6 (a) Power Piston. (b) Displacer (c) Power Piston. (d) Displacer.

first it was thought that this was an indication of compression loss. Eventually the running time increased as did the revolutions. The displacer cylinder was modified by further thinning down and reducing the cylinder wall considerably at the hot end with the result that engine response to heat was faster and revolutions increased substantially. A further modification was made much later - the hot end was reduced even more and a steel hot cap mounted over the entire hot space area. This resulted in slower heat conduction but more heat could be applied; another result was less conduction of heat along the cylinder.

Speeds of up to 1000 RPM can be obtained from this engine provided the power piston assembly is gas-tight fit, the displacer rod/guide bush fit is precise and there is minimum friction in the drive mechanism and elsewhere.

The engine can be scaled up to twice the specification size. Heating by gas and cooling by water jacket will obtain a good performance from such a model, especially if a thin-walled lightweight mild steel displacer is used.

CHAPTER ELEVEN

How to Construct "Dolly" II

DOLLY II is another basic engine built around two castings on a polished wooden base. This design was made to satisfy the request of fellow modellers for a simple, easily finished model with which they could identify some of the parameters of hot-air engine modelling. Originally two different castings were made for the engine block, one with round cylinder flanges (Fig 11.2) and another with a square finish (Fig 11.3) which was more pleasing aesthetically but proved too difficult for those who did not own a milling machine or attachment since it required a fair amount of bench fitting. The round casting is easier to machine on a small lathe.

The 'original' round castings were made from second grade aluminium and were just adequate but gave a dull finish. This pattern, together with a pattern for the crankshaft bearing bracket were

*Fig 11.1
DOLLY II,
constructed by
Roy Darlington
of Worthing,
from castings
supplied by
author.
(Courtesy of
Graham
Darlington).*

Fig 11.2 (Below) Two sets of round castings: the set on the right was cast in rough aluminium, the set on the left was cast in gunmetal.

Fig 11.3 (Right) Set of square castings - aesthetically more appealing, but requiring substantial lathework and milling.

Fig 11.4 (Bottom) DOLLY II - engine layout.

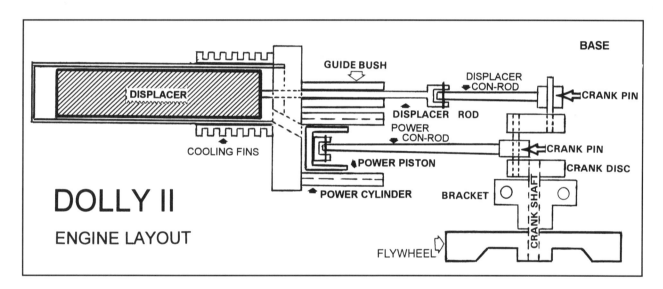

sent to John Tipton of Hollywood, Birmingham, who made a few castings in gunmetal far superior in finish than the originals.

The cylinder-block or engine-block is machined in a four-jaw independent chuck in a two-stage, multi-step operation (see Fig11.5 over page). The power cylinder end is first placed in the chuck such that the displacer side is centered and ready for boring. A ¹³⁄₆₄in hole is drilled right through to exit on the reverse side of the block. This is then enlarged by successive drilling and boring bar to 1in ID to a depth of 1¼in to take the displacer cylinder snugly - not too tight, not too loose. With the engine block still in place the displacer rod guide bush seating is prepared by threading the remaining bore with an 0 BA tap. The next step is cutting fins in the displacer cylinder flange to a depth just ¹⁄₁₆in short of the bore. These fins will be part of the cooling system of the engine. The final step of this

operation is facing the engine block to a smooth finish.

The engine block is then reversed in the chuck and aligned for the second stage of the machining operation, the power cylinder flange. This operation is a couple of steps simpler - a ⅞in bore is made to take the power cylinder sleeve which is a solid drawn steel tube, the outside of the flange and the engine block are faced in one single operation.

The final stage of operations on the engine block is opening a port hole between the two cylinders. The angle is rather acute and therefore care is advised not to damage the cylinder bores.

The power cylinder sleeve is prepared for insertion after being honed and lapped; when completed it is smeared with Loctite glue and pressed in. The displacer cylinder, displacer, and the displacer rod

DOLLY II: STEP BY STEP CYLINDER MACHINING SEQUENCE

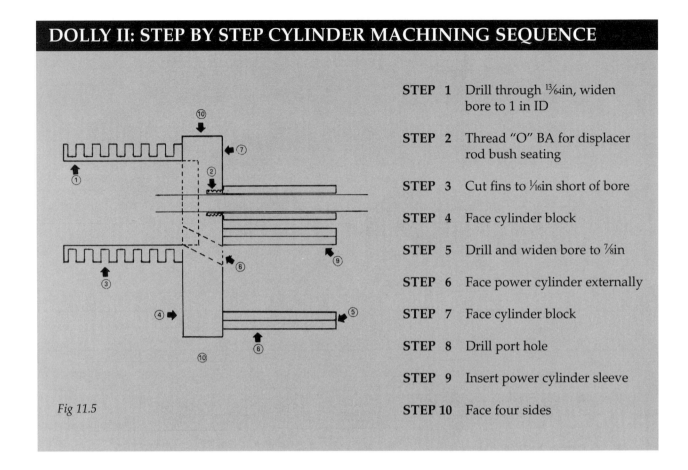

STEP 1	Drill through $^{13}/_{64}$in, widen bore to 1 in ID
STEP 2	Thread "O" BA for displacer rod bush seating
STEP 3	Cut fins to $^{1}/_{16}$in short of bore
STEP 4	Face cylinder block
STEP 5	Drill and widen bore to $^{7}/_{8}$in
STEP 6	Face power cylinder externally
STEP 7	Face cylinder block
STEP 8	Drill port hole
STEP 9	Insert power cylinder sleeve
STEP 10	Face four sides

Fig 11.5

guide bush are prepared and fitted as in DOLLY I. The power piston is lapped and fitted with the con-rod attached and ready for mounting to its crankpin.

The drive mechanism includes a cast bearing bracket with an integral overhung crankshaft housing, which is bored in the lathe to take two miniature ball bearings $^{1}/_{8}$in ID for smooth running. A 2½in flywheel is fitted on the outer side of the bracket (Fig 11.4), while on the inner side a 1¼in x

$^{5}/_{16}$in disc is inserted with a lateral long 6 BA grub screw and secured to the crankshaft. A $^{1}/_{8}$in dowel pin, threaded 6 BA at one end, $^{9}/_{16}$in long is screwed in the disc $^{7}/_{16}$in off-centre to give the power piston a $^{7}/_{8}$in stroke.

What happens now is a piece of geometrical drawing application. The displacer stroke is known to be approximately 1$^{3}/_{16}$in to give the right ratio of swept volumes. Therefore a second crankpin at right angles to the first is necessary; this can be

Fig 11.6 Side elevation - power side.

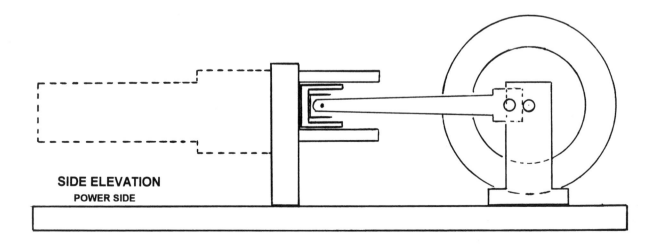

SIDE ELEVATION
POWER SIDE

Fig 11.7 Side elevation - displacer side.

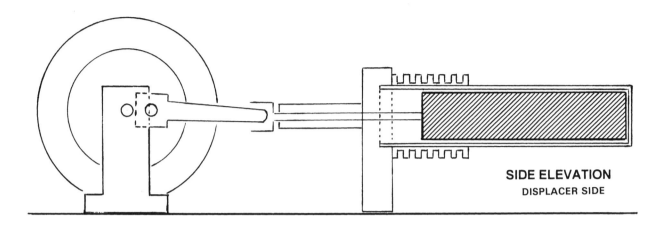

SIDE ELEVATION
DISPLACER SIDE

achieved in a number of ways, but the one offered by the author is simple and gives the opportunity to alter slightly the angle and the stroke. A piece of BMS flat bar, 1in long, ⅜in wide and ¼in thick is prepared, first by marking on its wide side two points ⁷⁄₁₆in from each other, leaving ⁷⁄₃₂in on either side, then drilling on the marks two ³⁄₃₂in holes. One of these holes is enlarged to ⅛in, the other is tapped 6 BA. The edge of the flat bar, on the side where the ⅛in hole is drilled, is tapped 6 BA to take a grub screw. A short ⅛in dowel, the second crankpin, threaded 6 BA is screwed into the corresponding hole, while the other end slips onto the first crankpin. Placed at right angles this should give the right stroke to the displacer (Fig 11.4).

The fitting of the con-rods to the crankpins is similar to that of DOLLY I.

ALTERNATIVE DISPLACER ROD / CRANKPIN FITTING

It is possible to shorten the overall length of the engine by fitting a scotch yoke on the displacer rod, thereby eliminating the con-rod and reducing the connection between the displacer and the crankpin by about 2in.

COOLING

Cooling DOLLY II has to follow a slightly different pattern than the first engine. The displacer cylinder flange has been machined and finned; unfortunately these fins do not give sufficient cooling, therefore additional fins are required. A 2in dural bar is first bored 1¼in ID to a depth of 1in, then 1in ID to an additional depth of ½in. While in the lathe, the total 1½ in length is finned, that part of the bar which is bored 1in in is finned to a depth of ⁷⁄₁₆in approx, that part which has an internal bore of 1¼in, is finned down to a depth of ⁵⁄₁₆in. The end

result is the second set of fins will readily fit over the finned displacer cylinder flange - careful and precise machining will ensure good contact between the two surfaces (Fig 11.8).

However one should not expect long runs with this type of fin arrangement - the total heat exchange area is far too small. Larger fins may be more adequate for a longer run, but the aesthetic appearance will be slightly marred.

HEATING

No special burner was originally made for this engine, in fact the first model had a small metal lid in the shape of a dish into which were placed two solid fuel cubes. Later on, when the time came to take it, along with other models, to the Maltese Engineering Association's annual exhibition, one could see that the graceful, almost petite appearance of DOLLY II was marred by the burner arrangement. A small furnace cover, made from 24 gauge brass, was cut and soldered, ensuring that the overall appearance was not affected. A small square container was adapted to hold the solid fuel. Eventually a fitting for a microtorch was made, the furnace cover opened up at the back to contain the flame and heat (Fig 11.9).

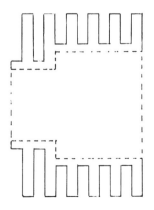

*Fig 11.8
Additional cooling fins fitted on the displacer cylinder flange.*

PERFORMANCE

Engine performance was calculated on the effect of two different burners. The solid fuel, at maximum heat, gave the engine a top speed of 720 RPM, with the average for a 5-minute duration of about 550 RPM. The microtorch gave far more heat, and in fact the rear, heated section of the displacer cylinder, being greatly reduced in thickness, started to grow red almost immediately. The engine ran so fast that it nearly ran off the table edge! A second attempt showed a speed of 950 RPM+. With a soft gas flame the speed hovered around the 760 RPM.

Many minor modifications can still be made to this engine; water-cooling, balancing the strokes by a bob weight or weighted disc and fitting a machined crankshaft to eliminate a cumbersome drive mechanism are just three other experiments.

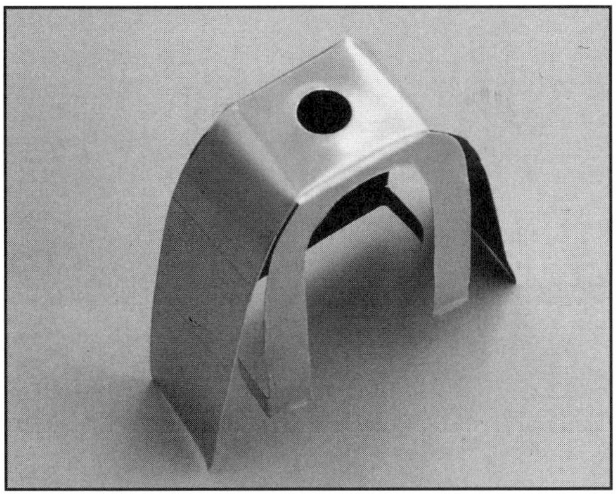

Fig 11.9 Flame canopy.

DOLLY II: ENGINE SPECIFICATIONS

	IMPERIAL SIZES	NEAREST "WORKING" METRIC EQUIVALENTS
Engine base	8½in x 4in	210mm x 100mm
Cast cylinder block	2in x 2in	50mm x 50mm
Integral displacer cylinder flange	1³⁄₁₆in OD ²⁹⁄₃₂in ID 1in long	30mm 23mm 25mm
Integral power cylinder flange	1in OD ⅞in ID 1½in long	25mm 22mm 38 - 40mm
Power cylinder sleeve	¾in ID	19 - 20mm
Power piston	¾in OD ⅝in long	19 - 20mm 16 - 17mm
Displacer cylinder	²⁹⁄₃₂in OD ¹³⁄₁₆in ID 3½in int. length	23mm 20mm 88mm
Displacer	¾in OD 2¼in long	19mm 57mm
Displacer rod guide bush	½in OD ⅛in ID 1¼in long	10 - 12 mm 3mm 32mm
Power stroke	⅞in	22mm
Displacer stroke	1³⁄₁₆in	30mm

C H A P T E R   T W E L V E

How to construct "DOP-YU", a double-acting Stirling engine.

(The design and construction of this engine was first described in ENGINEERING in MINIATURE of April 1987. This article elicited quite a number of comments due to its unusual configuration and construction. A number of modellers wrote to check on one of the measurements in the 'Engine Specifications', which as a result of typographical error was listed ½in too short.)

The second engine built by the Stirling brothers in 1827 was the first double-acting hot air engine recorded. It was also the first hot air engine designed to work under increased pressure. In their patent application No. 5456 of 1827, Robert and James Stirling described these two improvements on previous hot air engines as the "application of two or more such air vessels and plungers to one cylinder, so as to act alternatively and equally

*Fig 12.1
Completed
engine.*

upon opposite sides of the same piston" and "forcing... by means of air pump a greater quantity of air than could be introduced by the simple pressure of the atmosphere". Fig 12.2 shows an artist's illustration of the mechanical arrangement of this second Stirling engine.

This engine proves once more how far ahead of their time the Stirling brothers were in engineering concepts as well as in thermodynamic principles. Although it is recorded that a French engineer, Charles L. Franchot produced a two-cylinder twin-system double-acting engine in 1853, it was well over a century before the double-acting configuration was made use of again, albeit in a different manner. In Stirling's engine the power piston performs its function twice, that is at each end, compressing the working air before the displacer moves this volume to the hot side in order to raise the pressure. Moreover the power piston twice transmits force to the crankshaft.

In modern double-acting multiple cylinder engines, the displacer is done away with, leaving only an enlarged power piston to perform the same work - the cylinder is connected at its bottom end with the top end of the adjoining cylinder and at its top end with the bottom end of the other adjoining cylinder on the opposite side (Fig 2.11). The expansion space of each cylinder is connected to the compression space of the adjoining cylinder. In between each cylinder there is a heater, a regenerator and a cooler. This configuration is suitable for a four-square engine with four cylinders, or for a

four-in-line cylinder engine which has a drawback in that there is a considerable distance between the first and last cylinders and obviously too much dead space or dead volume. The four-square engine has a design problem in that it is difficult to find an 'easy' mechanical drive; on the other hand the wobble-plate drive is highly suitable allowing the engine to lie horizontally and connects readily to the transmission box.

METHOD OF CONSTRUCTION

It is relatively simple to progress from single-acting twin-parallel-cylinder engine construction (DOLLY I and II) to a double-acting triple-parallel-cylinder Stirling engine, particularly if the modeller uses as a straight-forward mechanical drive consisting of two flywheels with a single throw crankshaft in between. A double-acting engine requires greater attention to precision work and bench fitting since one of the more important requirements is perfect balancing of the components to give the model a smooth run with minimum vibration. No less important is the need to prevent air from escaping from any of the rod guide bushes, and to reduce the amount of dead volume to a minimum.

In a double-acting engine each of the displacer units is coupled to one end of the central power unit such that the power unit acts with increased pressure at either end. This means that both displacer cylinders and displacers are identical in construction and in volume/stroke ratio; it also

Fig 12.2
Stirling engine
with elevated
pressure, 1827.

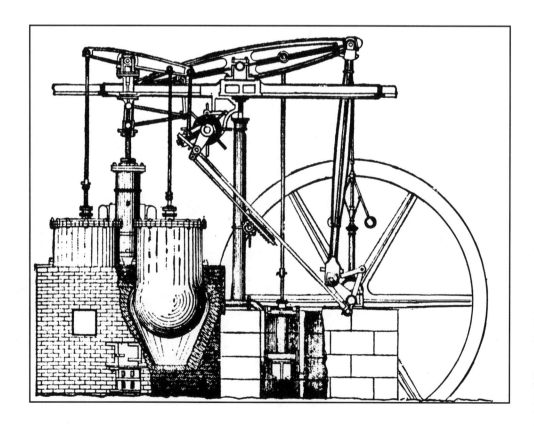

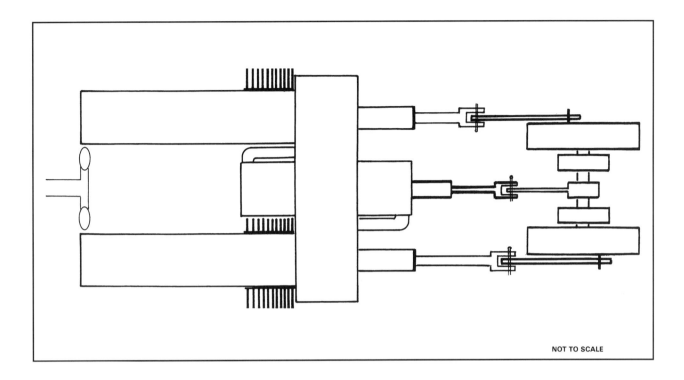

NOT TO SCALE

Fig 12.3 Engine layout.

means that the power unit is constructed in such a way that the volume swept by the power piston at each end is exactly the same, with minimum, but equal, dead space. The only difference between the two ends of the power cylinder is the piston rod outlet through a very precise fitting guide-bush.

The 1.5 : 1 swept volume ratio between the each displacer and each side of the power piston is maintained. To achieve this one of two methods is used during the construction: either different diameter of tubes are used for the displacer cylinders and for the power cylinder, or the stroke of the displacers is different from the stroke of the power cylinder. There is yet a third alternative, compensating a slight difference in the sizes of the displacer/power cylinders by a difference in the strokes. The engine described in this Chapter has identical cylinder diameters for the three components (¾in), and different length of strokes for the power piston and for the displacers. The power piston has a stroke of ½in while the stroke of the displacers is ¾in.

The construction of this model is well within the capability of a modeller with modest workshop facilities - the lathe work involved can be quite efficiently executed on a small table top lathe, EMCO Compact 5 or HOBBYMAT size, while brazing or silver soldering is only required to seal the hot end of the displacer cylinders. The rest is precise bench fitting.

Basically the engine consists of a dural block on

which are mounted the two displacer cylinders with the power cylinder in the middle, all three parallel, together with a drive mechanism consisting of a twin flywheel assembly on a crankshaft that has a central crank throw for the power piston. The displacers are driven off crankpins in the flywheels, (Fig 12.3).

GENERAL CONSTRUCTION DETAILS

The cylinder block is prepared by a series of drilled holes in preparation for assembly. The positions of the displacer and power cylinders are marked first; the next step is marking the positions of the air passage bores which will take the tubes connecting the two displacer cylinders to the power cylinder. Fig 12.4 shows details of the positions of the various drilled holes and enlarged bores as viewed from above, from the rear (backview, burner end), and from the front (flywheel end).

(In the designs of this engine, the FRONT is the FLYWHEEL END, the BACK is the BURNER END. Viewed from above in Fig 12.4, the displacer cylinder in bore No.2 is actually the RIGHT HAND displacer, the displacer cylinder in bore No.3 is the LEFT HAND displacer. This explanation should eliminate any difficulty in following the marking and drilling instructions.)

The CYLINDER BORES are drilled from back to front, while the air passage tube bores are first drilled from the sides of the dural block, and then one connecting port hole is drilled from the back (Step 6 of Fig 12.4), and another from the front

(Step 7 of Fig 12.4). The first holes drilled are the three which take the two displacer cylinders and the power cylinder. A pilot hole ³⁄₁₆in is first drilled right through, in each of the marked spots. The two holes, on either side of the power cylinder position, are widened, to take the displacer cylinders ¾in wide, (steps 2 & 3 of Fig 12.4). The centre hole is widened right through the block to take the power cylinder, also ¾in OD. Each of the two displacer cylinder bores is widened to two thirds of its depth; the remaining one third is then tapped ¼ in BSF to take the displacer rod guide bush. It is recommended that either when bench fitting or machining the bores in the milling machine or in the lathe, the drilling, bore widening, and tapping is done in one operation to ensure perfect alignment of the cylinders and the guide bushes.

The air passage connections are next to be completed, a bore of ³⁄₁₆in from the sides of the dural block (Step 8 of Fig 12.4) is recommended. The connecting port hole from the back of the engine block, i.e. Step 6, and the connecting port hole from the front, i.e. Step 7, are drilled ¼in to take a similar size copper or brass tube. The holes on the sides of the engine block (shaded part) are plugged and made airtight.

The DISPLACER CYLINDERS are machined from BMS solid drawn tubes, brazed or welded at one end and thinned down externally to 50% of the wall thickness for about one third of the length of the cylinder to lessen heat conduction, and to 75% for the last 1in from the closed end to enable the burner heat up the engine quickly. The fitting of the displacer cylinders should be precise, requiring only a smear of bonding agent.

The DISPLACERS are made in one of two ways: the easy way by making use of suitable hollow aluminium containers, in this model the first displacers were made from felt pen containers; these are quite rigid and lightweight. The more difficult and longer job is machining them from BMS thin gauge tubes, first silver soldered at one end, then thinned down considerably, internally or externally as required. to give a good fit inside the cylinders. Weight is a drawback as it can cause drag and friction on the displacer rod fitting in the guide bush. The annular gap between the displacer and the cylinder should not exceed ¹⁄₃₂in on the diameter, ¹⁄₆₄in on the radius. The displacers are sealed with aluminium plugs, which are first centre-drilled, then drilled and tapped 6 BA to take the displacer rods.

The DISPLACER RODS are made from ⅛in silver steel rods, threaded one end 6 BA to fit into the plugged ends of the displacers. The ROD GUIDES are machined from brass rod in a single operation, threaded one end ¼in BSF, centre-drilled, drilled

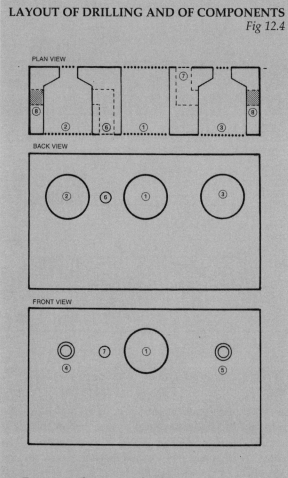

LAYOUT OF DRILLING AND OF COMPONENTS
Fig 12.4

1. Position of power cylinder
2. Position of right hand displacer cylinder.
3. Position of left hand displacer cylinder.
4. Position of left hand displacer rod guide bush.
5. Position of right hand displacer rod guide bush.
6. Port hole for right hand displacer from rear of cylinder plate.
7. Port hole for left hand displacer from front of cylinder plate.
8. Cross-drilled (and plugged) port holes to connect with 6 and 7 above.

and reamed ⅛in through. A perfect fit of the displacer rod in the guide bush is essential.

The POWER CYLINDER is an open-ended BMS tube, mirror finished internally by lapping after fine machining. It should fit into the engine block snugly, requiring only a smear of bonding agent. This cylinder is closed at the front end by an aluminium plug which is centre-drilled, drilled and tapped ³⁄₁₆in BSF. This will take the piston-rod guide bush. The plugged end is cross-drilled ¼in bore to a depth of ⅛in; a corresponding hole, ³⁄₁₆in, is made internally into the plugged end to meet the lateral hole, thus creating an air passage from inside the front end of the power cylinder ready for connecting to the left hand displacer cylinder. A similar plug is prepared for the rear end of the power cylinder, but at this stage it is just fitted on and NOT glued.

The POWER PISTON is best machined from cast iron, although other materials such as PTFE, brass or BMS make fairly good substitutes. The piston is solid and is centre-drilled, drilled and tapped 6 BA in a single operation to take the piston rod. The fitting of the power piston should be gas-tight but with minimum friction; compression can be enhanced by a few shallow grooves turned in the piston wall.

The POWER PISTON ROD is best made from ⅛in ground silver steel or chromed shafting. The GUIDE BUSH, made from brass, requires delicate fitting; in one operation it is threaded ³⁄₁₆in one end, then centre-drilled, drilled and reamed ⅛in through. A perfect fitting of the piston-rod in the guide bush is absolutely essential.

The engine requires three COUPLING BLOCKS, one for each of the connecting rods. A simple method is to take a ⁵⁄₁₆in brass rod, drilled through ⅛in, part off three pieces ⅝in long, each piece is slotted ³⁄₃₂in for half its length to take the connecting rod, while at the other end a lateral hole is drilled and tapped 6 BA to take a grub screw. Another hole is cross drilled where the con-rod slips into the slot, half way along its length, approximately ⁵⁄₃₂in from the end. Fig 12.3 gives a good indication of the coupling blocks in relation to the con-rods, guide bushes and the drive mechanism.

The COOLING FINS are machined from an aluminium or brass bar 1½in OD, which is first drilled and bored internally to fit the cold end of the displacer cylinders. While in the chuck the bar is finned using a parting tool leaving the narrowest of fins and diameter around the cylinders. One set of fins requires cutting away part of the fins so that it can accommodate the rear connecting air-pipe. The air passage connection is an area where prudence in purchasing an item, a ¼in copper bend, rather than machining it, comes uppermost. These copper bends, with a socket to take a ¼in brass or copper tube enhance the finish of the engine, and provide an airtight connection; the alternative is a deep V-cut in a brass tube, bend it at right angles, and solder the joint. Either way it has to provide for increased air pressure and compression to be transmitted to and from the displacer cylinders and the power cylinder.

The DRIVE MECHANISM consists of a crankshaft with the central throw connected to the power unit, and two 2in OD flywheels, each with a crankpin

connected to the displacer by a con-rod. The FLY-WHEELS have a 1¹⁄₁₆in outside boss to allow for the crankpin fitting ³⁄₈in off-centre. In this engine there is no inner boss - the flywheels are secured to the crankshaft by means of a grubscrew fitted into and through the rim thickness (½in).

The CRANKSHAFT with its crankwebs and throw may be machined in the lathe or fabricated from two BMS webs drilled in the middle to take a ³⁄₁₆in silver steel rod, and drilled ¼in off centre to take the crank. The whole unit is either silver soldered or pinned or both. The supporting CRANKSHAFT BRACKETS are constructed from dural with either brass bushes or ball bearings for easy running.

ASSEMBLING THE ENGINE

1. The various components are checked and prepared for final assembly. The displacers are checked for correct length taking into account the stroke and, if aluminium containers are used, a minimal expansion, usually in the shape of a dome at the hot end.

2. The displacers, displacer rods and guides are fitted first, the guides bonded to the cylinder block. Ensure free movement of each displacer in its cylinder.
AT THIS STAGE THE DISPLACER CYLINDERS ARE TESTED FOR ALIGNMENT AND FRICTION-FREE MOVEMENT BUT NOT PERMANENTLY FIXED IN PLACE.

3. The power cylinder, open-ended at the rear is then fitted but NOT bonded at this stage. The bend and pipe which transmits the air pressure from the front end of the power cylinder to the drilled hole in the engine block and connecting to the left-hand displacer cylinder (Step 7) are checked for correct fitting and alignment.

   Only when the modeller is convinced that the fittings are perfect, should this part of the assembly be glued.

4. The displacer cylinders are marked very, very carefully with their exact position in the engine/cylinder block, and with the position of the air vent holes which will connect to the power cylinder. When marked the cylinders are drilled ³⁄₁₆in, these holes aligning exactly with the connecting tubes. The displacer cylinders may then be secured in place.

5. The final part of the air connection is the right hand displacer (Step 6) to the rear end of the power cylinder and its plug. This is completed after the power piston has been checked for throw and correct length (next stage, 6).

6. The drive mechanism is prepared for assembly. The connecting-rods are measured and drilled.

DOP-YU: ENGINE SPECIFICATIONS

	IMPERIAL SIZES	NEAREST "WORKING" METRIC EQUIVALENTS
Cylinder block	3½in x 2in x1in	90mm x 50mm x 25mm
Displacer & power	¾in cylinders OD	19 - 20mm
Displacer cylinders	3¾in internal length	95mm
Displacer	2¹⁵⁄₁₆in length	74mm
Displacer OD	⅝in	16mm
Power Piston	1½in length	38 - 40mm
Power piston OD	⅝in	16mm
Power cylinder internal	2¹⁄₃₂in internal length (between plugs)	52mm
Guide bushes	1¼in long ⅜in OD	30mm 10mm
Con-rod lengths Power Displacer	2in approx 2⅜in approx	50mm 60mm
Flywheels	2in OD ½in rim	50mm 12mm
Stroke lengths: Power Displacer	½in ¾in	12.5mm 19mm
Cooling Fins:	1½in OD ⅞in long	40mm 22mm
Height of mid-centre, cylinders / drive	1¼in	32mm
Overall engine size	9⅝in x 4in	240mm x 100mm

The connecting-rods are measured and drilled. The power piston and rod are inserted from the rear and fitted with the coupling block. The con-rod is attached to a big-end which is split to mount on to the crank; at the other end the con-rod fits into the slotted coupling block of the power piston. The position of the piston on the up-stroke and on the down-stroke are carefully measured and any minor alteration is made through the fitting of the coupling to the power piston rod. The position of the plug at the rear end of the power cylinder is checked and marked, as is the air connection mentioned in Stage 5 above. When the fittings have been well and truly tested, this part of the assembly is glued on.

7. The coupling blocks on the displacer rods are fitted in place and the con-rods checked, drilled and fitted to the flywheel crankpins. Again some very minor adjustment may be made through the coupling fitting. At this stage the engine is very carefully turned over by hand to ensure smooth movement and free running.

8. The cooling fins are fitted to the displacer cylinder. A simple gas burner is made from a ½in copper bend soldered to a 2in length of copper tubing that fits on to a gas jet tube or a Bunsen burner. The space between the two ends of the bend is filled with coarse steel wool and the ends slightly flattened to give a better flame spread.

This a rather elementary burner but sufficient for trying out the engine. A double-ringburner would give much better heating to the displacer cylinders and would be more efficient.

9. Running-in is important to any engine, more so to a hot air engine and doubly so to this double-acting configuration.

PERFORMANCE

This engine is a very easy starter, and thereafter absolutely trouble-free. It has elicited very favourable comments during exhibitions. Running speed is relatively slow, hardly ever exceeding 600 RPM, though the author does not know why this should be so; a minimum speed of 850 - 1000 RPM was expected. Due to its small fin area, the temperature difference between the hot ends and the cooling fins, became markedly less after about a run of fifteen minutes.

CHAPTER   THIRTEEN

How to construct "Lolly", a V-type engine.

The engine in Fig 13.1 is another model designed for beginners.   The construction method is simple and the components are relatively easy to find or construct. It can be built with basic workshop tools and requires limited brazing facilities.

The principle of the V-type Stirling engine embodies a single crank and crankpin, thus reducing the

number of moving parts and obviously lessening friction. In this configuration the power and displacer cylinders are at 90 degrees to each other; this format can take different positions in relation to the engine base, the displacer cylinder placed horizontally to the base, the power cylinder horizontal to the base with the displacer cylinder standing vertical, or both cylinders "in the air",

Fig 13.1
"LOLLY"
constructed by
Ronald G. Smith
of Atherstone,
and exhibited at
the'94 Midlands
Engineering
Exhibition,
Stoneleigh.
(Photo:
Courtesy of
Ronald G. Smith).

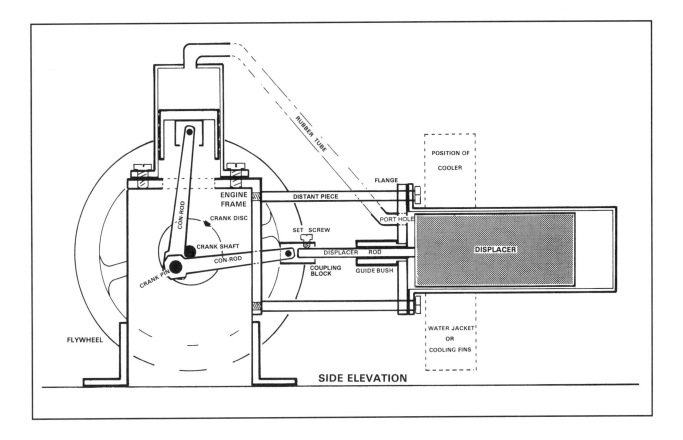

Fig 13.2 "LOLLY" Engine layout.

that is at 45° to the base. Somehow the design of "LOLLY" lends itself more to a horizontal displacer; it is definitely easier to heat and cool.

The V-type engine is one of the more efficient basic model engines for beginners since by its layout one parameter of engine construction is automatically absorbed in the design: the 90 degree phase. The position of the cylinders allows a variety of construction methods and the use of different materials for the engine frame. One such engine seen by the author had a polished hardwood engine frame and turned teak columns supporting the displacer cylinder, giving the engine a very elegant appearance; another constructed by Roy Darlington had such an excellent finish that the silver sprayed wooden engine frame was readily mistaken for dural!

ENGINE LAYOUT

This engine has a horizontal displacer cylinder and a vertical power cylinder bolted to an engine frame which consists of metal box in the form of a 3in cube which has one side missing, the side through which the fitting of the con-rods to the crank can be made without difficulty. The two cylinders are interconnected for the transfer of pressure through copper and rubber tubing, taking the shortest route between the two components. Brazing or welding

is required in three places, the displacer cylinder hot end, the displacer closed end and the power cylinder (unless the modeller would like to dispense with brazing and resort only to plugging this end).

The displacer cylinder is bolted on distant pieces screwed into the engine frame, to allow a long con-rod/displacer rod fitting, avoiding creep and lateral stress on the guide bush. In fact both con-rods (power and displacer) have purposely been made long, which ensures easy, flowing motions, and also less stress on the crankpin.

METHOD OF CONSTRUCTION

The ENGINE FRAME is prepared first. A dural flat bar, 3 in wide, 3⁄16in or 1⁄4in thick is ideal for the frame; an alternative is welding BMS flats, 3in wide and 1⁄8in thick. The position of the crankshaft bush is marked first, then the position of the displacer cylinder and finally the position of the power cylinder, taking into account that the positions of these two cylinders must offset each other by about 3⁄16in or the space required by the con-rod and spacer washers.

The seating of the crankshaft bush is drilled and tapped 3⁄8in BSF; the bores for the power piston and displacer con-rods are drilled and widened by boring. The positions of the displacer cylinder distant pieces are marked, drilled and tapped. The brackets which bolt the engine frame to the

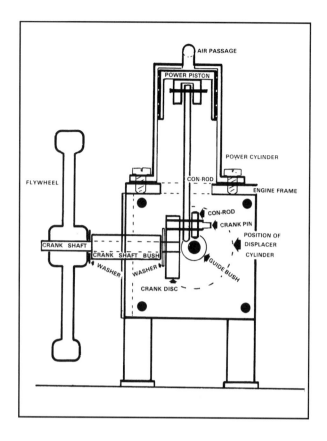

Fig 13.3 Side view, power piston side.

base are prepared for fitting.

The CRANKSHAFT GUIDE BUSH HOUSING is machined from ½in brass, reduced at one end to take a ⅜in BSF thread, then centre-drilled, drilled and reamed ¼in to take the crankshaft. The bush should be at least 1¼in long overall to support the flywheel and the crank disc without undue wear on the bush or crankshaft. Ideally the crankshaft bush should have as much length inside the engine frame as outside, (Fig 13.3).

The POWER CYLINDER is machined from good quality BMS solid drawn tube; the flange and the closed end are either silver soldered or fitted by the 'Heat and Freeze' method, (preferable as there is less probability of distortion). The cylinder is honed and lapped to a high degree of finish. The cylinder head is drilled and fitted with a 90° bend of ³⁄₁₆in brass or copper tube. The flange is screwed to engine frame by four 4 BA bolts.

The POWER PISTON is machined from cast iron, BMS or brass; a fine finish and gas-tight fit is essential for a successful engine. Two or three oil grooves are cut into the piston to aid lubrication and compression. The piston is bored internally to leave a ¹⁄₁₆ in skirt and a flat internal crown, which is the centre-drilled, drilled and tapped 2 BA to take the gudgeon block.

The GUDGEON BLOCK is machined from ½in BMS or brass, reduced and threaded 2 BA at one end, and slotted ³⁄₃₂in at the other end to take a ⅛in con-rod. The gudgeon pin fits half way along and into the slotted side.

The DISPLACER CYLINDER is best made from thin gauge BMS or steel tube, brazed or tig-welded at the closed end, and reduced to 50 - 75% of its wall thickness at the hot end. A collar flange is brazed or fitted on, with four 2 BA holes for bolting to the engine frame distant pieces.

The DISPLACER is made from thin-gauge BMS, brazed or silver soldered at one end and closed by an aluminium plug which is drilled and tapped 2 BA to take the displacer rod. An alternative is an aluminium medicine or perfume container of the right diameter.

DISPLACER SEALING FLANGE. This engine requires a second flange to contain and seal the displacer cylinder assembly. This flange should be sufficiently strong to withstand warping that may occur when mounting on the engine frame distant pieces. BMS, ⅛in thick or ³⁄₁₆in dural should be used for this sealing flange.

The machining of the sealing flange to fit the collar flange, and at the same time centering the displacer guide bush, is a delicate operation and should be handled with care as the slightest miscalculation will cause friction between the displacer and the displacer cylinder wall.

The first step will be to drill the sealing flange and tap ⅜in BSF to take the guide bush; the second step is to tape the displacer at its two ends (as in DOLLY) so that it will fit exactly into its cylinder; the third step is to fit the sealing flange with the guide bush epoxied in place, to take the displacer rod; the fourth step is to mark the four corresponding 2 BA holes which will take the four DISTANT PIECES from the engine frame, and the final step is to mark and drill the port hole which will take air connection from the displacer cylinder to the power cylinder.

The GUIDE BUSH is machined from ½in brass rod, reduced at one end and threaded ⅜in BSF to fit the sealing flange, centre-drilled, drilled and reamed ³⁄₁₆in to take the displacer rod.

A COUPLING BLOCK is machined from ⅜in brass, drilled ³⁄₁₆in at one end to take the displacer rod, and slotted ⁵⁄₃₂in to take the displacer con-rod. A set screw or grub screw is fitted at the displacer rod end; this fitting provides for fine adjustments to the displacer stroke and rod length. The CON-ROD is cut and shaped from ⅛in BMS flat bar, drilled one end to take a ¹⁄₁₆in wrist pin, and prepared for marking and drilling at the other end for final fitting to the crankpin.

CRANKSHAFT, CRANK DISC and CRANKPIN. This size and type of engine should take a ¼in crankshaft, threaded one end 2 BA to take the crank disc. (If it is desired to provide a brass bush, or ball bearings for the crankshaft, the sizes for the crankshaft housing, its seating, and possibly the crank-shaft itself should be altered accordingly. Obviously two ball bearings, one at each end of the guide bush, will be a more efficient method at providing friction free movement.) The crank disc is cut and machined from 1½in BMS, centre-drilled, drilled and tapped 2 BA to take the crankshaft, and marked, drilled and tapped 2 BA, ½in from the centre to take the crankpin. This will give the power piston and the displacer strokes a 1in throw. The crankpin is machined from ³⁄₁₆in silver steel, threaded 2 BA at both ends; one end is screwed into the crank disc, while the other end will take a retaining nut to secure both con-rods in place before the engine has a first run. The crankshaft and crank disc are assembled and tightened

with a smear of Loctite Screwlock 222.

The DISTANT PIECES are machined from hexagon brass rods, reduced and threaded 2 BA at either end; at one end the thread is ¼in long, at the other end the thread is ½in long.

ASSEMBLING THE ENGINE

The engine frame is screwed to a wooden base, heavy enough to withstand vibration; four rubber buffers or grommets will prevent the engine from running off the table. The four distant pieces supporting the displacer cylinder assembly are screwed in place and tightened. The displacer cylinder, with a thin gasket between the two flanges, is then mounted on the distant pieces, and secured by nuts on both sides. Care is taken to ensure perfect alignment of the displacer cylinder assembly.

The crankshaft is fitted into its housing, with washers where necessary and the flywheel bolted lightly in place. The power cylinder assembly is then screwed into the engine frame, and the two con-rods, power and displacer prepared for marking. The power piston is pushed in to TDC and the crankpin turned towards the power cylinder (highest point of the circle or turn); the con-rod is marked for fitting, after making a minimal allowance, paper thin, at TDC. The same procedure takes place for the displacer con-rod, again making a small allowance at the heated end, not exceeding ¹⁄₃₂in if a BMS displacer is used, or slightly more for an aluminium container displacer because of the possibility of a dome effect when heated. At this stage the drive mechanism is tested for full movement and for friction; if satisfactory, the first two stages of running-in are recommended.

The power cylinder compression can now be tested, and one should be able to obtain some engine bounce if the power cylinder air connection is finger sealed. A rubber tube is then inserted onto the air connections of the two cylinders and secured with clips or wire.

Cooling is provided by either of two methods, fins or water jacket. LOLLY was originally fitted with large rectangular aluminium fins, with thin brass spacers between each fin. This was sufficient for short runs of up to thirty minutes, eventually a water hopper replaced the fins, and later still, when this engine was used as a demonstration model, a water jacket attached to a tank, was used for cooling; this allowed runs of up to one hour without any overheating.

Heating is provided by spirit lamp, solid spirit cubes, or gas burner. As the prototype of this engine was designed for demonstration purposes

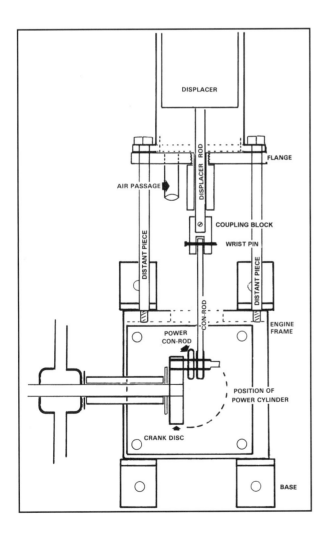

Fig 13.4 Plan view.

LOLLY: ENGINE SPECIFICATIONS

	IMPERIAL SIZES	NEAREST "WORKING" METRIC EQUIVALENTS
Engine frame	3in x 3in x 3in	75mm x75mmx 75mm
Power Cylinder	1⅝in OD 1½in ID 2½in length	40mm 38mm 63.5mm
Power cylinder flange	2⅜in x 2⅜in	60mm x 60mm
Power piston	1½in OD 1¼in long	38mm 32mm
Power con-rod	3³⁄₁₆in approx between centres	80 - 82mm
Displacer cylinder	2in OD 1⅞in ID 5in long	50mm 48mm 127mm
Displacer cylinder flange and second sealing flange	2½in x 2½in	65mm x 65mm x 65mm
Displacer	1¹³⁄₁₆in OD 3¹⁵⁄₁₆in long	46mm 100mm
Displacer rod	2¾in	70mm
Displacer con-rod	2¼in approx between centres	57 - 58mm
Displacer distant pieces	3½in	89mm
Flywheel	5in diameter x ½in rim	130mm x 12mm
Crank disc	1½in OD ¼in thick	40mm 6mm
Crankpin	³⁄₁₆in silver steel	5mm
Crankshaft	¼in silver steel or shafting.	6mm
Stroke of Power piston and displacer	1in	25mm

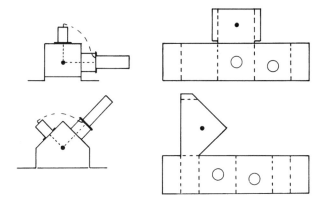

Fig 13.5 Alternative construction of engine frame.

at Technical Schools and Engineering Exhibitions, the first burner was an ordinary small dish on which were placed solid fuel cubes, two at a time, enough to give a good flame and sufficient heat for a good speed, but just as important to show the audience that these engines did not require excessive heating to make them run; after all demonstrating the principle of the Stirling engine was more important. Eventually, a Bunsen burner adaptor was fitted to LOLLY.

PERFORMANCE

The engine started at the first attempt and has given trouble-free running ever since. After months of shelf life it still runs without bother as soon as heat is applied. The engines reaches a speed of about 900 RPM with high heat, and a steady 600 - 650 RPM with solid fuel.

MODIFICATIONS

A number of modifications can be made to various components without effecting adversely the performance. The engine frame can be made from one piece of sheet metal, $\frac{1}{16}$in BMS or gauge 20 brass sheet, with suitable adaptation for bolting the cylinders/distant pieces, and the crankshaft bush, which side would need strengthening (Fig 13.5). The crankthrow can be shortened if the displacer length is altered, by bringing the crankpin nearer the centre, e.g. a $\frac{3}{4}$in throw, or even less; this necessitates alteration to both con-rod lengths. If desired, one can experiment with different swept volume ratios by altering the power cylinder or displacer cylinder size. A small dynamo, adapted from a cassette tape recorder or walkman with a small pulley, can be mounted on the engine base to light a small bulb - excellent for demonstration!

CHAPTER FOURTEEN

How to construct "Lolly II", a V-type engine.

The engine in Fig 14.1 is a later version of the V-type design and was constructed to take into account the following changes;

1. The displacer side was brought closer to the engine frame;

2. A shortened and narrower connecting air passage between the power and displacer cylinders;

3. A first attempt at using a scotch yoke and

4. the introduction of a counterbalanced crank web.

The construction was greatly facilitated by the use of an ex-military electrical equipment rectangular brass box similar to the one used in SUNSPOT (Chapter 19). The thickness of the brass was sufficient to enable tapping without having to use retaining nuts.

Fig 14.1
The finished engine.

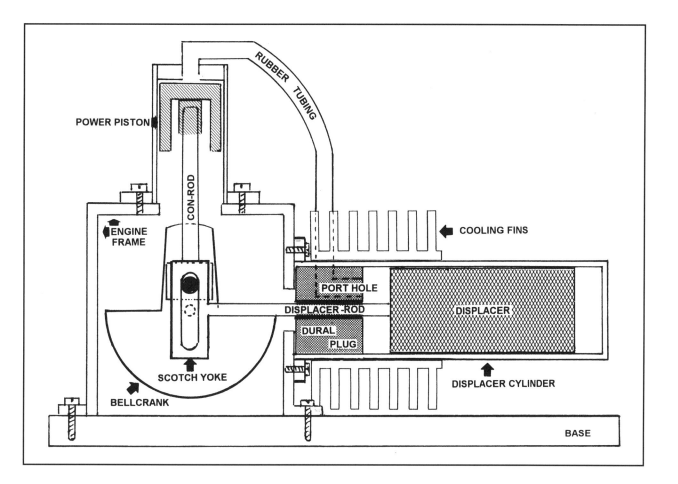

Fig 14.2 Engine layout.

A similar engine frame can be readily constructed from plate aluminium or from sheet metal as described in Fig 13.5. Since Lolly II is a more compact engine, and can be scaled down even more; an alternative polished wooden engine frame, made from teak or ebony, will make an attractive desk model.

CONSTRUCTION

The frame is first prepared as in the previous model with holes on adjacent sides, one of them off-centred by ¼in. If the preference is for a horizontal displacer, rather than a V-type, both cylinders "in-the-air" style, it is recommended that the power cylinder is first fitted centrally on top, with the displacer cylinder off-centre in the horizontal position. The crankshaft bush is then fitted to the third adjacent (front) side of the engine frame.

This engine can be made to run with moderate flame provided by a small spirit dish burner or by solid fuel cubes; therefore a space of 1½in between the base and the displacer cylinder will be sufficient, thus keeping the engine configuration low.

THE POWER CYLINDER is made from 1in ID BMS solid drawn tube honed and lapped before being closed at one end by a dural plug. "Heat-and-freeze" method has been used in this version for both the end plug and the flange which is machined from a 2 in dural round bar. The power cylinder assembly is fitted to the engine frame by four 6BA bolts. The air tube connection is ⁷⁄₃₂in OD brass which is cut and soldered at 90° and then inserted with a smear of Loctite into the power cylinder plugged top.

THE POWER PISTON is machined from cast iron and when finished is fitted with a short connecting rod in a gudgeon block within the piston. The same method of machining used in the previous model, both for the POWER PISTON and the GUDGEON BLOCK is used here, ensuring gas-tight fitting of the former and easy movement of the latter. A ¹⁄₁₆in skirt for the piston will allow the con- rod sufficient space to swing.

THE DISPLACER CYLINDER is machined from 1¼in ID BMS tube, brazed at the hot end and flanged at the cold end. In Lolly II, the flange has been silver soldered; however a ring flange machined from a 2in dural round bar and fitted on by "heat-and-freeze" is an adequate alternative. The flange should be prepared for fitting to the engine frame by four 4BA bolts

The DISPLACER is made from thin gauge BMS, first brazed at one end and then reduced further by careful machining to ⅟₃₂in thickness. An alum plug, ¼in thick drilled ³⁄₁₆in is smeared with epoxy glue and inserted half way down the length of the displacer. Another plug, tight fitting with a thin flange is drilled ³⁄₁₆in and epoxied into the end of the displacer which is now ready to receive the displacer rod. This step should be left for later.

The DISPLACER CYLINDER SEALING FLANGE and GUIDE BUSH have been machined in a different manner from LOLLY. In effect the guide bush is internal rather than external to bring the displacer cylinder closer to the engine frame.

Normally the end or sealing flange is a flat plate into which the displacer rod guide bush is fitted. In this way the guide bush protrudes from the displacer cylinder assembly by at least 1in. The alternative method used in this model brings the sealing flange, and therefore the displacer cylinder right against the engine frame.

The sealing flange is machined from 2in OD dural, stepped down to 1¼in for a length of 1in which fits into the displacer cylinder, leaving a ³⁄₁₆in collar (2 in OD). While still in the chuck, a ½in brass bush is inserted into the sealing flange, which is then centre-drilled, drilled and reamed ³⁄₁₆in to take the displacer rod. At this stage the port hole for the air connection is drilled into the outer flange from the front.

The final stage is drilling a port hole into the side of this cylinder to meet the front-drilled port hole at 90 degrees (Fig 14.2). The front end is then plugged. See Fig 14.3.

The WEIGHTED CRANK is another new feature which is included in this model. The crank is cut from a round BMS disc 2in diameter and ¼in thick. The disc is drilled and tapped 2BA in the centre and drilled and tapped 2 BA ³⁄₈in off centre.

The CRANKSHAFT HOUSING is machined from a ½in brass rod, 1½in long and threaded ³⁄₈in BSF at one end. While in the chuck it is drilled and reamed ³⁄₁₆ in to take the crankshaft.

The CRANKSHAFT is a ³⁄₁₆in silver steel rod or shafting which is cut 2½in long, threaded one end 2 BA to fit into the crank web.

The ENGINE FRAME is drilled and tapped ³⁄₈in to take the crankshaft housing.

The CRANKPIN is a ³⁄₁₆in silver steel rod, 1in long, threaded 2 BA BOTH ENDS.

It is recommended that initially a FINNED COOLER is prepared for fitting to the displacer

Fig 14.3 (Below left) Sectional view.
Fig 14.4 (Below right) Side elevation from displacer end.

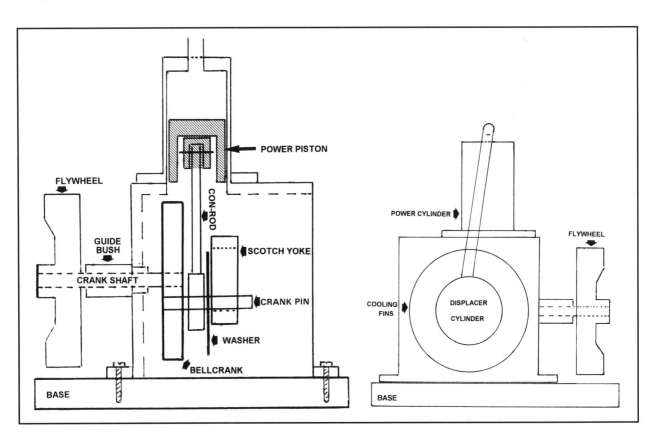

LOLLY II: ENGINE SPECIFICATIONS

	IMPERIAL SIZES	NEAREST "WORKING" METRIC EQUIVALENTS
Engine frame	3in x 3in x 3in	75mm x 75mm x 75mm
Power cylinder	1⅛in OD 1in ID 1¾in long	28mm 25mm 45mm
Power Piston	1in OD 1in long	25mm 25mm
Displacer cylinder	1⅜in OD 1¼in ID 4½in long	35mm 32mm 115mm
Displacer	1³⁄₁₆in OD 2¾in long	30mm 70mm
Round flanges for power and displacer cylinders	2in OD	50mm

Sealing flange for displacer cylinder:
    outer collar
    inner plug
	2in OD x ³⁄₁₆in
	1in inside the displacer
	1¼in OD
		50mm x 5mm
		25mm
		32mm

Stroke of power piston, displacer	¾in	19mm
Flywheel	5in diameter x ½in rim	130mm x 12mm
Crank Web counter balanced machined from	1½in OD	40mm

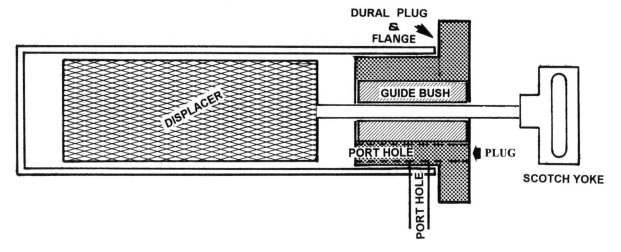

Fig 14.5 Displacer cylinder scaling flange with internal guide bush and scotch yoke fitting (indicative only - not to scale).

cylinder, prior to testing. A water jacket or water tank can be fitted later if desired.

There is only one item left to prepare, the DISPLACER ROD. A fair approximation of its length can be established, however a final fitting in place will confirm the exact length that needs threading 2 BA to take the scotch yoke. This fitting is performed later on during assembling.

ASSEMBLING LOLLY II

The crankshaft housing is epoxied in place; the crankshaft, fitted to the crank web, is inserted in the housing and tested for smooth turning.

The power cylinder, piston and con-rod are placed in position, tested for alignment; the cylinder flange and the engine frame face are marked and prepared for bolting with four 6 BA screws. Once this stage is completed the con-rod end is marked against the bell crank web/crankpin hole on the upstroke of the power piston (TDC) and checked again on the down stroke to ensure that there is sufficient clearance at both ends of the power piston stroke.

The fitting of the displacer cylinder, displacer, displacer rod and scotch yoke is next. The displacer sealing flange is marked against the engine frame face which takes this assembly and 4 BA holes are drilled and tapped accordingly. All the components are then fitted together temporarily and bolted to the engine frame.

The displacer is pushed back in the cylinder as far as it will go to the hot end. The crank web is turned so that the crankpin is nearest to the displacer flange; the scotch yoke is mounted on to the bell crank web by the crankpin. Any adjustments are made at this stage allowing a $\frac{1}{32}$in gap at one end between the displacer and the cylinder. This gap should eventually be distributed $\frac{1}{64}$in at each end. When all the adjustments have been made the components are taken out and bonded or bolted as indicated, leaving the port hole unobstructed. The air connection is made later.

The next step requires that the power and displacer cylinders are bolted in position and the crank assembled with washers where necessary. A few turns of the flywheel will confirm that there is no binding or hunting and the whole movement is soft and smooth.

The final stages include the fitting of the air pipe connection. A brass tube is placed in a spring bender and bent 90° at one end and connected by means of a short piece of rubber or plastic tubing to the power cylinder air pipe;

PERFORMANCE

Like its predecessor, LOLLY I, there was absolutely no problem in starting up. There was a minor snag where the scotch yoke face met the power con-rod, which was cured by a large washer. Otherwise the engine ran sweetly with the weighted crank balancing to a large degree the weight of the displacer and of the power piston as a result of which LOLLY II was not so prone to run off the table. The average speed was 750 RPM on gas heat and 500 RPM with the spirit burner. This model too proved to be a good demonstration engine, replacing LOLLY I.

CHAPTER FIFTEEN

How to construct "Sturdy", a twin cylinder Stirling engine.

This engine (Fig 15.1) is a compact twin Stirling engine designed as motive power for marine use. Originally the engine was designed to fit into a model cargo ship. This experiment is successful up to the point that the power generated is sufficient to move a model boat at a steady and sedate speed. The problem with using this particular design is

that the displacers are fairly high up and the burner, 6 in above the keel, is subject to wind influence. (The original engine had a 3in flywheel, and 1in height clearance - this has now been replaced by a 2in flywheel with a thicker rim and the engine base sits at keel level). The engine is constructed mainly from scrap material readily available, with some machining. It is well within the capabilities of a modeller who has successfully constructed the previous models.

GENERAL ENGINE LAYOUT

"Sturdy" is a combination of two separate Stirling engines built round one engine frame or compartment and having a common multiple crankshaft and flywheel. The engines are of the V-type with the displacers in a vertical position, one behind the other, while the power cylinders are in a horizontal position, on either side of the crank case. Each power cylinder is connected externally to its displacer cylinder.

The engine compartment is constructed from an aluminium box obtained from scrap aluminium sections. The power and displacer cylinders are cut from two different sizes BMS tubes while the displacers are taken from aluminium containers. Great care is taken in the construction of the crankshaft and in positioning the displacer and power con-rods.

As an experiment the 'heat and freeze' method of bonding flanges and cylinder ends is used

Fig 15.1 (Left) "STURDY"- Completed engine.

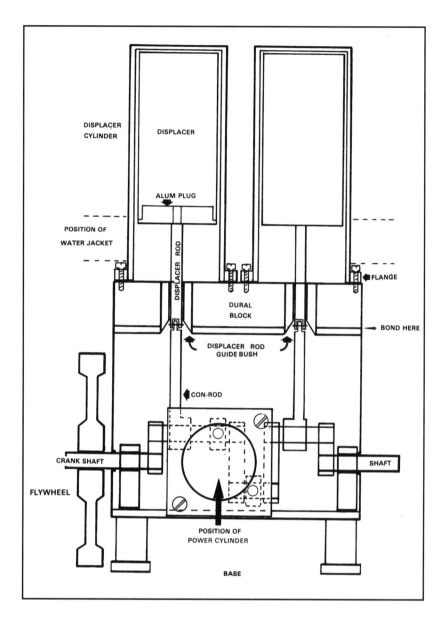

Fig 15.2 (Above) Aluminium scrap section used for engine compartment.

Fig 15.3 (Right) Engine layout - side elevation.

extensively, replacing six brazing areas and using brazing only on the displacer cylinder hot ends. The flanges and closed ends are completely airtight to the extent that an attempt to pressurise the engine had positive results.

METHOD OF CONSTRUCTION

The ENGINE COMPARTMENT is cut from scrap aluminium section (Fig 15.2) normally used in the construction of doors and windows. These sections have a number of projections internally and externally which are removed by filing, leaving a neat box with internal dimensions of 2½in height, 1⅝in width and 3½in length. The compartment is marked and drilled with holes for the power con-rods, bored and widened by a Conecut to a diameter of 1in to allow for con-rod movement.

The CYLINDER HEAD OR PLATE is cut from ⅝in dural flat bar (Fig 15.3) 1¾in wide and 3½in long.

The cylinder head is marked and drilled ½in where the displacer rod guides are to be inserted. Accurate drilling is essential in this operation. The air-vent holes are drilled from above to half way through the thickness of the plate and then cross drilled to provide for exit holes, (Fig 15.8). Further work on the cylinder head takes place later when the displacer cylinders are fitted.

The DISPLACER CYLINDERS are cut from BMS tube. The hot ends are brazed while the flanges are fitted with the 'heat and freeze' method. The normal method of brazing cylinder flanges may be used. The flanges are prepared with four holes for bolting to the cylinder head.

The DISPLACERS are cut to size from aluminium containers, and prepared to take aluminium plugs, centre-drilled, drilled and tapped 4 BA to take the displacer rods. The plugs are bonded in place and the displacer rods screwed in with a smear of bonding agent. The displacer/displacer rod assemblies are checked for accuracy and perfect alignment.

The DISPLACER ROD GUIDES are machined from ½in brass drilled and reamed ³⁄₁₆in. Before the final reaming operation, the bottom end of the bore is widened by a countersink to accommodate the con-rod/displacer rod wrist-pin fitting. The guides are inserted in the cylinder head and bonded in place leaving a projection of ¹⁄₁₆in into the engine compartment.

At this stage the cylinder head is bonded to the engine compartment with Loctite Multibond . This ensures that when the bond sets the cylinder head and engine compartment become one solid body. The next step is to fit the displacer cylinders to the cylinder head. In order to obtain perfect alignment and to avoid friction during the displacer movement, the method used in Chapter 10 (using tape round the displacer during the marking session) should be followed. The bolt holes are marked, drilled and tapped 4 BA, the tape removed and the displacer cylinders (with the displacer in place) assembled, and the bolts lightly tightened. The engine compartment is turned upside down (inverted) so that the displacers are at TDC, and the displacer rods are then marked with a felt pen where they just emerge from the guides.

The displacers are removed from the cylinders and

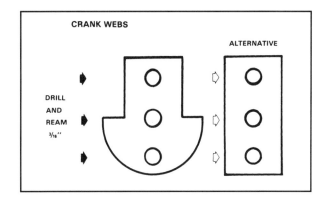

Fig 15.5 Crank webs for fabricated crankshaft.

each displacer rod is prepared to take its con-rod. The rods are cut ³⁄₁₆in longer than the mark, and then slotted ³⁄₃₂in for ¼in. A ¹⁄₁₆in hole is cross drilled in the slotted part of the displacer rod ¹⁄₈in from the end (i.e., midway in the slotted part). This part will take the con-rod and the wrist-pin or gudgeon pin. The displacer cylinder units are now re-assembled with a thin gasket between the flanges and the cylinder head.

The POWER CYLINDERS are cut from a solid drawn steel tube, the plugs and the flanges bonded in place with the 'heat and freeze' method. The closed ends of the power cylinders are drilled to take ¼in OD copper bends which will serve as port

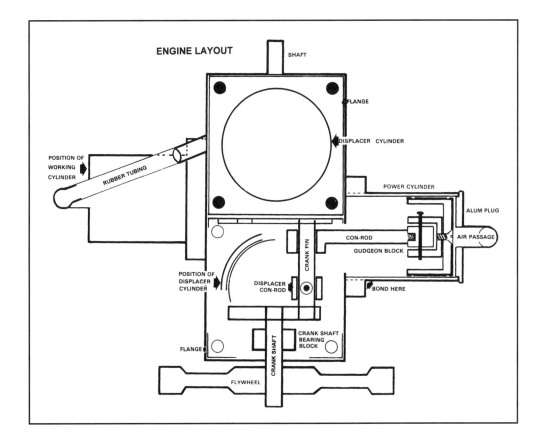

Fig 15.4 Engine layout - plan view.

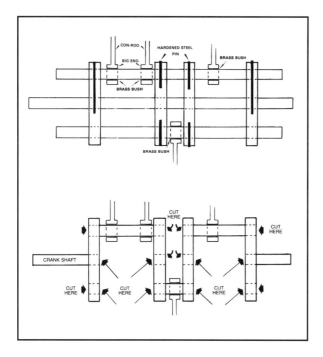

Fig 15.6 (Above right) First stages of the fabricated crankshaft assembly.

Fig 15.7 (Below right) Final stages of the crankshaft assembly.

holes. The cylinders are then lapped and prepared to take the power pistons. Finally the flanges are drilled for bolting into the engine compartment which is also prepared with four tapped 4 BA holes to take the securing bolts

The POWER PISTONS are machined from cast iron or brass, with a ⅛in skirt and crown. The crown is drilled and tapped 4 BA to take the gudgeon block. Two or three grooves may be cut into the piston walls - gas tight fitting without friction is essential.

The GUDGEON BLOCKS are machined from ½in brass or BMS, drilled and tapped 4 BA at one end and slotted ⁵⁄₃₂in to take the con-rods. It is essential that the gudgeon pin is placed as near to the piston crown as possible in order to obtain a long con-rod.

The MULTIPLE CRANKSHAFT. This engine is designed to have the two power pistons firing at the same time giving increased torque. The crank is fabricated from four webs and three ³⁄₁₆in silver steel rods.

The webs are cut from ¼in BMS and are shaped round or left square-sided as in Fig 15.5 . The webs are drilled and reamed with three ³⁄₁₆in holes, ½in between centres. In this operation the webs are secured together to obtain perfect alignment of the bores.

The next stages of the fabricated crank are illustrated in Fig 15.6. Three silver steel rods are pushed through the webs, the outer rods being 3½in long while the centre rod is 5 in long. Four big-ends, drilled and tapped 4 BA to take the con-rods, are inserted with brass bushes, in the rods before the crankshaft is fully assembled. The position for these big-ends is shown in the illustration Fig 15.7). The rods and webs are bonded in place after aligning the assembly so that the big-ends are directly opposite the displacer rods and the power piston gudgeon blocks.

The next operation is delicate and requires careful handling. The bonded fabricated assembly is placed and tightened in a vice and four ¹⁄₁₆in holes are drilled in the middle and right through the length of the webs. Loctite Superfast 415 is pushed into the drilled holes, and steel pins are hammered through the webs to secure the crankshaft assembly. When the bond has set the surplus pieces of crank are cut off with a fine hacksaw and the sides filed down, leaving the fabricated crank as in Fig 15.7 . Four 4 BA studs, 1½in long are screwed into the big-ends while small-ends are prepared to fit into the power gudgeon blocks and the displacer rods. The small-ends are screwed on temporarily to check for con-rod length before the final fitting. The crank assembly is also mounted temporarily in the engine compartment on bearing brackets, one at each end, bolted from underneath; the assembly is checked for friction-free movement. Brass bushes should be inserted in the con-rod big-ends and in the bearing brackets.

At this stage the displacer units are already assembled. The displacer con-rod small-ends are tried for fitting into the displacer rods with cotter pins and any adjustments to the length of the studs are made with the crank temporarily in place. The power studs are screwed into the big-ends from the side holes in the engine compartment, and the small-ends screwed on. The small-ends are then fitted into the gudgeon block and the power cylinders lightly bolted to the engine compartment. Again any adjustments required to the power con-rod studs are made before the power cylinder bolts are securely tightened.

At this stage all the crankshaft fittings are checked and with the flywheel on , several turns are given to the crank to ensure that there is no binding. When the fitting accuracy has been checked, the crank assembly is tightened and where necessary bonded. A slow running-in period is recommended, with the engine coupled to a slow running synchronous electric motor. The engine parts have to be well bedded before any attempt is made to start the engine under its own power. Finally the air vents are connected with rubber tubing.

A 3in by ¾in rim, 12oz flywheel is recommended

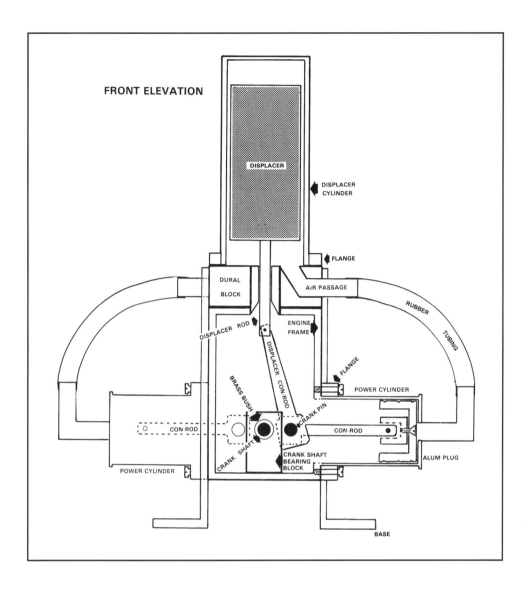

*Fig 15.8
Engine layout
- front elevation.*

for this type of engine, (later replaced by a 2in flywheel). A double ring gas burner, such as described in Chapter 4, is required. Cooling is by a double water jacket connected to a scoop when fitted to a boat.

PERFORMANCE
AND MODIFICATIONS

This engine is an easy starter. After an initial period of running-in the engine settles down to provide many hours of trouble-free running. On starting it picks up speed steadily, reaching and maintaining about 600rpm for long stretches. There is quite a considerable torque for an engine of this size.

The engine can be made to run with the power pistons firing alternately. This can be done by changing the fabrication of the multiple crank, keeping in mind that the displacer stroke precedes the power stroke by 90°.

This type of crank will probably increase engine

speed with a corresponding reduction in engine power.

With minor modifications the engine may be made to work at slightly elevated crankcase pressure. The experiment in pressurisation is explained in Chapter 5.

Fig 15.9 Burner and water jacket cooler for "STURDY".

ENGINE SPECIFICATIONS

	IMPERIAL SIZES	NEAREST "WORKING" METRIC EQUIVALENTS
Engine compartment	1¾in external width	45mm
	2⅝in external height	67mm
	3½in length	90mm
	1⅝in internal width	42mm
	2½in internal height	64mm
Dural block	1¾in width	45mm
	⅝in thick	16mm
	3½in length	90mm
Displacer cylinders (2)	1⅜in OD	35mm
	1⁵⁄₁₆in ID	33mm
	3¼in internal length	83mm
Displacer flanges (2)	1¾in by 1¾in by ³⁄₁₆in	45mm by 45mm by 5mm
Displacers (2)	1¼ in OD	32mm
	2¼ in length	57mm
Displacer rod guides (2)	½in OD	12mm
	³⁄₁₆in bore	5mm
	¹¹⁄₁₆in length	18mm
Power cylinder (2)	1¹⁄₁₆in OD	27mm
	1in ID	25mm
	1½in internal length	38mm
Power flanges (2)	1½in by 1¼in by ³⁄₁₆in dural	38mm by 32mm by 5mm
Power pistons (2)	1in OD	25mm
	½in length	12.5mm
Displacer stroke	1in	25mm
Power stroke	1in	25mm

C H A P T E R   S I X T E E N

How to construct "Mariner", a twin cylinder Stirling engine.

The second marine engine took into account the internal dimensions of a model boat together with the parameters of the marine Stirling engine. This called for an engine with a low profile and a low centre of gravity, as well as a low weight to power ratio. Several engine and boat designs were studied until it was decided that the minimum size of engine that can safely be built with any assurance that it works and generate sufficient power to move a 30 in - 36 in boat, should be 8in long, 5in wide and 3in high, and that the crankshaft is in line with the propeller shaft.

On the other hand, the boat design should allow this size of engine forward of the shaft, and the chimney stack, the superstructure and the upper deck should allow easy access to the engine, the burner and the cooling system.

Fig 16.1 "Mariner" - finished engine.

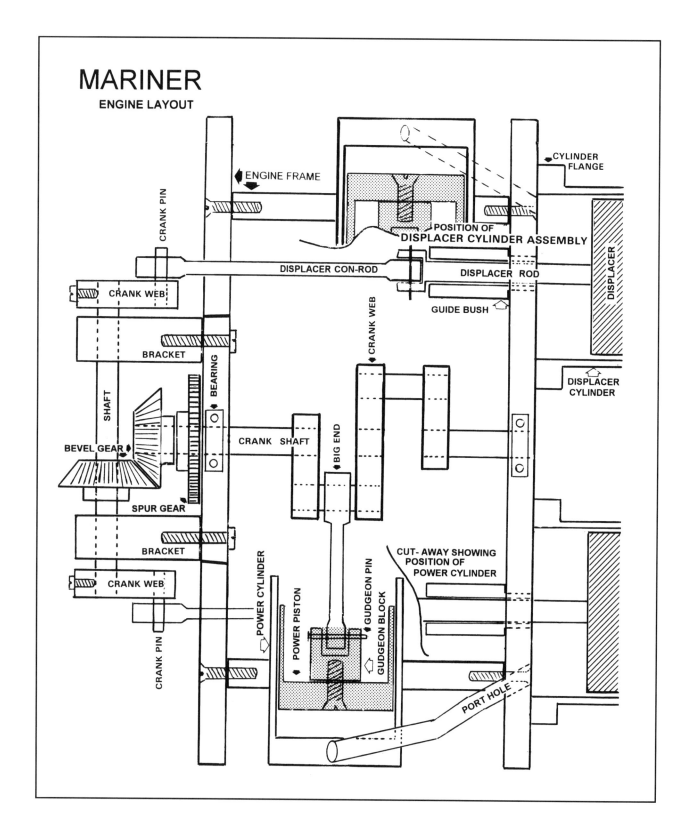

MARINER
ENGINE LAYOUT

Fig 16.2 Engine layout- plan view.

GENERAL ENGINE LAYOUT

The engine is based on a frame or compartment which is bolted to a 1⁄16in aluminium sheet, 5in x 8½in, although the engine dimensions are slightly smaller; however the space taken by the burner, any gas tank if used, and the cooler are not taken into account since this depends on the type of equipment the modeller prefers.

The innovation in this engine is the gear drive mechanism used to transfer crankshaft power to displacer movement. Two spur gears and two bevel gears are used. The power pistons operate simultaneously on a single crankshaft which drives the main spur gears and these in turn drive two bevel gears on a cross-drive shaft to which the displacer con-rods are coupled. The mechanism allows a slight adjustment in the phase angle. The gear drive gives lower speed but greater torque. The low front shaft exit, just ¾in above the base allows for easy coupling with the propeller shaft.

A small flywheel with a thick rim is required at the front end - a 1³⁄₁₆in diameter solid flywheel is the minimum one can use with any effect.

The engine is compact in length as the design allows the displacer con-rods to work above the power pistons; on the other hand the requirement for moderately long power con-rods does not allow for a narrower configuration. One could experiment with the scotch yoke for the power con-rods, however a short piston would require a type of guide bush for the piston rod which increases friction and probably lateral stress.

The use of ball bearings on the crankshaft and miniature bearings on the con-rods is recommended; where possible these bearings should be of the shielded type otherwise well protected with grease before the boat is put in water, especially sea water. The front, back and side plates of the engine frame should have the edges smeared with gasket compound to make the frame tight against water in the bilge.

Fig 16.3 Front elevation- relation of power pistons to displacer cylinders. Also shows position of gear assembly.

METHOD OF CONSTRUCTION

An aluminium sheet, 5in x 8½in is used as the base. The ENGINE FRAME or BODY is made up of four pieces cut from ³⁄₁₆in dural plate (although ⅛in may be sufficient for the front and back plates). The front plate is 5in x 2½in, with two pieces cut out or bored where the displacer con-rods fit into the cross drive shaft crankpins. The back plate is 5in x 2¾in and this takes the displacer cylinders and in fact serves as their end flange. The side plates, 2¼in x 1½in, serve also as power cylinder flanges.

The four plates are bolted to the base and to each other by means of 8 BA bolts. This arrangement should give a rigid structure.

The POWER CYLINDERS and PISTONS are prepared and machined as in "STURDY". The flanges which retain the cylinders are bored according to the position these have in relation to the cranks; Fig 16.2 gives an overhead view of the power cylinders and the position of the double-throw crank. With this illustration one can mark exactly where each cylinder fits into the engine frame.

The DISPLACER CYLINDERS and DISPLACERS are purchased ready-made from STERLING STIRLING of Newport, Gwent. These pressed steel cylinders come in sets of two, one inside the other, and have a very good annular fit. The wall thickness is approximately ¹⁄₃₂in. A ³⁄₁₆in dural

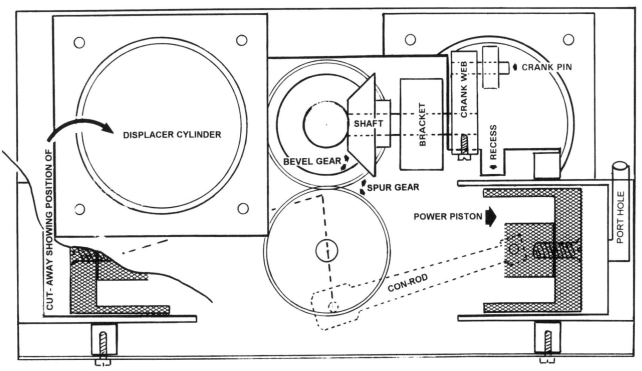

FRONT ELEVATION

MARINER: ENGINE SPECIFICATIONS

	IMPERIAL SIZES	NEAREST "WORKING" METRIC EQUIVALENTS
Base	8¼in x 5in	210mm x 125mm
Engine frame, outer dimensions	5in x 2½in	125mm x 65mm
Power cylinders	1⅛in OD 1in ID 1¾in long intern.	29mm 25mm 44mm
Power pistons	1in ID 13⁄16in long	25mm 20mm
Displacer cylinders	1¹¹⁄₃₂in OD 1¹⁹⁄₆₄in ID 3½in int length	34mm 33mm 90mm
Displacer	1¼in OD 32mm 2¹¹⁄16in long	 69mm

Stroke:
  Power
  Displacer
	
	⅞in
	²⁵⁄₃₂in
		
		22mm
		20mm

Gears:
  Spur
  Bevel
	
	1in
	¾in
		
		25mm
		19mm - 20mm

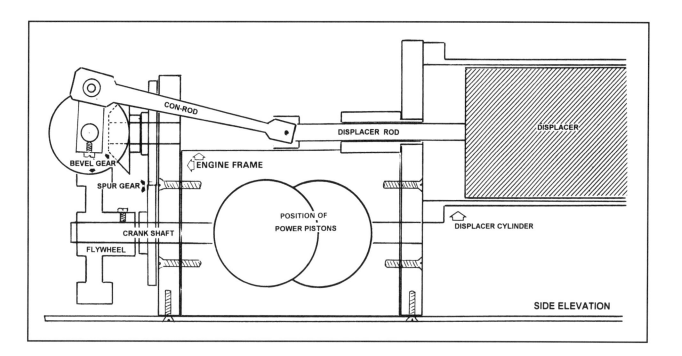

Fig 16.4 Engine layout - side elevation.

square flange, 1¾in x 1¾in is fitted to each cylinder by "heat and freeze" method. The second (inner) steel cylinder becomes the displacer, reduced in length to take into account the length of stroke; these are then sealed with an aluminium plug, drilled and tapped 4 BA.

The CRANKSHAFT is fabricated in the same style and method as the one used in "STURDY", but with a slightly smaller throw. Three webs, 1³⁄₁₆in x ½in x ¼in, are cut from BMS flat bar and together they are drilled ³⁄₁₆in in the centre and ⁷⁄₁₆in off-centre to give a ⁷⁄₈in throw.   Three silver steel rods, ³⁄₁₆in diameter, are inserted and pinned, brazed or silver soldered, the surplus parts cut off to give the crankshaft seen in Fig 16.2.

The GEAR MECHANISM consists of 1in spur gears for the main drive shaft and two ¾in bevel gears for the cross-drive shaft. The top spur gear and its adjacent bevel gear and their shaft rotate freely together on their axis. The ⅛in cross-drive shaft is mounted on two brackets bolted to the front plate from the rear.

The AIR VENT CONNECTION should be the shortest route possible between the displacer cylinder and the power piston. In this engine it is possible to drill a port hole that goes half-way through the power cylinder end from above and crossdrilled internally in the centre of the plug. At the displacer end, the port hole is drilled at the angle indicated in Fig 16.2, through the back plate which is also the displacer cylinder sealing flange.

The BURNER. This engine can be heated with gas or solid fuel. It is recommended that initially, at least until the full running-in is completed and the engine is working smoothly, a solid fuel burner is used. The hull area for and aft of the displacer hot end should have a ¹⁄₃₂in aluminium sheet on both sides of the engine to prevent accidental flame spread. At the same time a double cylinder canopy, should be fabricated irrespective of the type of burner used as this will give added protection and allow the exhaust from the flames to leave through the stack.

The COOLER. A fin cooler with forced air through the superstructure, will be suitable for short runs; a water cooling system with a water scoop that goes directly into the water jacket or into a tank tucked away in the bridge or in the superstructure, and feeding the water jacket, will be allow longer runs especially if a gas burner with an in-built tank is used.

PERFORMANCE and MODIFICATIONS

"MARINER" is a very easy starter after allowing for some initial friction in the gear drive mechanism until the necessary adjustments are made. The bevel gear settings may take some fine tuning with shims under the brackets until a smooth drive is obtained. All adjustments should be made with the engine outside the boat.

If the height of the hull allows, larger diameter spur and bevel gears will give a smoother drive with less friction. The use of larger spur gears will allow a bigger flywheel.

CHAPTER SEVENTEEN

The Ericsson Hot Air Pumping engines.

(Variations of the same theme! The design and construction of the first engine in this Chapter was described in MODEL ENGINEER of July 6, 1984).

This ERICSSON model was designed and built from reproductions found in various old publications, mainly from THE ENGINEER of that period. These engines were originally produced in large quantities and in various sizes, from around 1880. It is thought that this is the first type of engine built by John Ericsson which did not incorporate the usual valve system that Ericsson was so fond of. Ironically it is one of the more successful engines he designed; the problem that this brilliant engineer could not come to terms with was the persistent use of valves to induce a fresh charge of air into the cylinder with every cycle. The valves were usually placed near the hot end and they burnt out with regular monotony. It took Ericsson many years to accept the "closed-cycle" principle developed by the Stirling Brothers. On the other hand Ericsson was one of the very few engineers who accepted the principle of the regenerator, probably he was unique in understanding its function in those early days. Yet, this successful pump engine did not employ a regenerator; it was A.K. Rider who developed a similar style of pumping engine that first incorporated the regenerator for this type of engine layout.

The ERICSSON PUMP ENGINE is a concentric type, single cylinder, twin piston (power and displacer), with a series of linkages from a single crankshaft and crank. The water pump is an external attachment at the rear end of the main (walking) beam. The first engines built by Ericsson to this design had a single pump, but the engine proved to be sufficiently powerful to work two pumps simultaneously and later engines had a

Fig 17.1 (Left) Ericsson engine completed by author in 1983.

Fig 17.2 (Below) Sectional view of the Ericsson engine from the Engineer.

Fig 17.3 (Right) Ericsson engine parts (The Engineer). 1. The Flywheel. 2 Crankshaft bracket. 3. Crank. 4. Connecting rod crank to main beam. 5. Main beam. 6. Main beam centre bearing. 7. Bell-crank link. 8. Bell-crank. 9. Bell-crank bearing. 10. Crosshead assembly. 11. Displacer rod. 12. Power piston con-rod (2) 13. Pump link. 14. Pump. 15. Water jacket. 16. Main cylinder (above is the water jacket, below is the furnace). 17. Main cylinder flange. 18. Bed plate. 19. Supporting legs. 20. Furnace.

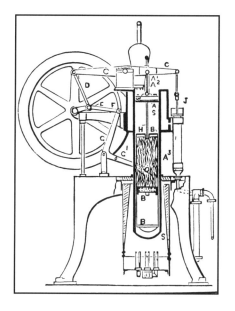

modification whereby the larger pump was used for water supply, while a smaller pump served as a cooler, pumping water round the hot cylinder before being used for domestic purposes.

The model designed and described here was built to a scale dictated by two main components available to the author at the time - a heavy duty shock absorber cylinder with an internal diameter of 1¾in and a flywheel, 6¼in, from an old sewing machine. The cylinder was particularly useful because of its 'mono' construction (solid drawn without any seam welding even at the closed end). It had a mirror-like finish which did not require any honing, just lapping. In addition the wall thickness (⅛in) allowed silver soldering and brazing without distorting the cylinder; at the same time it was possible to reduce the hot end substantially to lessen heat transfer.

This model can be scaled up or down according to the availability of materials or the workshop facilities at the disposal of the modeller. The model can even be enlarged further to perform work it

was originally designed for, long hours of water pumping for the house or garden! On the other hand it can be reduced substantially; in fact the author has seen a 6in high model built to this design which works quite efficiently and smoothly, but has no pump.

METHOD OF CONSTRUCTION

The PLATFORM (Fig 17.5) is fabricated from ¾in x ¾in angle bars, welded to form a base 6¾in x 4⅜in, and four legs, from the same material, welded to the base, splayed slightly outwards for greater stability. The bed-plate, ⅛in thick, is bored 2⅛in to take the working cylinder, which is bolted on by four 2 BA bolts.

The LINKAGES are machined to sizes from templates cut from the enlarged original design. The main beam is constructed from a ½in square bar, shaped according to the template; two BMS strips, ½in x ⅛in and 1in long are welded along the sides of the main beam at the point where an enlarged, elongated hole is slot drilled to take the

*Fig 17.4
Engine layout -
plan view.*

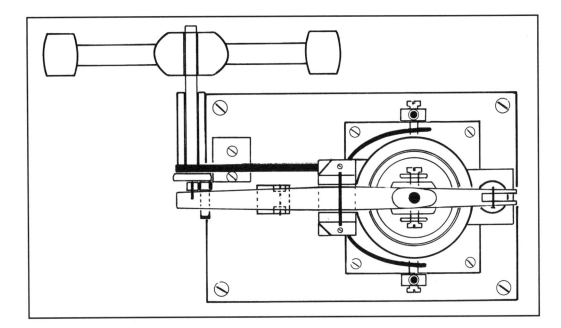

displacer rod. These two strips serve to reinforce the beam in its weak point, otherwise a wider bar, with more work to reduce the surplus metal, would be required.

The CONNECTING ROD from the crank to the beam, is an adjustable device consisting of two rods with left and right threads in a similar socket, for fine adjustments to the power piston stroke which may be required during the running-in.

The FLYWHEEL is 6¼in diameter dictated by the scale of the model; however a smaller flywheel, not less than 5½in diameter, will not adversely effect engine performance.

The WORKING CYLINDER. Very little work is required on this type of cylinder. A flange, ³⁄₃₂in thick, 2¾in x 2¾in and bored 2¹⁄₆₄in, is brazed to the cylinder one-third of its length from the hot end. This bolts the cylinder to the base. Ericsson constructed his working cylinder in two parts, bolted together on opposite sides of the base; however in this model the working cylinder is a single unit, having the advantage of avoiding loss of working air through the joint.

The cylinder wall in the hot space is reduced in thickness to at least 50%, preferably up to 75% to reduce heat conduction.

The WATER JACKET is made from scrap silencer pipe, 2½in ID, and brazed to the working cylinder to cool the upper third of its length. A BMS ring, 2in ID and 2½in OD fits the bottom of the water jacket for brazing on, (a simpler alternative is to cut a number of small segments, ¼ in long, in the water jacket, which are the gently hammered in and brazed to seal the bottom of the water jacket). A bracket made from ³⁄₁₆in BMS, 1¼in x ⅞in, is brazed

to the front and top of the water jacket. This bracket takes the main beam bearing block, and at the same time it supports the crankshaft bracket.

The FLYWHEEL (or CRANKSHAFT) BRACKET is cut from ⅛in BMS (brass will also do), and shaped according to the template. In this model the shape and the method of bolting to the base and the water jacket differ from some of the early designs; however a modification appears to have been made later to the Ericsson pumps whereby a stronger flywheel bracket was used, (Fig 17.3). This model's bracket has two short cross-pieces brazed on, one to bolt the bracket to the base, and the

*Fig 17.5
(Left)
Platform.*

*Fig 17.6
(Below)
Bell crank
assembly.*

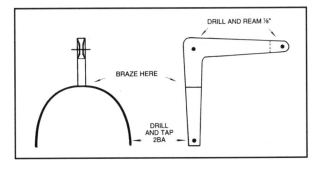

other to bolt the rear end of flywheel bracket to the water jacket/main bearing bracket.

The DISPLACER YOKE (or BELL CRANK) is fabricated from two separate pieces, brazed or bolted together, an L-shaped arm which pivots in the centre and is linked to the crank and flywheel, and a horseshoe bracket which lifts the displacer, (Fig 17.6). This assembly carries a fair degree of weight and force, and therefore it is essential to have a rigid unit. In some early models, the displacer yoke was pivoted on the flywheel bracket, in other models, the yoke has its own bracket bolted to the base. In this engine the displacer yoke has its own bracket/bearing bolted to the bed plate.

The DISPLACER LIFTING and CROSSHEAD ASSEMBLY is made up of a number of parts. The original engine had two ³⁄₁₆in silver steel rods bent at one end to form an inverted U-shape when fitted into the crosshead T-piece. (Subsequently this arrangement was altered and the straight rods fitted with square end brackets, threaded or capped as required, to provide a square shaped lifting yoke.The construction of the crosshead T-piece follows the illustration in Fig 17.7.

The MAIN BEAM BEARING BRACKET is milled from solid BMS 1in x 1in x 1½in, shaped to take the rocking beam and reduced at the sides to take two 2 BA screws for bolting to the water jacket front flange.

The POWER PISTON is machined from cast iron, faced, grooved and lapped while ensuring a good gas tight fit. It is bored internally to leave a ³⁄₃₂in skirt and a flat bottom. The crown is centre-drilled, drilled and tapped ³⁄₈in BSF.

The DISPLACER ROD GUIDE BUSH serves a dual purpose; it holds the connecting rods that provide motion to the power piston through the main beam, and it allows the displacer to maintain its alignment while in motion (while containing the elevated air pressure in the working cylinder). The guide bush is machined from 1in BMS or brass, reduced and threaded one end ³⁄₈in BSF for ¼in length; the next is a collar ½in length and reduced to ¾in OD, while the remainder, ⅞in in length is reduced to ½in OD. The bush is then drilled and reamed ³⁄₁₆in.

The ¾in OD collar is filed down by ¹⁄₁₆in on opposite sides, and drilled and tapped to take a 2 BA screw on both sides.

The DISPLACER is usually made of BMS tube, carefully machined to reduce wall thickness to the minimum - first to avoid a weighty displacer and secondly to avoid heat creep along its length. This type of displacer was tried, but it resulted that the

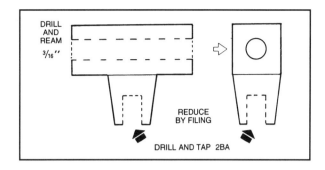

Fig 17.7 (Above) Crosshead T-piece.

Fig 17.8 (Left) Furnace cover.

displacer was still too heavy and the engine thump was deafening. (In the second attempt a lightweight aluminium perfume container was cut and prepared; its concave end was gently hammered outwards in the shape of a dome to fit into the profile of the working cylinder, then plugged, drilled and tapped 4 BA to take the displacer rod.)

The POWER PISTON CON-RODS are made from BMS flat bar, ⁵⁄₁₆in x ¹⁄₁₆in, cut, shaped and drilled at both ends (2⅜in between centres) to take 2 BA bolts.

The DISPLACER ROD is made from ground silver steel rod, ³⁄₁₆in, and 5⅛in long threaded one end 4 BA and the other end 2 BA.

The FURNACE (Fig 17.8). This model requires a furnace cover to conform with the designs of the old engines; however there appear to be two types of furnaces, the square shape and the round furnace - the latter has been adopted for this design. A piece of scrap silencer pipe, 3in OD, 4½in long, is welded with four lugs which will bolt to the engine plate. Inside the furnace cover a shield is placed 1½in above the heated end to contain as much as possible the heat from reaching the engine platform. A furnace door is constructed by cutting an opening in the side of the cover and fitting a hinged curved brass plate over the opening.

The PUMP ASSEMBLY consists of a pump box, a pump cylinder, a plunger and a water inlet. The

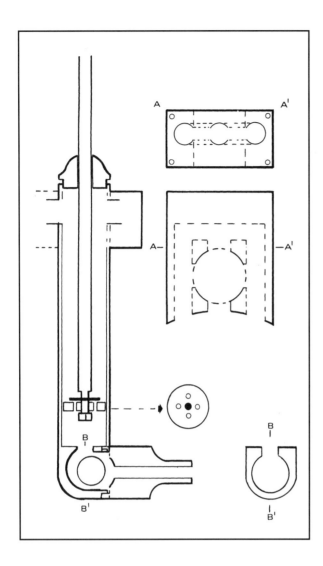

Fig 17.9 (a) Pump
assembly (above)
and (b) Plunger
assembly (right).

Fig 17.10 (Below)
Bell crank
counterweight.

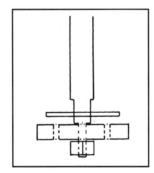

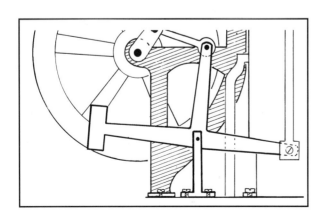

plunger is the item that requires most careful attention. It is constructed of a steel rod, ⅛in diameter, threaded one end 6 BA and reduced at the other end in two steps, first by ¹⁄₆₄in for ⅛in length, the next step by ¹⁄₃₂in for ³⁄₁₆in length. The very end is threaded 8 BA. A hard rubber washer, or a brass disc, is drilled with four ¹⁄₁₆in holes in a square formation (Fig 17.9). A thin brass washer is then prepared to cover the four holes; it should be able to slide without difficulty in the first stepped part of the rod. The plunger's downward stroke allows water to pass through and under the washer; on the upward stroke the pressure of the water in the cylinder closes the four holes with the washer and at the same time pushes the water into the pump box. The pump cylinder is drilled from ½in brass, 2½in long, threaded internally 32 TPI at the top end and reduced externally and threaded 32 TPI at the bottom end. At the top end a cylinder cover, drilled and reamed ⅛in, and threaded externally 32 TPI, is screwed on to seal the pump.

The lower pump inlet can be horizontal or vertical. A length of ½in brass rod is drilled internally ¼in and finished rounded to seat a brass or plastic ball; the water inlet is drilled ⅛in; the seating into the pump body is threaded internally 32 TPI to fit into the cylinder.

The pump box serves two purposes, one is to relieve water pressure from the plunger by containing a small volume of the water into a form of a tank around the pump exit bore, and the other purpose is to enable the pump to be screwed to the water jacket. The pump box is bored from the top to fit the pump cylinder tightly, the bore is then widened internally by ⅛in all round. Finally the pump box is filed down in the shape of a curve where it fits into the water jacket. The pump box is soldered to the pump cylinder.

PERFORMANCE AND MODIFICATIONS

This engine started at the first attempt, with reservations! The amount of heating and the length of time it took to reach the working temperature made it imperative to look for immediate modifications: reducing the displacer end of the cylinder by internal boring, no easy task with an 8 in+ cylinder until a kind fellow engineer offered an extra-long carbide tipped boring bar, and the external fitting of a shield half way up the displacer end to contain the heat. The engine still requires a fair amount of initial heating up until it picks up speed, but once the rhythmic cycle is under way, the flame is reduced by 50%. A no-load speed of around 250 RPM can be obtained with the pump disconnected: however, the engine bounces and thumps all over the place. Under pump load, with the water input at table level, the

ERICSSON: ENGINE SPECIFICATIONS

	IMPERIAL SIZES	NEAREST "WORKING" METRIC EQUIVALENTS
Table platform	6¾in x 4⅜in	170mm x 110mm
Height of platform	6in	150mm
Total height of engine	13in	330mm
Working cylinder	8¼in int. length 2in OD 1¾in ID	210mm 50mm 45mm
Water Jacket	2⅝in OD 67mm 2½in ID 4in long	64mm 100mm
Power Piston	1¾in OD 1½in long	45mm 38 - 40mm
Power piston con-rods	2⅜in between centres	60mm
Displacer guide bush	(Stepped OD) ³⁄₁₆in ID 1¾in long	5mm 45mm
Displacer	1¹¹⁄₁₆in OD 4½in long	43.5mm 115mm
Displacer rod	³⁄₁₆in diameter 5⅛in long	5mm 130mm
Con-rod beam to crank, adjustable	2in between centres	50mm
Crank throw	1¾in	45mm
Beam, main or walking	3⅛in crank pin to pivot centre 3½in pivot centre to pump link 5in crankpin to power piston con-rod centre	80mm 90mm 127mm
Bell crank (displacer lifting yoke)	2⅜in bell crank bearing centre to crankpin link centre 3⅛in bell crank bearing centre to lifting yoke centre	60mm 80mm
Furnace	3in OD 4½in high	75mm 115mm.

Fig 17.11 (Above left) Set of castings from Camden.

Fig 17.12 (Top right) Completed cylinder assembly.

Fig 17.13 (Above right) One piece working cylinder alongside the cylinder body casting.

pump load, with the water input at table level, the speed drops to 100 -120 RPM, but it still requires a strong arm to hold it in place.

Two other modifications are suggested, a counter-weight on the bell-crank and the adjustable connecting link mentioned earlier. A counter-weight at the other end of the bell crank (Fig 17.10) will largely equalise the weight of the displacer lifting yoke and the displacer assembly, though it may effect adversely the pump efficiency. It is a matter for experimentation, although apparently this device was used on some Ericsson engines. The adjustable connecting link between the crank and the main (walking beam) was originally used as a matter of expediency since no exact measurements were available to the author, just line drawings. This device was used to regulate the power piston stroke by fine adjustments; it consists of two pieces of ⅛in rod, one threaded 4 BA left at one end, the other threaded 4 BA normal. A short socket was tapped 4 BA left thread at one end and 4 BA right thread at the other. Put together the socket will lengthen or shorted the stroke accordingly. Later experiments showed that once the engine was running, a slight adjustment of this connection improved efficiency by altering the ratio of the swept volumes.

BUILDING THE RIDER-ERICSSON HOT AIR PUMPING ENGINE FROM CASTINGS.

The availability of castings for the Rider-Ericsson engine has encouraged modellers to build this historical and elegant model with comparative ease.

Camden Miniature Steam Services has been supplying these castings since 1982. Several hundred sets of castings have been sold, and judging by the standard of finish achieved and exhibited in various engineering shows and on Club Stands, the popularity of this model has been increasing as has the quality of finish and presentation.

The set of castings includes the major large components as well as the various small linkages; what is not included is the working cylinder, power piston and displacer, (Fig 17.11). Definitely the availability of the larger items is a boon for the modeller who does not have casting facilities, or finds it difficult to machine chunky components. The standard of the castings is high and what little bench fitting and machining is required does not detract from the pleasure of building this model, rather it is a worthwhile project for long winter evenings.

The castings are loosely based on a quarter-size Rider- Ericsson model described by Larry Kazyak in the book "STEAM AND STIRLING ENGINES you can build", edited by William Fitt, published by Wildwood Publications (Division of LIVE STEAM Incorporated) of Michigan, USA, and available in England from Camden Books of Rode, nr Bath, Somerset. The high standard, well written and documented article does justice to an extremely well designed scaled-down model of an 8in original held at the Ford Museum, Michigan. The article is well supported by high class photographs taken by the author, Larry Kazyak. One can easily follow his machining techniques and fitting procedures and relate the processes to the set of castings by CAMDEN.

An alternative method of machining the power and displacer cylinders is described hereunder. In Kazyak's model, as in the original, the two cylinders are separate and are bolted together above and below the engine plate, therefore technically liable to pressure leakage should the gasket give way, or the bolts work loose. The modification made by this author calls for machining the working cylinder in one piece; having used this method on the "home-made" Ericsson and on "DYNA", both of which have an 8¼in solid drawn BMS cylinder, no problem was anticipated with another slightly longer cylinder. Some differences stand out: the previous working cylinders were also mono construction, the base an integral part of the cylinder - not altogether a good thing since this part of the cylinder tends to be very thick and rounded, and needs careful machining. Contact was established with MODEL ENGINEERS SUPPLIES of Burton Joyce, Nottingham and a request for a high grade BMS solid drawn tube 2in OD promptly delivered. A request to another supplier, BRUCE ENGINEERING for a large diameter hone and oil got the same fast treatment.

The machining procedure is not too complicated, it is rather a long drawn affair with a component that requires treatment with respect and care! The internal bore is lightly faced from both ends to half the cylinder length plus ½in more, then honed from both ends to overlap the centre section by 1in each way. The last step in this stage of operations is reducing ½in length of one end of the cylinder to give a ¹⁄₁₆in wall thickness. This end is brazed closed with a ¹⁄₃₂in thin BMS strip. Care and speed in brazing is recommended to avoid any possible slight warping - not probable in view of the heavy thick walls still surrounding the brazed area.

The second stage, after careful measurement, is reducing the outer diameter to conform with the cylinder body casting and the requirements of the working cylinder. The top and central collars, retained at 2in OD, form part of the water jacket around the power cylinder. The length between these collars is reduced to ¹⁄₁₆in wall thickness. The remaining part of the cylinder from the central collar to the heated end is reduced in three stages, the

Fig 17.14 Roy Key in his workshop - the original Ericsson engine can be seen in the background.

middle part to fit tightly into the end seating of the cast cylinder body internal bore, the displacer area to a ¹⁄₁₆in wall thickness and the heated part, ¾in, reduced to ³⁄₆₄in wall. The very final stage is lapping the top (power) end of the cylinder until a mirror finish is obtained.

The cast cylinder body has the water jacket and the cylinder seating collar machined as described by Larry Kazyak in his article, with different internal dimensions in view of the type of cylinder size being used; in fact all the steps for completing the engine may well follow these instructions.

The above process of using a solid drawn working cylinder from 2in OD has the disadvantage (?) of giving a narrower working bore, 1½in ID as against the 2in+ bore used by Larry Kazyak, however it should not effect the performance of this engine.

ROY KEY'S ELEGANT ERICSSONS

Two remarkable and extremely well finished Ericsson engines are the handwork of ROY KEY, of Muir Heath, Stoke-on-Trent (Fig 17.14). Roy is well known for his meticulous and painstaking finish to his engines some of which are also dealt with in Chapter 9. Here, however, his two Ericssons are selected for their high class presentation; one of them has an interesting deviation from the original designs and castings, and should be studied for the ingenuity shown by the modeller in this scratch built engine.

Roy's first Ericsson, (Fig 17.15), is built from CAMDEN castings like hundreds of others similarly built; however the bench-work and paint finish of this engine gives it an outstanding appearance and elevates the model to a standard which is equivalent to the best exhibits of other types of engines in any Engineering Exhibition. To put a value to one's handwork is difficult, but the fact that this model was sold at CHRISTIE'S in October 1988 for £1,200 is an indication of the precision and high standard achieved.

Roy Key's second Ericsson (Fig 17.16) is a scratch built model and is described by him in an article well worth reading called "Elegant Ericsson Engine" in MODEL ENGINEER of February 18, 1994. Roy's departure from castings is intentional. It is an air-cooled design, totally independent of water supply, and geared to drive ancillary equipment rather than the normal use for pumping. The model retains the general appearance of the Ericsson but its gear drive has heightened the alternative uses of this engine. The superb finish of the model and the high quality of its engineering and bench fitting has earned it a special mention in CHRISTIE'S Catalogue and this is reflected in the price for which it was sold: £2,420!

Fig 17.15 (Above) Roy Key's Ericsson built from Camden Castings.

Fig 17.16 (Left) Roy Key's scratch built Ericsson with geardrive. (Courtesy: Christies Images.)

CHAPTER EIGHTEEN

How to construct 'Prova II', a competition type co-axial Stirling engine

'Prova II' (winner of the Brian Thomas Memorial Trophy, 1984 Model Engineering Exhibition, Wembley) is a test-bed engine designed for experiments on external annular regenerators (see Chapter 3).

The concept is for an engine which allows the regenerative matrix to be changed fairly easily without disturbing the engine mechanism. The design therefore incorporates a number of important features; a main or working cylinder that can be taken out and modified without removing the power piston/displacer assembly; a regenerative matrix that can be enclosed between the working cylinder and the regenerator cover, the whole assembly being gas tight; and thirdly a gap between the working cylinder and the regenerator cover which can be enlarged as

Fig 18.1 Completed engine pictured with Brian Thomas Memorial Trophy.

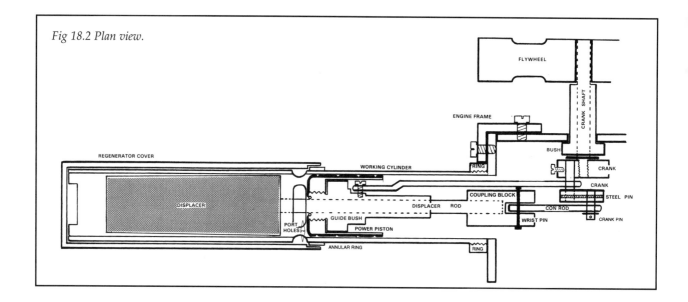

Fig 18.2 Plan view.

required to accommodate larger matrices. The engine design also incorporates a construction feature which consists of an easily dismantled engine frame so that any part of the engine can be removed without disturbing the rest.

The materials for the engine can be obtained from scrap or surplus supplies with the possible exception of the stainless steel shim (regenerative matrix), the silver steel rods and the flywheel. The outer regenerator cover, the retaining ring and collar, the working cylinder and the displacer cylinder of the winning engine were all obtained from the internal cylinders of various different sizes of shock absorbers.

GENERAL ENGINE LAYOUT

The working cylinder is open-ended, the front part threaded to fit into a ring brazed on a flange. The rear end, apart from being open is partly filed down to allow the uninterrupted flow of gas during the expansion stage. Four ports are milled (or drilled) about midway along the length of the cylinder. A regenerator cover is machined to fit on to the working cylinder, long enough to cover the port holes, while leaving a narrow gap. The working gas moves through the rear opening, through the regenerator gap, through the port holes back into the main cylinder. The assembled cylinder is mounted onto an engine frame which allows for stroke and timing adjustments with comparative ease.

METHOD OF CONSTRUCTION

The MAIN WORKING CYLINDER. The front end of the main cylinder is threaded 32 tpi for ¼in but other fine threads would also be suitable. Alternatively the cylinder may be brazed to a

flange. The back end is segmented by fine saw cuts into eight equal sections, alternate sections filed down by ⅛in. Four portholes are machined in the cylinder, their position being at the place where the power piston reaches TDC. The portholes are milled, with the use of a dividing head to give four points where the slot drill, 3⁄16in, makes its first cut. Each cut is slowly lengthened sideways to give four portholes of 3⁄16in by ⅝in (Fig 18.3). Alternatively, 12 holes, 3⁄16in may be drilled, equally spaced around the circumference. Care is taken not to damage or to twist the cylinder. Finally a boring tool is used to remove any sharp metal edges left by the milling/drilling operation.

The final stage of construction on the cylinder involves the mounting of a ring just forward (1⁄32in) of the portholes. This ring, which is tight fitting, is lightly bonded in place. It is important to ensure that the OD of the ring is slightly over the unmachined ID of the regenerator cover. In this engine the ring OD is 1⅛in while the regenerator cover ID is 1 1⁄32in.

A flange is machined to fit the working cylinder; this involves a two step operation. First a collar is threaded 32 tpi to fit the threaded cylinder; then the collar is silver soldered to a brass flange, 3⁄32in thick, 1⅜in by 1⅜in. The flange is then bored to internal diameter of the working cylinder. Finally four 4 BA holes, one at each corner, are prepared for fitting to the engine frame.

The REGENERATOR COVER (Fig 18.4). Two stages of operation are required here - welding with oxyacetylene and iron filling rod, and the use of a boring tool to widen the first ¼in length of this cylinder to 1⅛in to give a nice sliding fit on the ring which has been bonded to the main cylinder. The regenerator cover may be externally thinned down for two-thirds of its length to lessen heat conduction.

The DISPLACER. Machining this component requires more attention than any other part of the engine, probably as much as the power piston itself. A thin-walled cylinder is found or machined to obtain a sliding fit in the working cylinder. This is brazed at one end using thin gauge sheet metal. The displacer is sealed at the other end by a dural plug, drilled and threaded 4 BA. Since the working air is not required to pass along the annular gap between the displacer and the working cylinder, but is pushed outside of the working cylinder into the regenerator cover, it is essential that the annular gap is reduced to the barest minimum without friction.

The last job on the displacer assembly is the coupling block/con-rod fitting (Fig 18.5). There are several ways of making a coupling block - the simplest type is made from a ⅜in by 1in brass bar, drilled ³⁄₁₆in to a depth of about ½in. The other end is slotted ⅛in by ½in deep, and prepared to take the con-rod. In line with the slot and about ³⁄₁₆in from the bored end, a hole is drilled and tapped 4 BA to take a set screw. The coupling block is then crossdrilled to take the gudgeon pin across the middle of the slot. The con-rod should fit nicely without friction or binding. The coupling block gives an adjustment of about ¼in, that is ⅛in each way.

The POWER PISTON is machined from cast iron or suitable bright mild steel bar (Fig 18.6). Work on the piston is a multi-stage operation, first reducing the diameter to obtain an almost perfect fit, cutting four oil grooves, finishing off the top (crown) in a fairly rounded end - required in view of the portholes arrangement, and then parted off. In the final stage the piston is reversed in the chuck drilled and bored and then faced internally with

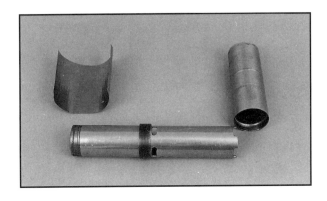

Fig 18.3 Regenerator components.

an end mill to ensure a tight fit when the displacer rod guide bush is screwed in.

The DISPLACER ROD GUIDE BUSH (Fig 18.7). The machining of this guide is a four stage operation at one go. A ¾in mild steel bar is faced along its length. The first ⅜in is reduced and threaded ⅜in BSF with a slight undercut at the end of the thread. A collar of ¼in long is left untouched (¾ in OD), a second collar is machined to ½in OD while the remaining length is reduced to ⁵⁄₁₆in OD. The guide is first centre-drilled, then drilled and reamed ³⁄₁₆in and parted off.

The second collar (½in OD) above is filed on one side to remove about ¹⁄₁₆in of its diameter; a hole is then drilled in the centre of this part and tapped 4 BA to take a bolt which will be the wrist pin of the power piston con-rod. Once the power piston con-rod has been prepared, it is bolted to the guide bush, ensuring free movement. The guide bush is then assembled into the power piston with a fibre

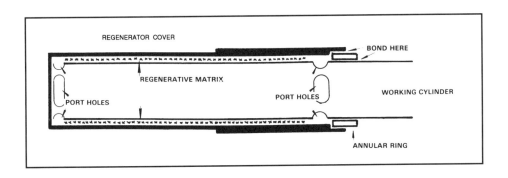

Fig 18.4 (Left) Layout of regenerator.

Fig 18.5 (Below) Gudgeon or coupling block.

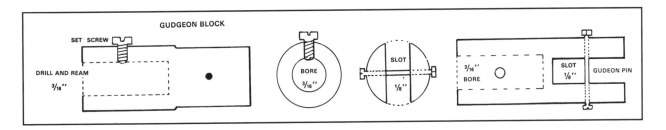

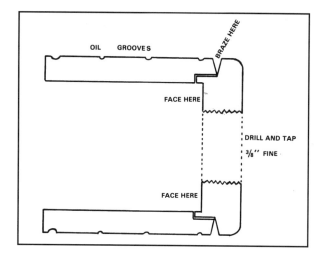

OIL GROOVES

BRAZE HERE

FACE HERE

DRILL AND TAP
3/8" FINE

FACE HERE

Fig 18.6 (Above) Machined power piston.

The DRIVE MECHANISM. At this stage it is required to provide the power piston with a stroke of ⅜in; to provide the displacer with a stroke of ⅞in; and to provide a variable phase angle of between 90° and 110°, Fig 18.8.

A ³⁄₁₆in shaft is machined and threaded 4 BA to take the power crank, made from a BMS square section ¼in by ¼in by ¾in long, marked at the centre and ³⁄₁₆ in from the centre. The centre hole is drilled and tapped 4 BA while the other hole is drilled ⅛in clear. The crank is then drilled laterally and tapped 4 BA on the side of the ⅛in hole to provide a grub screw.

Another piece of BMS square section, ³⁄₁₆in by ³⁄₁₆in by ¾in is then prepared for the second crank (the displacer stroke). Two holes, ½in apart, are marked and drilled ⅛in clear, into which are inserted two tightly fitted dowel pins, exiting on opposite sides of the square section. The crank assembly is shown in Fig 18.9 It is advisable to thread the dowel pin which takes the displacer con-rod in order that a lock nut can be used; alternatively a split pin/washer arrangement can be devised. With the two cranks completed, it remains only for the stroke and timing mechanism to be fitted and set.

washer and a smear of Loctite Screwlock 222, and the whole assembly tightened.

The ENGINE FRAME consists of two plates, a cylinder plate and a crankshaft bearing plate which are bolted to a bracket in turn screwed to a base. This type of construction allows for either plate to be removed without the necessity of unscrewing the other. The plates are cut and shaped from ⅛in to ³⁄₁₆in brass or BMS, 2½in long and 2in wide. The centre point of the displacer cylinder ring is 1½in from the L-corner, while the centre point of the crankshaft bush is 1¾in from the L-corner. Two important requirements should be kept in mind. The first that the plates must be at 90° to each other and the centre points of the cylinder ring and the crankshaft bush are perfectly aligned.

The CRANKSHAFT HOUSING, 1½in long, is machined from BMS ¾in bar stock. Machining is a multi-stage operation at one-go. The housing is faced, then 1¼in length is reduced to ½in, centre drilled, and then drilled and reamed ³⁄₁₆in. One or two oil holes may be drilled for lubrication. The housing is fitted to the side plate and sweat soldered or brazed. It is advisable to re-finish the bore with a reamer if any heat is applied.

The first part of the stroke and timing operation involves the power piston. The fitting of the piston at TDC should just reach the portholes in the working cylinder. Any adjustment to the con-rod is made at this stage before the displacer crank is fitted to the drive mechanism. The working of the power piston is checked carefully at this stage. In the second stage, the displacer/displacer rod is fitted into the power piston and guide bush from the open rear end of the working cylinder. The coupling block is fitted to the displacer rod, and the con-rod fitted between the coupling block and the displacer crankpin. As explained in Chapter 6 the closest the displacer is to the power piston during its movements in the cycle is when is when the cranks are at approximately 10 past 11, that is the piston con-rod is at 5 mins to the hour, while the displacer con-rod/crank-pin is at 10 mins past the hour. Fig 18.10 explains this position clearly.

Fig 18.7
Displacer
rod guide
bush.

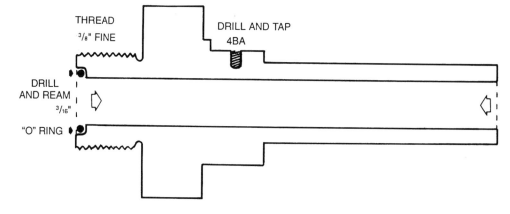

THREAD
3/8" FINE

DRILL AND TAP
4BA

DRILL
AND REAM
3/16"

"O" RING

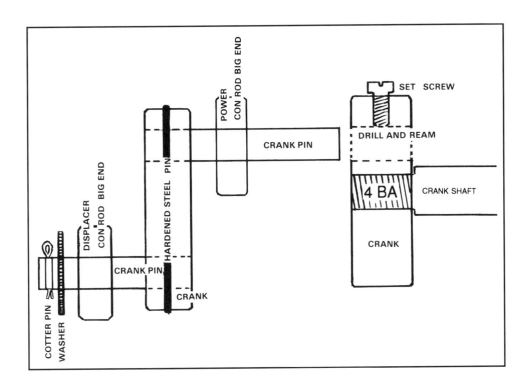

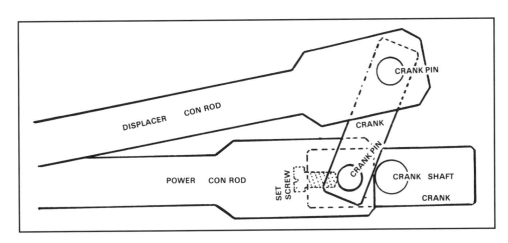

The space between the power piston and the displacer should be at its minimum in this position; this is the starting point of the engine setting. Any small adjustment can be made later from the coupling block. Major adjustments on the other hand involve either the length of the displacer rod or the length of the con-rod. In this position (10 past 11), the cranks are approximately at 90° to each other, and therefore marking and drilling for the hole where the crank pin should fit into the displacer con-rod should be made here. Throughout the fitting of the power piston and the displacer the rear of the working cylinder is uncovered.

The REGENERATOR MATRIX. The first experimental matrix is made from 0.002in stainless steel shim, similar to that used by Robin Robbins and Andy Ross in their engines. The steel shim is ruled by a scriber every 1⁄8in, the lines alternating

on opposite sides of the shim, along the path of the working gas - these lines cause the shim to pleat and to bend naturally along the circumference of the cylinder. This construction allows the working gas to pass on both sides of the shim, thus doubling the surface of the matrix exposed to the working gas. The gap between the regenerator (outer) cover and the working cylinder is of 1⁄64in, enough to accommodate the pleated shim while at the same time limiting dead space.

The final stages of assembly with the power piston and the displacer in position and the mechanism fully adjusted, involve the positioning of the steel shim regenerator between the outer cover and the working cylinder. Care is taken that the matrix does not slip forward to cover the portholes and some juggling with the shim may be necessary to ensure correct positioning. A smear of bonding agent around the annular ring should hold the

*Fig 18.10
The position of the displacer and power piston at their closest point of "near" contact - for timing purposes.*

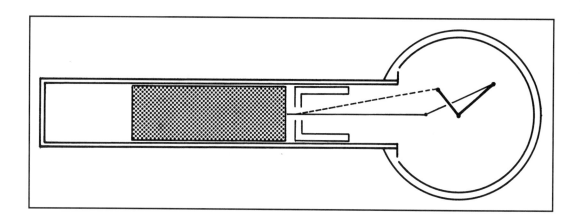

regenerator cover quite fast preventing any gas leakage.

COOLING is by waterjacket attached by tubes to a cooling tank. The working cylinder has two outside diameters, the regenerator cover and the power cylinder. The water jacket should be placed as far forward on the regenerator cover as possible. If it is found that during test runs, the power cylinder becomes too hot, a second smaller water jacket for this area is advisable: Fig 18.11.

The BURNER consists of an enclosed ring with 24 jets of $\frac{1}{16}$in diameter; the mixing tube holds a Camping Gaz burner jet while a copper pipe connects the burner to a Camping Gaz blowlamp through a special adaptor fitted for the purpose, Fig 18.12. The engine responds quickest to heat if the burner is positioned at the extreme end of the cylinder such that the last row of jets throw a curtain of flames to the rear of the cylinder, while the first row of jets heat the rear $\frac{3}{4}$in of the regenerator cover. In this way the working gas is

forced to make constant contact with the closed end of the regenerator cover, picking up more heat and more quickly.

RUNNING-IN the engine is advised before the regenerator cover is bonded to the working cylinder. When the regenerator cover has been fitted and the bond set, another but shorter running-in is given to the engine. In the initial stages care is taken to run the engine for short periods at slow speed, increasing both the speed and duration over a number of runs.

PERFORMANCE

The first run of 'Prova II' under power clocked a no-load speed of 1,200 rpm. Subsequent runs, after a slight adjustment to the phase mechanism by

Fig 18.11 (Below left) Cooler assembly.

Fig 18.12 (Below right) Burner assembly.

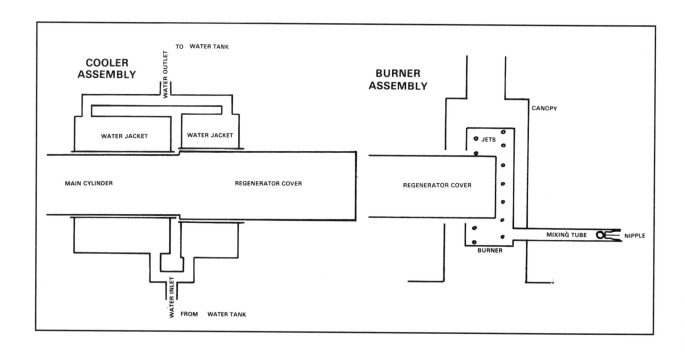

increasing the angle from 90° to 100° gave an increase of speed to a steady 1,830 rpm. Two other results are evident. This engine takes longer to start than other co-axial engines due to the particular regenerator cover construction. The other interesting point is that on turning off the heat the engine takes a long time to stop, again due to the type of regeneration. Obviously other types of regenerative matrices may be experimented with. Stainless steel mesh gauze, stainless steel wire, fine glass rods or ceramic strips are all possibilities.

It will be noticed that the volume of air swept by the displacer and the power piston is in the ratio of almost 2:1. This is explained by the fact that in this engine there is much more dead space or cushion air than any other engine described so far. The volume of air contained in the annular space accounts for a substantial proportion of this cushion air.

PROVA: ENGINE SPECIFICATIONS

	IMPERIAL SIZES	NEAREST "WORKING" METRIC EQUIVALENT
Working cylinder	1in OD	25mm
	29⁄32in ID	23mm
	6in length	150mm
Outer cylinder (regenerator cover)	1³⁄₁₆in OD	30mm
	1¹⁄₃₂in ID	26.2mm
	3½in length	90mm
Power piston	29⁄32in OD	23mm
	1¹⁄₁₆in length	27mm
	⅜in stroke	9.5mm - 10mm
Displacer	⅞in (approx) OD	22.6mm
	2¹⁷⁄₃₂in length	64.3mm
	⅞in stroke	22mm
Portholes	4 of ³⁄₁₆in x ⅝in	5mm by 16mm
Crankshaft and displacer rod	³⁄₁₆in silver steel	5mm
Annular ring	1⅛ in OD	29mm
	1in ID	25mm
Displacer rod guide bush	¾in OD	19mm
	1¾in length	45mm
	³⁄₁₆in bore ID	5mm
Cranks: Power	¼in x ¼in x ¾in	6mm by 6mm by 20mm
Displacer	³⁄₁₆in x ³⁄₁₆in x ¾in	5mm by 5mm by 20mm
Coupling block	⅜in OD	10mm
	1in length	25mm

CHAPTER NINETEEN

How to Construct "Sunspot" a solar-powered Stirling Engine

'SUNSPOT' is a small concentric solar-powered Stirling engine (Fig 19.1). Heating the engine is by means of the concentration of the sun's rays on the hot end of the cylinder with the aid of a parabolic reflector. There are some disadvantages to this type of heating, mainly because of the total dependence on bright sunlight and the need to aim the reflector directly into the sun but these disadvantages are outweighed by the satisfaction of using free energy. In fact this method of obtaining mechanical energy is one of the most direct ways of tapping the power of the sun.

The use of a parabolic mirror or reflector is not the only method of using the sun's rays to power a

Stirling engine; an alternative method is the use of the Fresnel lens which also concentrates the rays on a focal point (see Chapter 4). The main difference between the parabolic reflector and the Fresnel lens is that the parabolic reflector heats the circumference of the hot end of a cylinder while the Fresnel lens heats one particular area or point, although the temperature at this spot can be higher. Another difference is that the cylinder with its hot end heated by the reflector is almost always perpendicular or nearly so, whereas an engine heated by the Fresnel lens can stay horizontal. The engine described in this chapter can be made to work with other common fuels and is not entirely dependent on the sun's energy. It works just as

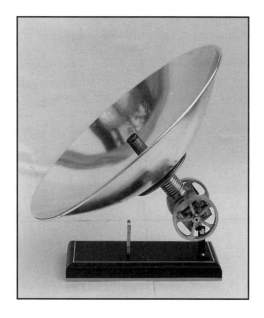

Fig 19.1 SUNSPOT - with reflector (a) left, and as normal stationary engine heated by other conventional means (b) right.

Fig 19.2 Scrap reflector - original state.

easily with gas, or methylated spirit. The engine can be made to stand in any position to work with the fuel or energy chosen.

The construction of this engine is only slightly different from that of 'Prova II' described in Chapter 18 and of 'Dyna' in Chapter 20, the difference being in the crank assembly. The materials used in the building of the original 'SUNSPOT' were mainly from scrap or surplus supplies involving minimum expenditure. No doubt luck played a great part with the finding in a scrap heap of a parabolic reflector, part of some clinic equipment, which was in reasonably good shape and condition (Fig 19.2). The reflector was chromed for a small sum by a private firm specialising in this work. The most important part of this particular project is the reflector. It should be perfectly parabolic in shape so that maximum concentration of the sun's rays can be focused on the hot end of the working cylinder. A parabolic mirror or reflector has the property of bringing the rays parallel to the axis to a point of focus.

The greater the circumference of the reflector, the greater the concentration of the sun's rays. A minimum circumference of 15in diameter is required although a diameter of between 18in to 24in is more desirable.

ENGINE CONSTRUCTION

The reflector used in 'SUNSPOT' has a focal point of 3in, the cylinder length is 5½in, of which 3¼in is within the reflector sphere. A fin cooler is machined and mounted directly in front of the reflector base, while a similar but smaller fin cooler is mounted behind the reflector. The two fin coolers, apart from their use in cooling the cylinder, are also used to retain the reflector

rigidly in place. The cylinder is ring-mounted on an engine frame which holds a multiple crank and supports flywheels. A BMS displacer and a cast iron piston are used for the working mechanism.

The CYLINDER is machined from bright mild steel, (ex-shock absorber internal cylinder), brazed at the closed end. Careful machining on the lathe is essential to the success of the project since the collection of sufficient heat at the hot end is as much dependent on the reflector as it is on the cylinder wall thickness. The most important part of machining is the reduction of the wall thickness of the hot end of the cylinder for a length of ¾in from the brazed end, ensuring that the brazing is not touched or removed, that the cylinder is not distorted and that the wall is greatly reduced.

A further 2¼in length of the cylinder is slightly reduced to prevent heat conduction along the length of the cylinder covered by the displacer and the displacer stroke. At the other end the cylinder is threaded 32 tpi for ¼in. Alternatively a flange may be brazed on the cylinder, care being taken to avoid distortion. Any internal boring , honing and lapping should be completed at this stage, after extensive external lathe work has been undertaken.

The ENGINE FRAME . There are different ways of constructing the engine frame. The method described in Chapter 18 is an excellent alternative to the one described here. So, for that matter, is the drive mechanism which can be adapted to this engine.

The engine frame illustrated here (Fig 19.3), taken from surplus electrical equipment is 2½in by 2¼in by 2¼in. A ring, bored and threaded internally 32 tpi to take the main cylinder, is silver brazed on a side of the box which is 2¼in by 2¼in; this arrangement allows for con-rods to be fitted on to the crankshaft housed within the frame. One minor modification to this frame is necessary in view of the need for the crank assembly to slide into its place within the engine frame. Two holes, ⁷⁄₃₂in, are drilled in the sides of the frame and slots cut with a fine hacksaw blade (Fig 16.4).

Two Dural plates, 1¼in by 1¼in by ¼in are drilled ⅝in to take ball bearings for the crankshaft, and fitted to the engine frame by four 2BA bolts. This assembly allows for the crankshaft, bearings and con-rods to slide out of the frame without difficulty when any adjustment is required. Alternative engine frames may be constructed to allow for adjustments as necessary.

The DISPLACER/REGENERATOR is best constructed from thin-walled BMS tube brazed at one end and sealed at the other end with an aluminium plug, drilled and tapped 4BA to take ⁵⁄₃₂in silver

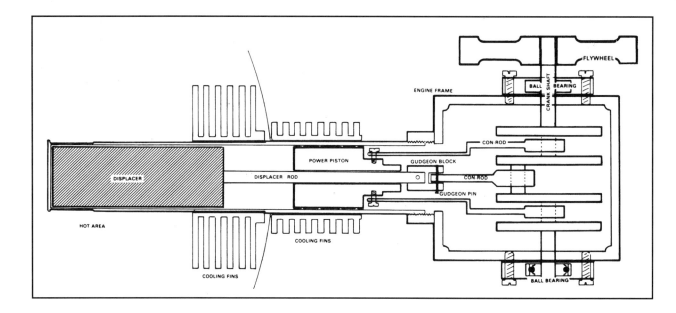

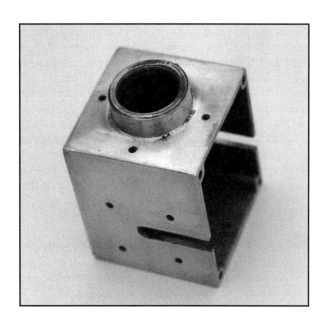

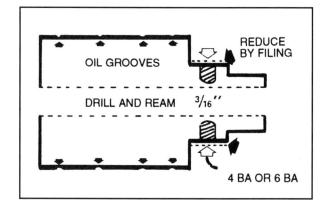

Fig 19.3 (Top) Plan view.

Fig 19.4 (Left) Engine frame with brazed ring and slotted sides.

Fig 19.5 (Above) Power piston.

steel rod. The original version of 'Sunspot' had an alloy displacer (ex-perfume container), whose regenerative effect was barely adequate. To complement regeneration a 0.002in stainless steel shim, raised on both sides by dimples, was inserted to press against the cylinder wall and reduce the annular gap. Eventually this assembly was replaced by a BMS displacer.

The POWER PISTON is machined from 1in cast iron, reduced to ⅞in OD for a length of 1¼in, ⁹⁄₁₆in OD for a further ¼in, and ⅜in OD for ¼in (Fig 19.5). While in the lathe the power piston assembly is centre-drilled, drilled and reamed ⁵⁄₃₂in (³⁄₁₆in bore is a suitable alternative), and finally parted off. The ⁹⁄₁₆in OD collar is filed ¹⁄₃₂in on opposite sides and prepared to take two con-rods. Two holes, drilled and tapped 4BA will take the wrist pins for the con-rods.

The CRANK is constructed from four discs or webs, with crank pins fitted in the discs and silver soldered in place. The construction (Fig 19.6), although delicate in execution, is quite straight forward provided that the steps explained here are followed in the right order.

1. A bright mild steel bar, 1½in OD, is faced and prepared in the lathe. It is centre-drilled, then drilled ³⁄₁₆in to a depth of 1in.

2. The bar is then drilled ³⁄₁₆in at a mark ⁵⁄₁₆in off-centre.

3. In the next stage the bar is marked ²⁵⁄₆₄in off-centre, but at right angle from step 2 above. These two bores are both one inch in depth.

4. Four discs, ⅛in thick are cut from the drilled end of the bar either by parting off on the lathe, or

SUNSPOT: FABRICATED CRANKSHAFT ASSEMBLY *(Fig 19.6)*

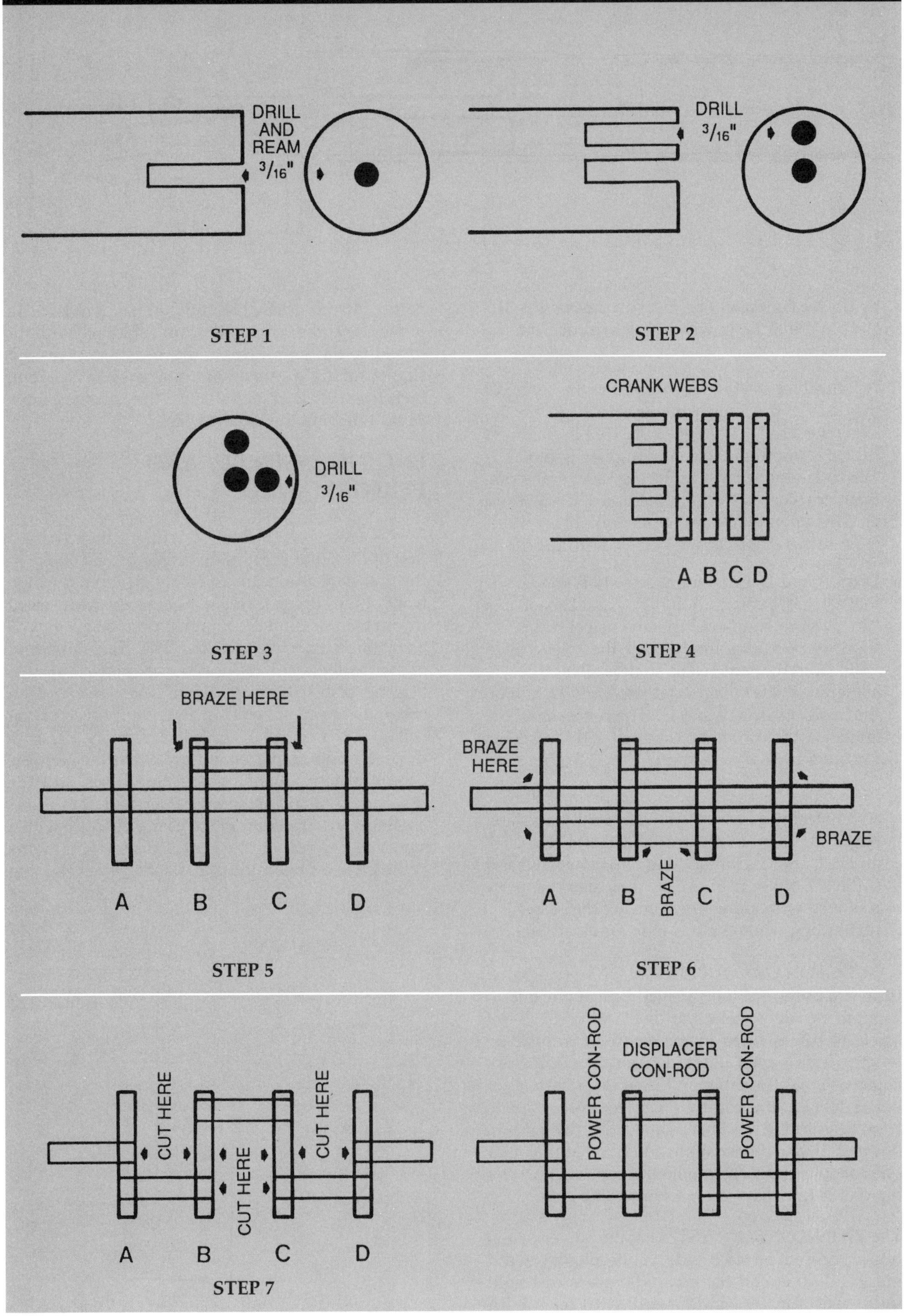

DRILL
AND
REAM
³/₁₆"

STEP 1

DRILL
³/₁₆"

STEP 2

DRILL
³/₁₆"

CRANK WEBS

A B C D

STEP 3

STEP 4

BRAZE HERE

A   B   C   D

STEP 5

BRAZE
HERE

BRAZE

BRAZE

A   B   C   D

STEP 6

CUT HERE

CUT HERE

CUT HERE

A   B   C   D

STEP 7

POWER CON-ROD

DISPLACER
CON-ROD

POWER CON-ROD

Fig 19.7 Side elevation

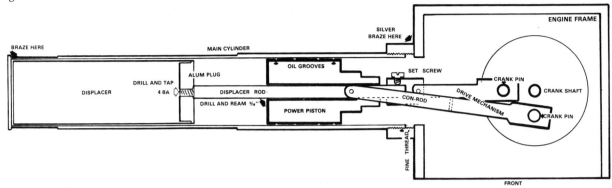

by power hacksaw. The discs are marked A, B, C, D in the order in which they are cut from the bar stock.

5. A ³⁄₁₆in silver steel rod is inserted in the centre of the discs in the same order as above. A ³⁄₁₆in silver steel rod, ⅝in long, is inserted in the holes drilled ²⁵⁄₆₄in from the centre in discs B and C. The rod, which serves as the displacer crank pin, is silver soldered from the outside of discs B and C. This operation will give a crank throw of ²⁵⁄₃₂in to the displacer when the con-rod is fitted.

6. Discs A and D are brought close to B and C, so that the gap between A and B, C and D is of just ¼in. A 1½ in length of ³⁄₁₆in silver steel rod is then inserted in the four discs in the holes drilled ²⁵⁄₆₄in from the centre. The shaft is silver soldered on the outside of discs A and D, and on the inside of discs B and C. The centre shaft or crankshaft is also silver soldered at this stage on the outside of discs A and D.

7. With a fine hacksaw the surplus parts of the silver steel rods are cut off. In all eight cuts are required, six for the centre crankshaft between A and B, B and C, C and D, and two between B and C (Step 7 of Fig 19.6). All surplus material is removed with a fine file to ensure that there is no binding when the con-rods are assembled.

A GUDGEON OR COUPLING BLOCK is prepared from ⅜in brass, ½in long, drilled ⁵⁄₃₂in at one end to a depth of ¼in to take the displacer rod. A set screw, 4 BA, is fitted in the centre of the drilled length. (See Chapter 18 for identical coupling block construction). The other end is slotted ⅛in for ¼in depth to take the con-rod. The con-rod is made from bright mild steel bar ³⁄₁₆in by ¼in, drilled ¹⁄₁₆in one end to take the wrist pin and fitted at the other end to a big-end. (The method of construction of a big-end is fully covered in Chapter 20).

The TWIN-CONROD SYSTEM of the power piston has a con-rod on each side of the displacer rod guide. At one end the con-rods, made of bright mild steel ³⁄₁₆in by ¼in, are drilled to take 4 BA

bolts. At the other, big-ends are soldered on. In order that the con-rods can function without touching the crank-webs, the rods are bent and shaped at right angles (as in Fig 19.3). Careful measurement is essential since the con-rods must avoid touching the engine frame.

ENGINE ASSEMBLY AND PERFORMANCE

The assembly of 'SUNSPOT' differs slightly from that of the other engines described in this book. In the first stage the crank assembly is placed through front of the engine frame; the con-rods are inserted through the cylinder retaining ring, and screwed on to the respective cranks. The crankshaft and crank assembly is slipped into place and the bearing plates screwed down. The power piston con-rods are next screwed into the power piston collar with a smear of Loctite Screwlock 222. The displacer and displacer rod are fitted through the power piston, then the coupling block and the displacer con-rod is screwed on and the whole assembly inserted into the working cylinder with a smear of light oil on the power piston. Finally the cylinder is screwed into its place in the retaining

Fig 19.8 Tilting mechanism.

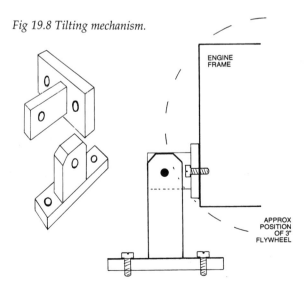

ring. At this stage the crank is turned by hand from the flywheels to ensure that there is no binding. Any adjustments to the displacer stroke are made at this stage.

It is advisable to give a good running-in (without heat) to the engine assembly until the mechanism is working smoothly. Finally, before the reflector is mounted, it is advisable to run the engine under power heated by a methylated spirit burner or a low gas flame (such as a bunsen burner at 50% power). In northern countries, above the 45th parallel (latitude) experiments with the reflector may be best attempted around noon on a bright sunny day. Care should be taken not to point the reflector in the eyes of the operator or of other people standing by.

The engine frame requires a tilting mechanism to allow it to move from horizontal to vertical positions with minimum effort. This pivot mechanism (Fig 19.8) should neither be too low to obstruct the flywheels nor too high to make the engine unsteady during its run. A height of about 1in between the engine frame and the engine base is adequate. If the engine is to be used constantly in a horizontal position, it is worthwhile to devise an engine support so that the main cylinder can avoid vibrations.

Engine performance depends on the amount of heat generated at the hot end of the cylinder. With a gas burner or a good methylated spirit flame the engine easily reaches the 1,300 rpm range. With bright sunlight and a good-sized reflector, speeds of 600-800 rpm can be attained. If the engine is being used with a reflector only, it is advisable to spray the hot end with a matt black paint to aid the absorption of heat.

EXPERIMENTS WITH A FRESNEL LENS

Various experiments were undertaken in the early days of 'SUNSPOT' to gauge the performance difference between a parabolic reflector and Fresnel lenses. In fact two different sizes of lenses were used, a 12in and a 15in.

There are two main problems in using these lenses : in the first place they are too pliable and require a rigid wooden circular frame, hinged to a stand to find the right angle to the sun's rays. Secondly, it required manoeuvring of the engine to obtain the right focal length. Every minute the frame has to be adjusted and the engine moved to find the right position. However, for that short period that the rays are focused on the hot end, the engine develops very high speeds equivalent to a high gas flame.

ALTERNATIVE ENGINE CONSTRUCTION

The design of the solar powered engine in Fig 19.9 and 19.10 by fellow modeller Alphonse Vassallo of California, allows for a simple engine frame machined from dural, mounted on a wooden base. The engine is a concentric Stirling with a cylinder of 1⅜in ID, fin cooled with a double-throw crank and a tilting mechanism independent of the crankshaft and flywheel bracket, a neat and functional assembly which allows for easy adjustment. The addition of a hot cap in the shape of a small glass jar has increased the engine power by 20%. The reflector used on this engine is an 18in diameter, although Alphonse Vassallo has used a 24in reflector, on another solar powered engine, with much greater effect.

Fig 19.9 (Top) Alphonse Vassallo's Solar powered engine showing tilting mechanism and Fig 19.10 (Above) showing 18 in reflector.

SUNSPOT: ENGINE SPECIFICATIONS

	IMPERIAL SIZES	NEAREST "WORKING" METRIC EQUIVALENTS
Engine base	10½in x 4¾in	270mm x 120mm
Engine frame	2½in x 2¼in x 2¼in	63mm x 57mm x 57mm
Working cylinder	5½in long intern. 1in OD	140mm 25mm
Power piston	⅞in OD 1¾in total length	22mm 44mm
Displacer	⅞in OD 2⁷⁄₁₆in long	22mm 62mm
Stroke: Power Displacer	⅝in ²⁵⁄₃₂in long	16mm 20mm

CHAPTER TWENTY

How to Construct "Dyna" a demonstration engine

This engine was built specifically as a demonstration engine for exhibitions, lectures and other club promotional activities. It is designed to show that a hot air engine, even as a model, can produce enough power to provide a modest work output. The engine was made to drive a small dynamo (generating enough power to light a torch bulb), drive a fan to cool the engine radiator and to drive a pump which circulates water from the engine to the radiator. "DYNA" performs all the above work and that in itself is a great attraction during exhibitions; however the talking point is usually a list placed near the engine giving details of scrap materials used for the various parts and their origin. This list is given at the end of the chapter.

GENERAL ENGINE LAYOUT

"DYNA" is a single cylinder concentric engine similar to "PROVA", "SUNSPOT" and the "ERICSSON HOT AIR PUMP ENGINE". Planning an engine layout with a number of accessories, all driven off the same shaft, that had to be accommodated without cluttering a base of given dimensions, was a challenge in itself. The base was probably a chassis of some type of radio or transmitter, carrying a number of valves and relays.

The starting point, and a lucky find, was this particular heavy duty shock absorber (damper). The construction of the cylinder is in itself unusual in that it is high quality BMS, solid drawn and seamless even at the closed end which is domed. Its mono construction proved ideal for machining, especially for reducing the hot end. The internal wall surface did not require finishing, and micrometer readings gave an accurate round bore. All the same the first three inches were lapped to ensure a good finish. An alternative working cylinder would obviously require more attention.

The crankshaft is fabricated to give the required stroke to the power piston and the displacer. The original crankshaft spanned the width of the base and had three pulleys to provide drive to the accessories; this was later modified and cut into two separate parts, one part being the crankshaft attached to the flywheel, the other became a drive shaft with pulleys to drive the dynamo, pump and fan. In between a clutch mechanism was assembled; its purpose is to activate the drive shaft after the engine picks up speed.

The cooling system appears to be a complex one, in reality it is a piece of showmanship; there is no need for a pump and a cooling fan with the radiator when a simple thermosyphon system coupled to a water tank will suffice. The dynamo and bulb on the other hand, give an impressive effect during demonstrations, particularly indoors when the bulb lights up the drive mechanism, the clutch assembly and the pulleys.

METHOD OF CONSTRUCTION

The ENGINE BASE is to a large extent also the engine frame since all the components are bolted directly to the base. Drilling is only required for the brackets and supports where necessary.

The MAIN (WORKING) CYLINDER is cut and

Fig 20.1 DYNA - completed engine.

machined from a heavy duty shock absorber, cleaned and faced on the outside, and, if required, honed and lapped on the inside. This particular specimen did not require much internal work, just lapping although the bore had a mirror finish. Any other cylinder requires internal boring, honing and lapping. The material, high quality machinable BMS, ⅛in thick, requires considerable thinning in the heated area.

Machining the working cylinder entails the following :

1. Reducing the external wall thickness by 60-75 % for a length of about 2in from the heated end;

2. Silver soldering a flange, L-shaped at one end, about one-third of the way from the heated end, for bolting to the base;

3. Silver soldering a water jacket to the flange (only). This water jacket covers 40% of the length of the length of the working cylinder, with inlet and outlet water pipes on opposite sides, top and bottom.

4. Fitting of a small bracket at the top end of the working cylinder for bolting to the base.

The WATER JACKET is cut from BMS tubing, 1⁄16in thick, 2½in ID; one end is segmented by many cuts with a fine hacksaw blade, ¼in deep, which are then gently hammered inwards to close up on the working cylinder. The other end is silver soldered to the flange. Finally, the segmented end is sealed water tight by Loctite Quickmetal. This system is as good as silver soldering the water jacket to the cylinder, without the danger of distorting it.

The DISPLACER is machined from BMS tube either 1¹¹⁄16in OD, reduced internally to a wall thickness not exceeding 1⁄64in, or 1¾in OD reduced externally to the same wall thickness. The first displacer made from 1¹¹⁄16in OD BMS tube had the wall thickness reduced by internal boring, plugged, drilled and tapped 2 BA to take a

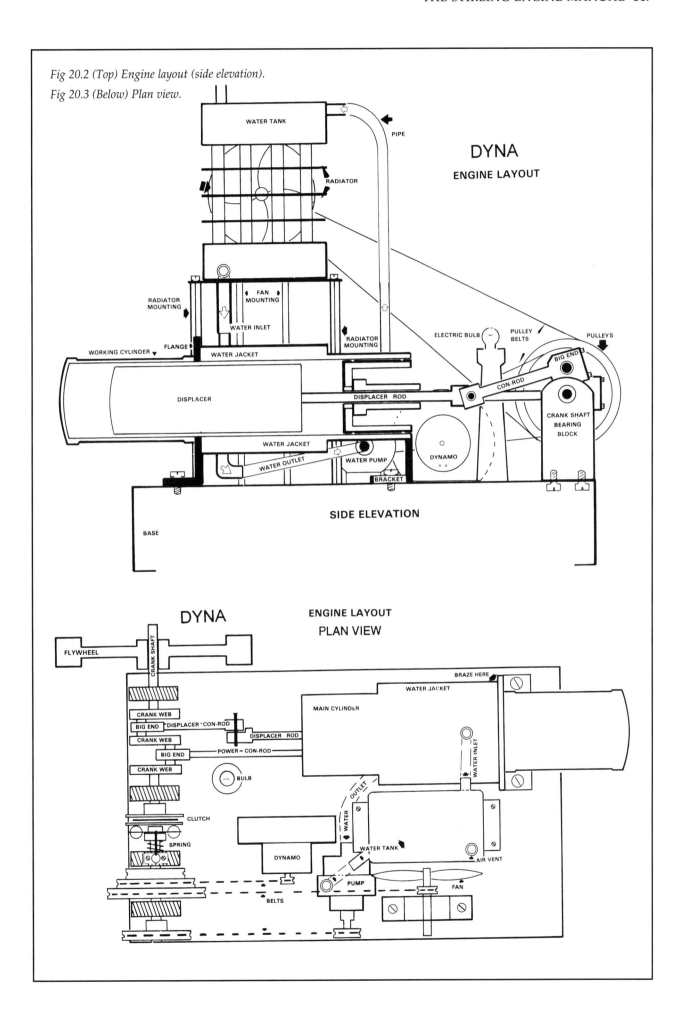

Fig 20.2 (Top) Engine layout (side elevation).
Fig 20.3 (Below) Plan view.

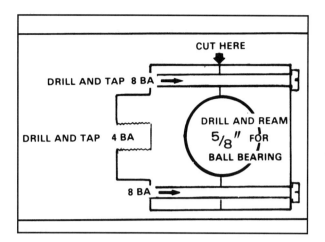

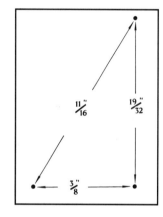

Fig 20.4 (Above)
Big-end
construction.

Fig 20.5 (Right)
Crank-web
marking.

rod. The other end is filed down or reduced by ³⁄₃₂in to allow side mounting of the displacer con-rod, (Fig 20.3).

The DISPLACER CON-ROD is best fabricated from BMS flat bar and silver steel rod. The big-end and the small-end are machined and fitted as explained further on. The rod connecting the two ends is threaded 4 BA at both ends.

The POWER PISTON is best machined from cast iron, finished, lapped and grooved externally, then bored internally to give a ³⁄₃₂in skirt and a flat internal surface at the crown. In the same operation the crown is drilled and tapped ³⁄₈in BSF. The piston used in "DYNA" was actually machined from cast iron water pipe, and has given excellent service.

The POWER PISTON CON-ROD is prepared in the same manner as the displacer con-rod, with a big-end and a small-end, (see below), and a silver steel rod joining the two.

The BIG-END is a multi-step operation, mostly bench-fitting. Fig 20.4 shows the more important steps and really only the measurements are necessary here. These big-ends are cut and shaped from ³⁄₁₆in flat bar, 1¼in x 1in, reduced at one end to leave a stepped side and an 1in x 1in big-end bearing surface which is drilled ⅝in to take a brass bush or ball bearing. The stepped side is drilled laterally and tapped 4 BA to take the displacer or power piston con-rod.

The opposite side to the stepped end is drilled laterally in two places as shown in Fig 20.4, and tapped 8 BA. The big-end is then cut in half by a fine hacksaw blade. To facilitate bolting the two halves together, the outer half of the big-end tapped holes are re-drilled ³⁄₃₂in. The big-end assembly is tightly bolted together and the ⅝in bore is re-drilled to its original size.

When fitting the threaded silver steel rods to the big-end, a retaining nut is used to tighten the assembly.

The SMALL-END is a much simpler operation; these are cut and shaped from ³⁄₁₆in BMS flat bar, ³⁄₈in x ³⁄₈in x ³⁄₁₆in, drilled in the centre to take a 4 BA bolt (preferably with a brass bush), and drilled and tapped 4 BA along the narrow side (³⁄₈in x ³⁄₁₆in) to take the displacer/power piston con-rod.

(See ENGINE LAYOUT for a general description of the crank and drive shafts.)

The DRIVE MECHANISM is fabricated from BMS flat bar ³⁄₁₆in thick, and from ³⁄₁₆in silver steel rod. Three webs are cut, 1¼in x 1in, drilled together and

displacer rod. Although the engine worked satisfactorily initially, it soon developed friction problems due to its length, weight and thin displacer rod, (see PERFORMANCE and MODIFICATIONS). The second displacer is made from a deodorant container, plugged and prepared for the displacer rod.

The DISPLACER ROD GUIDE is machined from BMS or brass, 1in thick, in several steps in a single operation. The first ¼in is reduced and threaded ³⁄₈in BSF, a collar ³⁄₈in wide is reduced to ¾in, and a length of 1¾in is reduced to ³⁄₈in. The guide is then centre-drilled, drilled and reamed ³⁄₁₆in. The guide requires some bench fitting in that the collar, ¾in OD x ³⁄₈in, is filed down on one side by ⅛in. The centre of this area is drilled and tapped 4 BA to take the power piston con-rod.

The DISPLACER ROD is machined from ³⁄₁₆in ground silver steel rod or shafting, threaded 2 BA at one end to fit into the dural plug in the displacer while the other end fits into the gudgeon or coupling block.

The COUPLING OR GUDGEON BLOCK is a BMS flat bar, ³⁄₈in x ³⁄₈in x 1in, drilled ³⁄₁₆in at its square face (³⁄₈in x ³⁄₈in) to a depth of ½in and fitted with a grub screw ¼in from that end to take the displacer

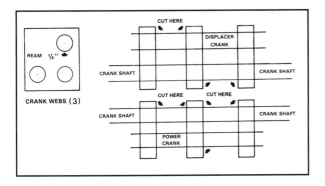

Fig 20.6 Fabricated crankshaft assembly.

reamed ³⁄₁₆in. The remaining holes are marked in a triangular formation, with distances shown in Fig 20.5. The crank is assembled together leaving a ⁵⁄₁₆in gap between the three webs, and the silver soldered or pinned together as in Fig 20.6. This crank will give a ¾in throw to the power piston and a 1³⁄₁₆in throw to the displacer. A length of 1½in shaft is left for the flywheel and 1in for the clutch disc. The crankshaft is then mounted on the brackets with bushes or bearings.

The CRANKSHAFT and DRIVE SHAFT BRACKETS are fabricated together. Four pieces are cut and shaped from ³⁄₈in BMS flat bar 1¼in x 2in, drilled ⁵⁄₈in to take ball bearings (or brass bushes). The position of these brackets is marked on the base and drilled accordingly, with corresponding holes, tapped 2 BA, on the brackets. The crankshaft is first tried in position, mainly for alignment, then with the big-ends in place. Finally the clutch plate

with a collar and set screw, is fitted on this side of the mechanism.

THE ENGINE SHOULD BE RUN-IN AND TRIED OUT AT THIS STAGE.

The DRIVE SHAFT is an assembly put together with care. These directions should be read together with Fig 20.7 and Fig 20.8. As seen from the front, the drive shaft is a straight shaft, between two brackets. On the far right is the pulley which drives the water pump. In between the brackets a multistep machined pulley block drives the fan and the dynamo. To the left of the drive shaft is the clutch mechanism, which seems complicated, but in fact it is a delightful mechanism and quite efficient in operation.

The CLUTCH MECHANISM has two clutch faces both lined with rubber (or cork); in this case rubber from the inner tube of a car tyre is used, the rough part on the outside, the smooth rubber face glued by LOCTITE Superfast 495 to the metal face. The drive-shaft clutch plate has a two step collar, ⁵⁄₁₆in ID against the plate, and ½in ID facing the bracket. This two-step collar does NOT have a set screw and is allowed to move freely along the shaft. The drive shaft has a slot drilled ³⁄₃₂in by ½in long, which starts ¼in from the end, (Fig 20.8, left side). The outer collar of the clutch plate has a ¹⁄₁₆in pin inserted whose work is to pull back the clutch plate when a lever is moved, while retaining its ability to turn the drive shaft, and replacing the usual set screw.

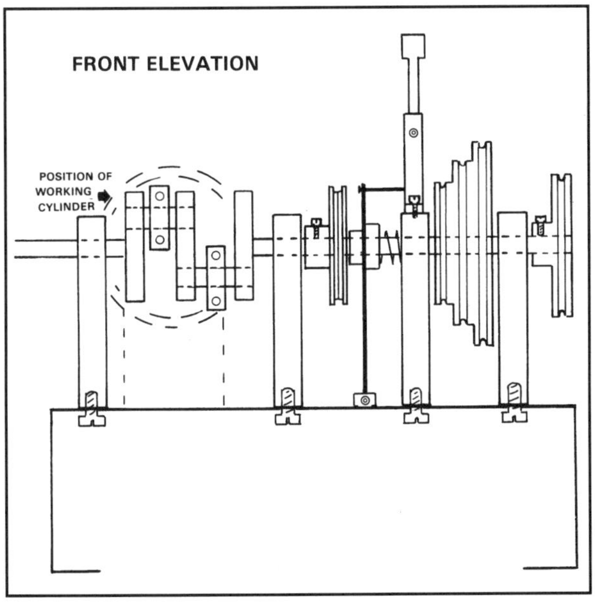

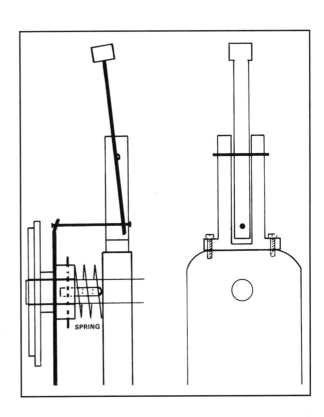

Fig 20.7 (Far left) Front elevation.
Fig 20.8 (Left) Clutch assembly.

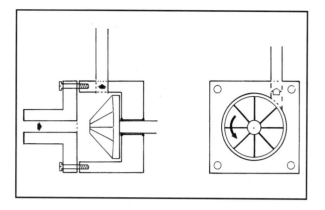

Fig 20.9 (Above) Water pump.

Two levers are employed to declutch the drive shaft; the lower lever is hinged at the base. It is made from a ¹⁄₁₆in BMS flat bar ½in wide. At a point ¾in from the top it is bored ¹¹⁄₃₂in to fit the inner collar of the clutch plate. A ³⁄₃₂in hole is drilled just beneath the top edge; this will take a long 10 BA bolt which serves as a connecting rod to the top lever. This part of the assembly can be tried out once a ¼in soft compression spring with thin brass washers on either side is inserted between the outer collar and the bracket. In practice the drive shaft will remain in place while the clutch plate is levered back.

The top lever, which is in effect the clutch lever, is mounted on a dural bracket machined as in Fig 20.8 (right side), bolted to the top of the drive shaft bracket. Half way along the length of this bracket a ¹⁄₁₆in hole is cross drilled to take the pivot for the top lever. This lever is a ¹⁄₁₆in brass strip, ¼in wide which has a narrow brass tube soldered crosswise halfway along its length, through which a ¹⁄₁₆in bolt or dowel can be inserted to serve as a pivot. The lower end takes the connecting rod from the lower (base mounted) lever. When pushed to the left, the top lever activates the declutch operation.

Any other type of clutch can be machined for this engine - a cone clutch will serve just as well.

The COOLING SYSTEM consists of a water jacket round the working cylinder, a pump, a radiator and a fan. As explained earlier, the pump and fan are not absolutely essential, although they function very well together with the radiator.

The RADIATOR is fabricated from two small tin containers (these particular tins used to contain OXO cubes!), a number of brass tubes and five layers of ¹⁄₃₂in brass sheets inserted are between the upper and lower tanks, acting as heat dissipaters. The top lid of one tank, the bottom of the second tank and the five brass sheets are drilled together to obtain correct alignment of the brass tubes. The

tubes are first sweat soldered in the top lid of the bottom tank; the brass sheets are inserted with spacers or drop of Loctite Superfast 415, and finally the tubes soldered into the bottom of the top tank. The next step is to seal both tanks - there are two ways to do this, solder the top and bottom parts together or use Loctite Multibond which eventually can be removed by the use of a burner. The final step of assembly is to mount the radiator on four hexagon rods, threaded 2 BA both ends, one end screwed into the engine frame and the other end screwed into a nut glued or soldered to the bottom of the radiator, (Fig 20.1).

(An alternative radiator with fan attachment was constructed later for another model. The container, a Colman Mustard tin, was drilled and a number of thin gauge brass tubes inserted and soldered. The fan has a cylindrical sleeve - mentioned later.)

The WATER PUMP is constructed mainly from perspex; the body is drilled and bored from a solid cube 1½in x 1½in x 1¼in to give a 1in bore, ½in deep, with a flat bottom, and then drilled through ⅛in to take a shaft running through a precise fitting bush or tube. A ¼in perspex cover, with a ⅜in boss drilled through ¼in to serve as the water inlet, is fitted to the pump body with four 6 BA bolts, and a thin rubber gasket, (Fig 20.9).

The rotation of the engine determines the position of the water outlet in the pump body. If the impeller is turning clockwise, the outlet is on the top left corner of the pump; if the impeller is turning anti-clockwise, the outlet is on the top right hand corner.

The IMPELLER may be constructed from perspex or solid rubber; it is shaped into an open cone with ridges and troughs cut and filed at equal distances radiating outwards from the hub. An alternative type of impeller is one made from a hub to which are fitted a number of blades made from hardened rubber or soft plastic. An "O" ring between the impeller and the rear of the pump body will assist to prevent seepage. The pulley fitted to the shaft should give a 1 : 4 ratio with the corresponding pulley on the drive shaft. The pump is connected to the exit water pipe from the working cylinder.

The DYNAMO or GENERATOR is a matter of experimenting with various small brushed electric motors and small low voltage/wattage bulbs; the engine speed and the drive pulley are also determining factors. For the on-load engine speed achieved an 8 : 1 ratio of pulleys is suggested. The electric motor used in "DYNA" comes from a cassette tape recorder main drive, and lights up a 6V 0.6W bulb quite brightly.

The FAN ASSEMBLY is a hotch-potch of materials

MATERIALS USED IN THE CONSTRUCTION OF "DYNA"

Engine base	Surplus radio equipment chassis
Main or working cylinder	Heavy duty shock absorber (damper)
Water jacket	Scrap silencer (muffler) pipe
Displacer	Deodorant alum container
Power piston	Cast iron water conduit pipe
Crank webs, big-ends, bearing blocks	Scrap BMS off-cuts
Radiator	Two old OXO tins, scrap brass sheet, brass tube
Fan	Scrap alum sheet and brass material
Radiator and Fan supports	Hexagonal rods used in old equipment
Flywheel	From an old German sewing machine
Dynamo	Ex-PYE cassette tape recorder drive motor

"DYNA": ENGINE SPECIFICATIONS

	IMPERIAL SIZES	NEAREST "WORKING" METRIC EQUIVALENTS
Base	11in x 6 ½ in	280mm x 165mm
Working cylinder	2in OD	50mm
	1¾in ID	45mm
	8in internal length	200mm
Power piston	1¾in OD	45mm
	1½in long	38mm
Guide bush	1in OD unmachined	25mm
	1¾in long	45mm
	³⁄₁₆in ID	5mm
Displacer	first - 1¹⁄₁₆in OD	43mm
	{second - 1³⁷⁄₆₄in OD	40mm}
	{annular wire - ¹⁄₁₆in	1.6mm}
Power Stroke	¾in	20mm
Displacer stroke	1³⁄₁₆in	30mm

which together make an impressive array, it is remarkably efficient pushing a steady breeze through the radiator. A modification made later which consisted of a cylindrical sleeve surrounding the blades, raised the efficiency level and made it look more professional. The fan blades are cut from a ⅟₁₆in aluminium sheet, rounded and fixed to a hub by four 8 BA bolts. Four blades are cut and shaped to give the same pitch. The hub is bonded to a small pulley fixed on a shaft fitted in a tube in a brass square section, the whole assembly standing on two long hexagon rods, threaded 2 BA both ends.

The DRIVE BELTS are cut from a 1.6mm LOCTITE NITRITE rubber "O" ring cord, the ends being fixed by Loctite Superfast 495.

PERFORMANCE
and MODIFICATIONS

Two modifications made to the original design may be of interest to modellers. The first displacer was made of BMS tube with greatly reduced walls; however this turned out to be unsatisfactory as it was still too heavy for the ³⁄₁₆in displacer rod fitting, and was soon scraping along the working cylinder wall causing heavy friction. The second displacer was cut from a deodorant container, which was much lighter, but left too wide an annular gap. As a matter of expediency and also as an experiment it was decided to fill the gap with a tightly wound spring 5½in long, made from ⅟₁₆in steel spring wire and inserted carefully right inside the working cylinder. The net result of this modification was a quicker response to heating and longer run-on with the burner turned off - a sign of good regeneration. There was no effect on the speed/power of the engine.

The second modification was to install a 'snifter valve' in the power piston which operates when the mean pressure inside the engine falls below atmospheric. The installation of the valve was made easy as a result of an "O" BA hole which had been drilled previously in the crown of the power piston as an aide to running-in the engine without compression (see Chapter 8). There were no visible benefits from the 'snifter valve', either in speed or torque.

The engine requires substantial heating to start off, but once it is running, the heat output can be reduced by 50%. The no-load speed is now 320 RPM; when the clutch engages the drive shaft with all accessories going, the speed falls down to about 150 RPM. The dynamo, fan and pump are quite efficient and as far as the purpose for which the engine was designed, that of demonstration, this aim has been successfully reached as it has proved to be quite an attraction in exhibitions. The debate that has gone on for some time is whether to fit an annular burner with a canopy, or just leave the Bunsen burner to do its bit in the open.

CHAPTER TWENTY ONE

Low Temperature Differential & Ringbom Stirling engines

AN OVERVIEW

A **Low Temperature Differential Stirling Engine** is one that operates efficiently with the minimum temperature difference between the hot and cold ends of the displacer cylinder or chamber.

Whereas in other Stirling Cycle engines, the greater the difference of temperature between the two ends, the more power the engine develops (subject to machining, mechanical-drive efficiency and to minimal friction), the LTD engine runs at the lowest scale of temperature difference possible. This new development, singularly suitable for demonstrating the Stirling Cycle principles, has aroused considerable interest in the last few years.

The imagination of several Stirling enthusiasts has been fired by the slow-running, sometimes hand-held and hand-warmed, engines constructed from perspex, plastic, polystyrene/Styrofoam and a mix of other materials. The starting point of the LTDs can be traced to Professor Ivor Kolin of Zagreb, who over a period of some years experimented with and built a number of engines, until finally in 1983 he presented a model which worked on a temperature difference as low as 15°C between the hot and cold ends of the displacer chamber. This engine inspired a number of experiments both in classical Stirling configuration as well as on the Ringbom principle.

The **Ringbom Stirling engine** bears the name of its inventor, Ossian Ringbom, who in 1907 patented a type of Stirling cycle engine which in its configuration dispensed with almost half of the

moving parts from the drive mechanism, on the displacer side, leaving the displacer to be lifted by pressure build-up as a result of compression. When the expansion of gas has taken place, the displacer falls by gravity to its lowest position which is the hot end of the displacer cylinder. The Ringbom engine has one other major difference from the normal Stirling engine in that the displacer rod has a larger diameter than usual, working in a precise fitting guide bush with rubber-type stop cushions at the top and bottom of the rod strokes.

The Ringbom development came at an age when hot air engines were being superseded by the internal combustion engine and electric motors and for many years this unusual engine remained forgotten and undeveloped. With the advent of the Low Temperature Differential concept, the Ringbom has re-emerged also in its small format, since its design essentially favours low operating speeds and short displacer strokes.

A model engine of the Ringbom principle, in the shape of "TAPPER", a hybrid Stirling engine (Fig 21.1), was designed and constructed by Professor James Senft, of the University of Wisconsin (River Falls, U.S.A.) and described in ENGINEERING IN MINIATURE of September, October and November 1982. 'TAPPER' aroused a great deal of interest as can be seen by the number of similar and modified models that appear in various Engineering Exhibitions.

(Enthusiasts who wish to learn more about the Ringbom concept and its adaptation as a Low Temperature Differential engine are well advised

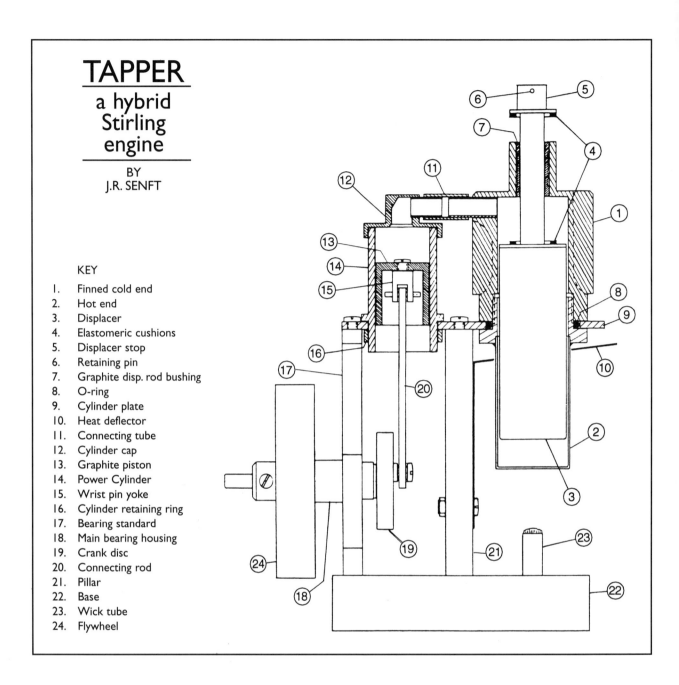

TAPPER
a hybrid Stirling engine
BY
J.R. SENFT

KEY
1. Finned cold end
2. Hot end
3. Displacer
4. Elastomeric cushions
5. Displacer stop
6. Retaining pin
7. Graphite disp. rod bushing
8. O-ring
9. Cylinder plate
10. Heat deflector
11. Connecting tube
12. Cylinder cap
13. Graphite piston
14. Power Cylinder
15. Wrist pin yoke
16. Cylinder retaining ring
17. Bearing standard
18. Main bearing housing
19. Crank disc
20. Connecting rod
21. Pillar
22. Base
23. Wick tube
24. Flywheel

Fig 21.1 (Left) Sectional view of TAPPER.

to read Professor Senft's latest book on the "Ringbom Stirling Engine" published in 1993, by Oxford University Press Inc. and obtainable from Camden Miniature Steam Services.)

Professor Senft's experiments with Low Temperature Differential Stirling Engines resulted in a unique and most interesting engine, the P-19, which has an ultra-low temperature differential of 0.5°C, (Fig 21.2 and 21.3). The engine's heat source is the human hand on which the engine rests where after 15 seconds of heat transfer it starts to run, and within a few minutes reaches a speed of 60 RPM. An alternative way of obtaining the temperature difference is by placing a tumbler with ice cubes on top of the displacer chamber surface, thus reducing the temperature of this side to below ambient temperature.

It is extremely difficult to envisage any further development which can better this result. According to Professor Senft (ISEC Paper presented in Dubrovnik 1991) the principal motivation for the engine was a simple demonstration engine for Stirling and general heat engine principles and as a goal, the aim was to produce an engine capable of operating at a temperature difference of 2° or lower. The engine's displacer chamber is constructed from perspex and for a power piston Professor Senft used graphite for low friction, together with balanced linkages for both displacer and piston.

Professor Senft has also made an in-depth study of the Ringbom Stirling engine as a vehicle for Low

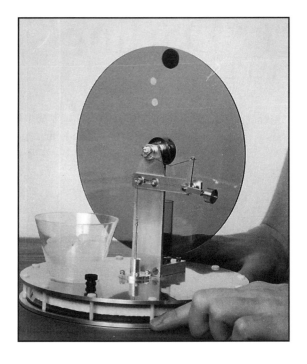

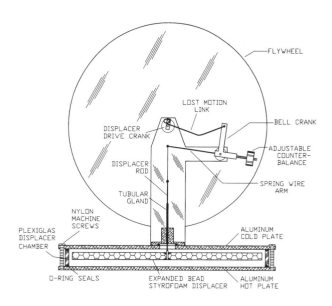

Fig 21.2 (Left) Professor Senft's P-19.
Fig 21.3 (Above) Plan view of the P19.

temperature differential development. Some of these smaller engines operate for long hours on a cup of hot water, or, when fitted with a conicial reflector, on solar energy.

A company in Germany, Delta Photon Energietechnick of Nurnberg, has gone into development of large scale Low Temperature Differential Solar Stirling engines which are suitable for pumping water, filtration, desalination by reverse osmosis, cooking and refrigeration, grain milling and electric power production (Fig 2.15).

There is intensive development of LTD model engines in Germany, and a number of projects are under way both in Universities and by private individuals. Dieter Schager of Offenbach M., Germany, has an on-going production of a "Handwarmer Motor" (Fig 21.4) which, as the name implies, works well on the warmth of the

palm of the hand. This LTD engine works on the Ringbom principle. At a temperature difference of 3 KELVIN, the engine works perfectly; however, with a higher temperature difference of 6 - 8 K, the engine goes much faster with a speed as high as 250 RPM. The overall height of the engine is 5½in (140 mm) and the diameter is 4¾in (120 mm). Dieter Schager has developed a variety of Ringbom Stirling engines with quartz displacer cylinders which are particularly instructive and appealing.

Another LTD model, devised on Ivor Kolin's Solar Stirling motor, and presented by Bernhart Scharl of Munich (Fig 21.5) has a 7⅞in (200 mm) x 7⅞in (200 mm) x 1⁹⁄₁₆in (40 mm) or 5½in (140 mm) x 5½in (140 mm) x 1³⁄₁₆in (30 mm) square configuration with a transparent displacer chamber made of Madrolon, heated with solar energy or a small lamp and operates on a temperature difference of 20 K.

SOME CHARACTERISTICS OF THE LOW TEMPERATURE DIFFERENTIAL STIRLING ENGINE

- Large diameter displacer chamber and displacer
- Short displacer body
- Short strokes, especially on the displacer side
- Large ratio of displacer to piston swept volumes
- Effective heat transfer surfaces on both end plates of the displacer chamber
- Preferably a longer dwell period at the end of the displacer stroke than with normal Stirling engine models
- Low operating speeds

Fig 21.4 Dieter Schager's
"HANDWARMER MOTOR"

How to Construct "Darling"
A LOW TEMPERATURE DIFFERENTIAL ENGINE

Designed and constructed by ROY DARLINGTON.
Photographs by GRAHAM DARLINGTON, text by the Author.

Roy Darlington's LOW TEMPERATURE DIFFER-ENTIAL ENGINE works on the principle of moving a mass of slightly warmed working gas from the displacer cylinder past a lightweight polystyrene displacer to the working cylinder on expansion and returning this mass to the displacer cylinder on compression. In Roy's engine the difference between the warm (rather lukewarm) expansion state of the working gas and the cooler compressed gas is a bare 8°C.

The versatility of this engine is amazing; it is also a crowd-puller, as could be seen at the Model Engineering Exhibition at Olympia and at the Brighton Modelworld. What is more amazing to the onlooker is the variety of heating methods that can be used to run this engine - from a bowl of hot water, to a spot lamp and also direct sunlight. It can run for hours on a bright and sunny day, provided the engine is "upside-down", with the hot end facing the sun (Fig 21.8).

The beginning of this project is the lucky find of a piece of Worthing gas mains plastic pipe, 9¾in OD, which happened to suit the size of the engine Roy had in mind. Thereafter, through established designs and parameters, the engine becomes an exercise which requires skill and high quality workmanship especially in two areas, the power or working cylinder/piston, and the mechanical drive.

The power piston is machined from graphite. This is not a material which is readily accessible to model engineers, and Roy's contacts stood him well in this regard. However, before the reader gives up hope, a recent advertisement in HOME SHOP MACHINIST (USA) by Steelhead Industries Inc. offered a sample pack of graphite at a very realistic price. (The author managed to obtain a solid block, 4in x 4in x 1¼in from this firm; however the cost of air parcel post to Malta was almost double the cost of the material).

The mechanical drive, although on paper appearing complicated, is in fact a bench fitting exercise, which requires a few evenings' patience and precise work in a worthwhile effort to create an impressive movement which is delightful to watch particularly because of its slow action.

The precise counter-balancing of the power piston

and the displacer enables the engine to work with relatively little effort, while the use of ball-bearings ensures frictionless movement of the working parts.

GENERAL ENGINE LAYOUT

The engine consists of a wide and low displacer cylinder, a precision power unit, a well-adjusted and balanced mechanical drive and a flywheel in the shape of a disc. The displacer cylinder has a substantial wall thickness which makes it relatively easy to obtain an airtight cylinder when the top (cold end) and bottom (hot end) discs are bolted to the wall. The power unit is bolted to one side of the engine to allow the mechanical drive assembly enough space between the displacer guide bush and the power cylinder. The bottom disc has a finned heat sink fitted underneath for quick and extensive heat transfer.

Much of the working metal is dural plate of various thickness, mostly however ⅛in which allows for versatility and lightness.

METHOD OF CONSTRUCTION

The DISPLACER CYLINDER. Roy's engine makes use of a gas mains plastic pipe. Not everyone is so lucky and neither can pipe laying be interrupted to provide model engineers with odd pieces of pipe for the next generation of L.T.Ds or for Ringbom engines. In looking for alternatives, the author

Fig 21.5 Solar Stirling motor to Professor Kolin's specification.

Fig 21.6 (Above) Roy Darlington's Low temperatue differential model "DARLING".

Fig 21.7 "DARLING" (Right) - plan

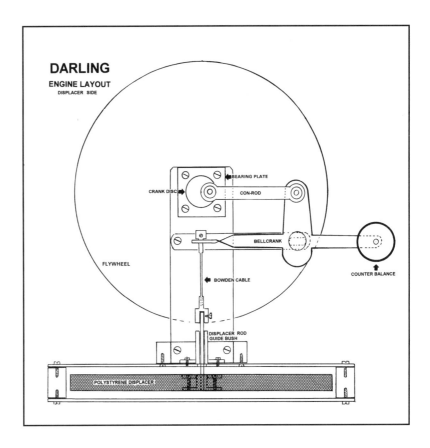

found two suitable from limited sources, one a 8in water mains plastic pipe socket (thick end) and the other a tailor-made ring or cylinder made from perspex sheet, heat formed and glued by a local sign-making firm. Both have the disadvantage of a ¼in (actually 6mm) wall thickness, therefore requiring even greater precision drilling for bolting the discs, although an alternative method is available. The heat formed cylinder is not a precise round ring, but it still serves its purpose. (Fig 21.9).

In Roy's engine the top and bottom discs are each drilled with 60 holes to enable 8 BA bolts to thread into the plastic pipe. In order to avoid conduction of heat through these fasteners, the bolts are short reaching. At the same time, the displacer cylinder, that is the plastic pipe, has 120 8BA holes tapped into the wall, 60 on either side, but not directly opposite each other.

The top disc is prepared to take the displacer cylinder guide bush, and at 3in off-centre, the power cylinder. The guide bush requires a through hole of ³⁄₁₆in to give sufficient clearance to the displacer rod (⅛in) and six 8 BA tapped holes for the guide bush flange fitting (using a flange as a jig). The power cylinder requires a 1in. diameter clear hole and six 8 BA tapped holes for the power cylinder flange, using the same method above.

Other work required on the displacer cylinder includes locating the base block securing bolts on the top disc (holding up the main drive brackets),

and the heat sink - if used - underneath the bottom disc. In the first stage of assembly only the bottom disc is bolted to the cylinder wall.

The DISPLACER is an expanded polystyrene disc, ⁷⁄₁₆in thick, 8¼in diameter. The polystyrene is clamped in the centre by a double disc assembly which also carries the displacer rod. One dural disc, ⁵⁄₃₂in thick, 1¼in OD, is drilled centrally ⁵⁄₁₆ in clear, and drilled to take six 6 BA screws with countersunk heads. The other disc is turned from a 1 ¼ in. dural bar, reduced to give a ⁵⁄₁₆ in. OD collar, ⁵⁄₁₆ in long, and finally drilled through ⅛ in ID. Using the first disc as a jig, the same number of tapped 6 BA holes are prepared; the two discs are bolted together sandwiching the polystyrene to give this fragile material a rigid dimension.

Finally the displacer rod, ⅛in precision ground silver steel 2 ⁷⁄₁₆in long, is loctited into the displacer clamp assembly.

The DISPLACER ROD GUIDE BUSH is machined from ⅜in phosphor bronze rod, drilled and reamed ⅛in ID. The bush is reduced at one end to ¼in to fit into a brass flange, 1¼in. OD, ⅛in thick, drilled to take the phosphor bronze bush and glued together. The flange should be faced true while the bush is in the chuck.

(An alternative method, using brass, is to machine the bush and flange from solid bar in one operation, including drilling and reaming ⅛in).

The POWER CYLINDER is machined from stainless steel tube. Considerable effort is required to ensure a high degree of mirror finish after the cylinder has been machined, honed and lapped. When this operation is completed, the cylinder is fitted into a dural flange, ⅛in thick, 2⅜in OD, (heat and freeze method or simply very precise fitting with a smear of Loctite). Six 6 BA clearance holes are drilled for fitting to the cold end, the flange serving as a jig to the top cylinder plate or disc.

The POWER PISTON is machined from graphite rod. The success of this engine depends on the piston fitting - high precision without the slightest hint of friction. Several fine cuts, taking off microns of graphite, are required to approach the precision fitting. There is no second best in this particular assembly.

The GUDGEON BLOCK is machined from ½in dural bar, ¾in long, and slotted ⁵⁄₃₂in to a depth of ½in to take the con-rod. The GUDGEON PIN is cut from ⅛in silver steel rod, while the POWER CON-ROD is cut from ⅛in dural flat, 4¾in long, ⁹⁄₁₆in wide at one end, tapering to ⅜in at the other end. Two pilot holes, ¹⁄₁₆in are drilled 4¼in between centres. At the narrower end (gudgeon pin end) a phosphor bronze bush is inserted to give free movement to the gudgeon pin, while at the other end, the wider end of the con-rod, a ball bearing ⅜in OD, ⅛in ID is inserted. This will take the crankpin on the power side.

The FLYWHEEL is an assembly of an 8in. OD dural disc, ⅛ in thick, a clamp plate and an "O" ring. First the clamp plate is machined from 1¼ in brass bar; this consists of a flange ⅛ in thick and a ⅜ in collar, ³⁄₁₆ in long. The clamp plate is reversed so that the collar is in the chuck and the flange on the outside. The flange is centre drilled, drilled and reamed 5 mm, slightly countersunk-recessed to fit a 5 mm ID "O" ring, and finally faced true. The clamp plate has four holes, 8 BA clearance, drilled around the flange for bolting to the flywheel. The clamp plate flange serves also as a jig for drilling identical holes in the flywheel.

At this stage one should explain the purpose of the "O" ring and the method used by Roy to fit the flywheel to the crankshaft. The flywheel/crankshaft assembly is a friction drive system caused by the compression of the "O" ring betwen the clamp plate and the flywheel, hence the need for recessed countersinking on the flywheel and the clamp plate. When these two components are bolted together, the "O" ring is squeezed and acts on the crankshaft to create a friction-drive.

The FLYWHEEL BEARING BRACKETS or SUPPORTS are cut from ⅛in dural plate, 2in wide, each 5¹⁵⁄₁₆in to 6in long. The brackets are bolted on opposite sides of the base block which is bolted to the cold (top) cylinder disc, at a point approximately 1⅜in from the centre, and between the displacer guide bush and the power cylinder. Each bracket is prepared by drilling a number of holes - two 4 BA clearance holes at a distance of ⁵⁄₁₆in from the bottom, four in a square formation (Fig 21.10) to take the main bearing housing, using this housing as a jig. Finally the brackets are drilled 5mm to take the crankshaft.

The MAIN BEARING HOUSING (BRACKETS) - two in number - are cut from ⅜in aluminium flat bar. Since both brackets are identical and should correspond in the number of drilled holes with each other, and with the main engine supports, it is advisable to use either one as a jig, or to drill all four components together. It should be noted that the bracket adjacent to the displacer guide bush has two extra holes drilled to take the bellcrank support.

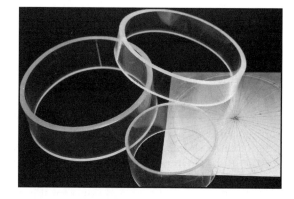

Fig 21.8 (Left) Roy Darlington running his engine in the garden.

Fig 21.9 (Above) Heat formed perspex displacer cylinders

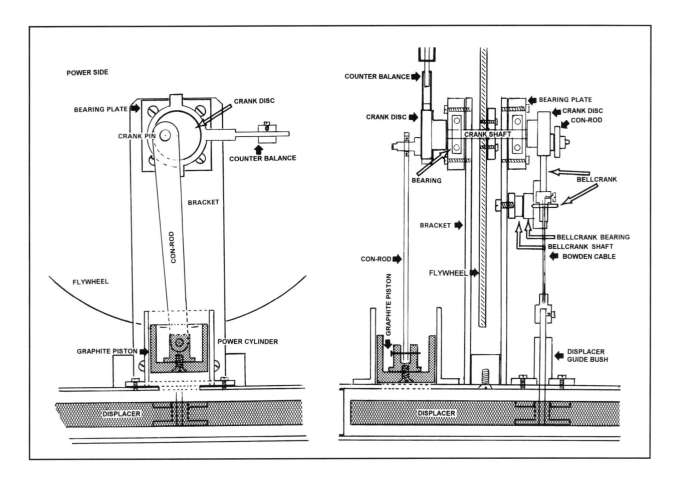

Fig 21.10 (Above left) Side view - power side.

Fig 21.11 (Above right) Side view showing relative positions of power piston and flywheel.

Each main bearing housing bracket carries a ball bearing, 5mm ID x 16mm OD, through which passes the crank shaft.

The CRANK DISC and CRANKPIN. The stroke movement to the power piston is applied by means of a crank disc and a crankpin. The crank disc is 1in OD and the crankpin is inserted ¼in off centre to give a ½in stroke. The size of the crankpin depends on the size of the ball bearing used in the power con-rod, in this case it is ⅛in ID x ⅜in OD.

The POWER PISTON COUNTER BALANCE is an assembly of components machined and fitted together to provide an equivalent weight, when in motion, to the power piston assembly. The components of the counter-balance are: a lock-ring which fits over the power crank disc; an extension to it which takes a ⅛in silver steel rod; and a brass bar ⅜in OD x ⅜in long which slides over the silver steel rod (Fig 21.11). Once the bar is adjusted for counter weight, it is locked in place by a 6 BA grub screw.

THE DISPLACER DRIVE IS PROVIDED BY A MECHANISM WHICH IS SLIGHTLY MORE COMPLEX IN THAT THERE ARE MORE MOVING PARTS WHICH INTERACT TO GIVE THE NECESSARY MOTION. THE CONSTRUCTION IS DESCRIBED HERE IN REVERSE ORDER FROM THE POWER MECHANISM, AND STARTING FROM THE TOP.

The drive mechanism on the displacer side consists of the following components (refer to Fig 21.10 and 21.11).

1. Crank disc and crankpin
2. Con-rod
3. Bell crank support
4. Bell crank
5. Counter weight
6. Bowden cable attachment
7. Displacer rod

The CRANK DISC (No.1) is ⅞in OD with a ⁹⁄₁₆in collar which fits directly to the crankshaft. The CRANKPIN is ⅛in off centre.

The CON-ROD (No.2) is 3 in. between centres and has a ball bearing at each end (⅛in ID, ⅜in OD).

The BELLCRANK SUPPORT (NO.3) is bolted to the displacer side of the FLYWHEEL BRACKET at a height of 3¾in from base. The support is 3¾in

"DARLING": ENGINE SPECIFICATIONS

	IMPERIAL SIZES	NEAREST "WORKING" METRIC EQUIVALENTS
Overall dimensions	11¼ in high 11⅛ in wide	285mm 283mm
Displacer cylinder	9¾in OD 8½in ID ¹⁵⁄₁₆in high	248mm 216mm 23.8mm (24mm)
Displacer	8¼in ⁷⁄₁₆in thick	210mm 11.2mm
Power cylinder	1½in OD 1¼in ID 1⁷⁄₁₆in high	38mm 32mm 37mm
Power piston	1¼in OD 1in long	32mm 25mm
Power con-rod	4¼in between centres	108mm
Displacer Bowden cable	2⅝in long	66.5mm
Bell crank con-rod	3in between centres	76mm
Bell crank	5½in between centres	140mm
Flywheel	8in diameter	205mm (200/210mm)
Power stroke	½in	12mm
Displacer stroke	⁷⁄₁₆in	11.2mm
Temperature difference	8°C	
R.P.M.	60 approx	

between centres; however to ensure adequate adjustment it is advisable to slot drill the bolt hole for ½in, a quarter of an inch either side of the centre which takes the BELLCRANK BEARING HOUS-ING pivot.

The BELLCRANK (No. 4) is cut to shape from ⅛in dural. The three dimensions given below are fairly critical and it is advisable to adhere to them as closely as possible.

> From the centre of bell crank **(A)** to con-rod pivot **(B)** = 1½in;
> From bell crank centre **(A)** to counter balance centre **(C)** = 2½in;
> From bell crank centre **(A)** to cable clamp centre **(D)** = 3in

The end arm **A** to **D** is twisted 90° to provide a flat surface to which the cable clamp can be fitted.

The COUNTER WEIGHT (No. 5) is a ¼in thick brass disc, 1½ in diameter.

The BOWDEN CABLE (No. 6) between the bell crank and the displacer rod is attached to both ends by cable clamps; the drilled hole of the clamps suits the bowden cable diameter. The fitting to the bellcrank is a matter for bench fitting according to the size of the cable, which in turn affects the size of the clamp. The fitting of the cable clamp to the displacer rod is again a bench fitting exercise as long as the clamp fits over the displacer rod (No. 7).

TIMING and ADJUSTMENTS

As in all Stirlings the normal phase timing is 90°, the displacer leading the power piston. A few test trials with marginal variations of the phase may give either slightly higher revolutions or a lesser degree of temperature difference. All that is required is an adjustment to the displacer crank disc.

The bowden cable assembly also allows for minor adjustments to the displacer gap at top or bottom of the stroke.

PERFORMANCE

One word of caution first - extensive heating should be avoided, gnat power heat is more than ample. Application of high heat may destroy or warp the delicate polystyrene displacer and the plastic/perspex body of the displacer cylinder.

The efficiency of this engine is calculated on the lowest degree of temperature differential possible.

(ROY'S LTD ENGINE WORKS ON A TEMPERATURE DIFFERENCE AS LOW AS 8° C. PROFESSOR J.R. SENFT'S EXPERIMENTAL ENGINE, THE P.19 (Fig 21.2) WORKS ON A DIFFERENCE OF 0.5° C. ANYWHERE BETWEEN THE TWO LIES THE CHALLENGE FOR THE MODEL ENGINEER.)

The model described here can possibly be improved with better heat transfer, better cooling, even more precision machining (?), better regeneration, etc. All these lie within the scope of the modeller.

Roy's engine developed a speed of approximately 60 RPM. Revolutions within this range are normal - with such models one is not looking for speed but efficiency through the lowest temperature differential possible.

C H A P T E R   T W E N T Y   T W O

How to Construct "Tuba"

Designed and constructed by Richard White
Photographs and text by Richard White

Author's Note: "TUBA" is an exercise in model Stirling engine pressurisation. It is designed and constructed for this purpose and its selection has been automatic since it fits in with the aim of this book - to introduce the STIRLING ENGINE in all its varied forms.

The author saw "TUBA" running on the Worthing Club Stand at the 1994 Brighton Modelword. The engine was first run at atmospheric pressure. While still running, Richard applied a few strokes of a bicycle pump which increased the internal pressure of the working gas, and raised the engine speed substantially.

The design and construction of "TUBA" is well within the capabilities of a Modeller who has worked on engines from the previous chapters.

INTRODUCTION

"TUBA" is a Stirling engine with co-axial displacer and power piston, and uses a simple return crank to give the displacer approximately 90° lead over the power piston. The idea in designing and building "TUBA" was to see whether it is worth pressurising a simple engine where heat is applied to a hot cap without additional heater tubes or fins to extend the heating surface. The tubular construction is a way of producing a pressurisable crankcase which also offers plenty of buffer space below the piston.

Fig 22.1
TUBA -
completed engine.

The dimensions of "TUBA" were decided by a matched pair of deep drawn stainless steel caps, fitting nicely and with little radial clearance into each other, the outer cap being used for the displacer cylinder hot cap while the inner and smaller cap is used for the displacer. There are added advantages in these matched pair of steel caps (obtainable from STERLING STIRLING), in that they are mono construction without seams or joints, and being stainless steel, they have low heat conductivity.

Like all co-axial engines, the alignment of the piston and the displacer rod guide is critical. The engine can be run on a very small heat source for demonstration purposes or, alternatively, with a more powerful gas flame when significant power is needed. In practice "TUBA" will run happily unpressurised on a standard night light or stub of a candle. For experimental purposes the stainless steel cap can be run at a medium red heat without fear. A specially designed silent gas burner, using a ceramic element, allows the engine to be run at full power, using easily available miniature cylinders of butane/propane mix or the same gas loaded into a rechargeable tank. As always with small Stirling engines, careful machining and accurate alignment pays dividends in reduced friction and greater power output. This engine can be made with fairly simple workshop facilities; some simple silver soldering is involved. For pressurisation purposes the use of a leather cup washer for the main power piston seal has eased slightly the problem of obtaining a good seal between the piston and the liner.

GENERAL ENGINE LAYOUT

The main framework of the engine is a piece of aluminium tube which forms the crankcase and the cylinder jacket. The part of the tube forming the cylinder jacket is thinned down from inside, leaving an internal ledge which locates the inner end of the cylinder liner. The cylinder liner is machined from cast iron in the form of a bobbin with enlarged end flanges which are grooved to take "O" rings, which form the water and air pressure seals.

The water cooling space is, therefore, an annulus defined by the outer surface of the liner, the end flanges and the inside surface of the aluminium cylinder. Water is fed in and out through small bushes Loctited into opposite sides of the tube. Water fed into the jacket can be thermo-syphoned into a cooling tower.

METHOD OF CONSTRUCTION

The ENGINE FRAME is machined from a dural tube, $6\frac{5}{8}$in long with an OD of 2in (50mm) and an ID of $1\frac{11}{16}$ in (43mm). The tube is reduced internally to $1\frac{13}{16}$in ID in two areas, the front end (flywheel end) is $3\frac{3}{8}$in long, the rear end is $2\frac{9}{16}$in long, thus leaving a central collar $\frac{11}{16}$in long with the original wall thickness. This serves as an internal ledge which locates the position of the internal, front end of the power cylinder or liner.

The front end of the tube is finished off with an angled recess which will take a sealing cap with an "O" ring to make it airtight.

A $\frac{7}{8}$in hole is bored through the flywheel-end of the engine frame which will eventually take the crankshaft and its housing. The exit is located $1\frac{1}{8}$in from the end.

The FLYWHEEL/CRANKSHAFT BEARING HOUSING is machined from a solid aluminium block and a dural bar, $1\frac{3}{8}$in long, 1in OD. The block is reduced to $1\frac{5}{8}$in square x $\frac{1}{4}$in thick and shaped to conform to the ID of the engine frame/tube. The dural bar is reduced to $\frac{13}{16}$in, then bored to take the two ball bearings; the central part is $\frac{1}{16}$in smaller in diameter than the bearing OD, to act as a spacer. The two components are Loctited together and finally fitted into the engine frame with a smear of silicone jointing compound or liquid gasket cement and bolted on to the frame from outside.

The POWER CYLINDER LINER is machined from a 2in cast iron bar in the form of a bobbin, with an internal diameter of 1in and an internal length of $3\frac{3}{16}$in. The liner has two enlarged flanges, both recessed with grooves to take tight fitting "O" rings which when inserted in the liner and slid into the cylinder, serve as water and pressure seals. The exterior diameter of that part of the bobbin which serves as a water annulus is $1\frac{1}{4}$in OD. The lower flange (flywheel end) is tapped 6BA on two opposite sides of the diameter to take two long reach studs.

The front end of the bore should take a long chamfer to allow insertion of the leather cup seal without catching or damaging the delicate edge.

The internal machining of the liner is critical and every effort should be made to give an absolutely smooth bore with a mirror finish. If there is any doubt about the bore being truly parallel along its length, a plug gauge test is suggested, finishing off any deficiencies with a suitable hone.

The POWER PISTON is machined from cast iron leaving a thin shell thus reducing its mass. The stresses on this type of engine are not high, and the lighter the running components are the better, because the out-of-balance forces will be smaller. The piston crown is bored through to take the

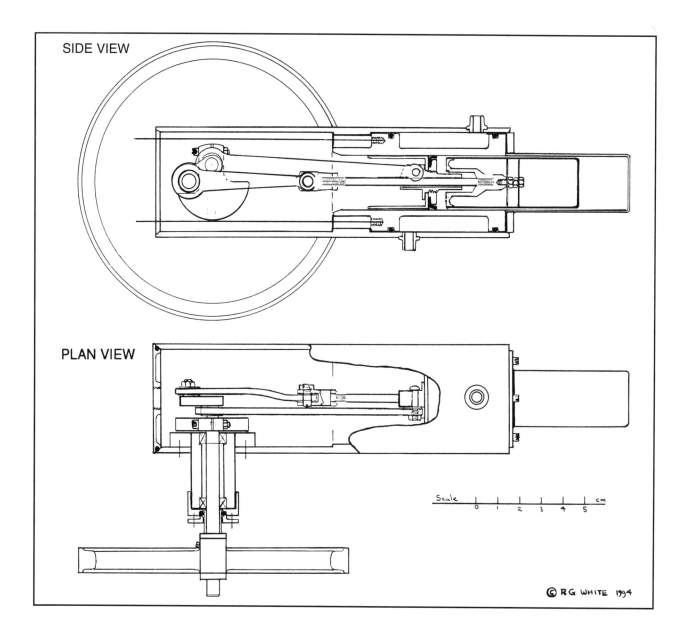

SIDE VIEW

PLAN VIEW

Scale

© R G WHITE 1994

Fig 22.2 TUBA - engine layout.

extended nose of the yoke piece. The YOKE combines the functions of gudgeon pin bearing and guide for the displacer rod; the extended nose is threaded externally and an aluminium ring is used to screw and lock the yoke and the piston together. The ring has an additional function, to locate and retain the leather cup washer.

The CUP WASHER is home made from thin leather from the back of a gardening glove, and is a rough pliable leather. It has a large central hole which registers on the ⅝in diameter spigot of the aluminium ring, and the outer part of the ring is turned to a 'gramophone record' finish to grip the leather.

The virtues of cup leather seals for hot air engines have been extolled in MODEL ENGINEER, and in TUBA this has been proven. The leather is soaked

overnight in water and then pulled down over the end of a piece of scrap nylon rod which has been turned to a flat face, a radiused shoulder and an outside diameter equal to the cylinder bore, less three times the thickness of the leather. When pulling the leather over the former, it is vital to avoid puckering; with care this is possible and the wet leather is then retained on the rod by a metal ring with radiused edges, and polished to prevent cutting the leather. A scalpel will cut away the excess leather cleanly.

A leather punch is used to cut the ⅝in hole in the centre and make it a neat fit over the aluminium ring which locks the piston and yoke together. Before assembly the leather is thoroughly soaked in oil and it is the work of a few minutes to period-ically withdraw the complete running gear for lubrication.

Once the components are screwed together, the aluminium ring and the piston crown make a metal-to-metal seat for better heat conduction and prevent the assembly loosening. The depth of the aluminium ring is sufficient to minimise dead space.

A secondary reason for extending the nose of the yoke is to bring the rod further into the displacer, lengthen the bearing to reduce gas leakage along the rod, and reduce overhang.

The DISPLACER is made from the smaller of the two stainless steel cups. It is closed by a thin brass end cap. After machining the cup, and anti-radiation baffle made of discs of thin steel shim is screwed to it, and a small vent hole drilled through the brass cap to vent air during the silver soldering operation which then unites the cap with the stainless cup. After soldering, hold the cap carefully in the chuck to avoid distortion, centre drill, drill recess and core diameter for the displacer rod thread and tap the thread.

Clearance between the displacer and the hot cap is small, so it is vital to maintain the alignment and concentricity of the displacer on its rod. Finally the fine drilled hole in the displacer end is blocked with a threaded plug sealed with Loctite.

The DISPLACER CYLINDER/HOT CAP is the second or larger stainless steel cap which now becomes the top end of the displacer cylinder and the area which is subjected to heating. (The component which in other engines is known as the displacer cylinder is, in this engine, made up of two parts, the upper end or hot cap and the lower end which is part of the cast iron liner. The cast iron liner performs two functions throughout its length, the lower part is the power cylinder, while the upper part is the cold end of the displacer cylinder.) The unheated trunk of the hot cap gives some regenerative action.

The stainless steel hot cap is silver soldered to a brass ring (acting as a flange) which, in turn, is secured by four cup screws to the upper flange/bobbin end of the cylinder liner. The hot

cap flange and the liner flange are of the same diameter and they register in the aluminium tube to give accurate alignment of the components. A smear of silicone jointing compound provides the necessary seal between the hot cap flange and the liner flange. THIS STAGE OF ASSEMBLY IS UNDERTAKEN AFTER THE DRIVE MECHANISM HAS BEEN MOUNTED AND TESTED.

The SEALING CAP for the lower end (flywheel end) of the engine frame is prepared to fit the cylinder and is one of the last stages of assembly. The cap is machined from a disc of steel, ⅛in thick, with a recessed groove at the edge to take an "O" ring which provides an airtight seal to the engine. Two long reach studs are inserted into the tapped 6 BA holes in the lower flange of the cast iron liner, and they exit in corresponding holes drilled in the sealing cap (6 BA threaded long studs are suitable).

Before removing from the chuck, the disc/sealing cap is drilled and tapped to take a bicycle inner tube valve kit.

In the final stages of engine assembly the sealing cap is set against the edge of the engine cylinder such that the "O" ring has complete seating; the studs are then screwed in, and bolted with tight fitting washers and gasket compound. This end should be completely airtight.

The DRIVE MECHANISM is straightforward and relatively simple. The crank web is fabricated from ¼in steel disc, cut away for balancing, and split at the crankpin with a clamping bolt to nip the web once the pin is in place. This unit is secured to the crankshaft by a grub screw.

The ¼in ground stainless steel crankshaft has a flat filed to give a secure seating to the crank web grub screw. The shaft runs in two miniature ball bearings in the main bearing housing.

The CRANKPIN, RETURN CRANK and RETURN CRANKPIN are individual units fastened together with Loctite 601 for a permanent assembly. The

Fig 22.3 Working pistons and drive mechanism.

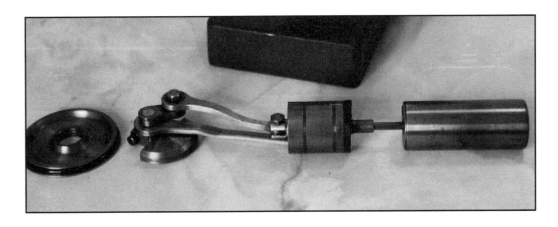

crankpin is inserted into the crank web, the return crank (which drives the displacer) adjusted to its correct offset which is precalculated to give the right stroke and phase difference, then locked by tightening the clamp bolt which is a high tensile cup screw.

The DISPLACER ROD is provided with a small amount of extra thread which together with a lock nut enables the final balancing of the hot end and cold end clearances, while allowing for fine adjustment when the displacer is following the power piston during the cycle (see Chapter 6).

The DISPLACER CON-ROD is cut from ⅛in brass flat, shaped, drilled at one end to take the return crankpin bearing, and at the other end drilled and reamed to take the gudgeon pin. The con-rod is given a slight dog leg for final alignment; this is

Fig 22.4 TUBA - main components.

unavoidable due to the design of the mechanism, and the angle depends on the thickness of the return crank (normally ³⁄₁₆in). With the displacer rod and the yoke (guide bush) being fairly long, the asymmetrical bearing load of the displacer con-rod (and of the power con-rod) is relatively unimportant.

The displacer rod/guide bush fitting is a potential pressure leakage point and care should be taken to provide a precise fitting with a ground and lapped displacer rod, and a finely reamed (preferably using a selectively stoned down reamer) guide bush. Although this is not the perfect way to finish a guide bush since a reamer tends to produce a series of splines rather than a perfect circular bore, in practice the result is reasonable and often acceptable.

The displacer con-rod is connected to the displacer rod through a small clevis, the wrist pin being screwed into the cheek of the clevis and secured by a lock nut.

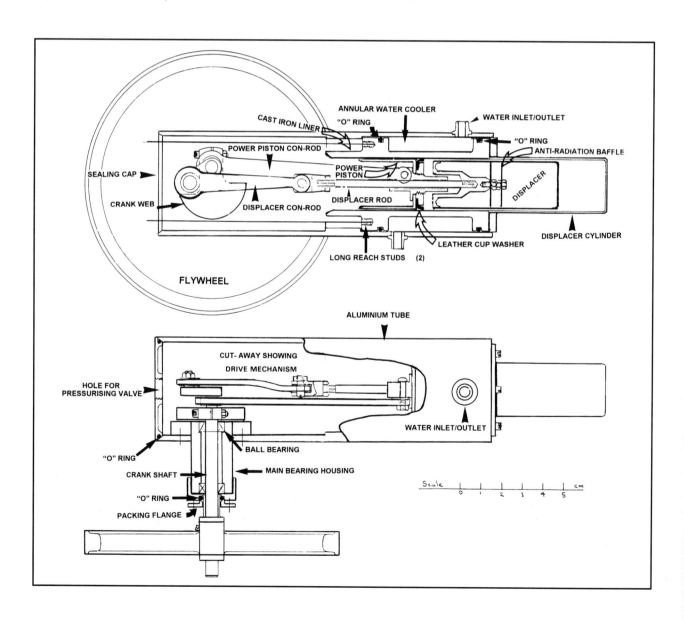

The POWER PISTON CON-ROD is cut from ⅛in brass flat, shaped and drilled to take the crankpin bearing at one end and the gudgeon pin at the other. The gudgeon pin runs in the guide bush/yoke inside the power piston which is then secured when the cup leather washer is screwed on.

The third potential pressure leakage point is the crankshaft housing. In order to reduce this leakage a device is inserted between the housing and the flywheel. A SUBSIDIARY HOUSING is machined and Loctited on the main housing and this contains a seal formed by an "O" ring. The inner diameter of the "O" ring is pressed against a thin, polished sleeve which is also Loctited to the shaft. In its relaxed form the "O" ring is slightly larger than this sleeve, and is loaded radially inward by tightening the packing flange with three small set screws, the housing having a bevelled face so that axial movement causes radial compression. The whole device can be tightened to prevent pressure leakage without excessive friction.

FINAL ASSEMBLY

Putting the engine together is reasonably straightforward. The main bearing housing is Loctited into the radiused aluminium block and the two bearings pushed into place. The complete assembly is then fed from inside the engine cylinder through the hole in the side of the crankcase tube, with liquid gasket between the block and the inner wall, and secured by two set screws.

The "O" rings are placed on the flanges of the cast iron power cylinder liner, the register in the crankcase tube lubricated and the liner pushed into place, ensuring that the tapped holes for the tie bolts (long reach studs) are at the correct angle to miss the crank web and mechanism. The water jacket inlet/outlet bushes are Loctited in place; for later dismantling ensure they do not protrude into the jacket space.

The complete running gear can then be assembled. Secure the displacer crank pin and main crank pin in the return crank with Loctite 601 (or a comparable product). Fit the bearings to the conrods and assemble on the crankpins. Fit the main crankpin in the crankweb, adjust the offset of the return crank to give the correct displacer stroke, then clamp the split crankweb to lock the pin in place.

Next screw the displacer rod into the displacer, with some thread-lock adhesive. Screw the gudgeon pin into the main conrod and add the locknut. Slide the gudgeon pin into the yoke, then slip the nose of the yoke through the piston crown, fit the cup leather and tighten the aluminium lock ring.

Assemble the clevis and pin on the displacer conrod then feed the displacer rod through the yoke, put the lock nut on the thread and engage the displacer rod thread in the clevis.

Lubricate the whole assembly, and feed displacer and piston into the cylinder bore from the flywheel end, taking care not to damage the leather seat. Align the crankweb with the main bearing housing, insert the main shaft and tighten the grub screw on to the flat of the shaft.

The displacer rod is progressively screwed into the clevis while the flywheel is being slowly turned by hand until the displacer just kisses the top of the piston at that point of the cycle where the two components are next to each other. The displacer is then slightly slackened to allow a minimum gap (0.5mm) between the two. The flywheel is kept turning until it is confirmed that there is no hunting, binding or contact.

To tighten the displacer rod lock nut, release the crankshaft grub screw, withdraw the shaft slightly and pull out the running gear, taking care not to alter the position of the displacer clearance. Then refit the running gear and secure the grub screw.

The fitting of the hot cap is the next stage of assembly. Initially, with the hot end upright, the hot cap is just placed in position, while the flywheel is being turned by hand. If there is insufficient clearance this will show immediately as the hot cap is lifted by the displacer. One can judge the amount of lift and a joint washer interposed between the hot cap and liner flange. It may be that in machining the components, errors have crept in.

The reverse may happen and there is too much gap at TDC. This can be gauged by inserting thin cardboard pieces (120 gsm) until lift occurs. If the gap is excessive the hot cap flange may be turned off in the lathe, reducing the metal by small amounts at any one time.

In principle, the clearances between the cap and the displacer faces need to be as small as possible to minimise dead space; in practice about 0.5mm is reasonable; excessive clearances are more likely to reduce power than to prevent the engine running at all.

The hot cap is then bolted permanently with a smear of jointing compound between the faces of the outer bobbin flange and the hot cap flange.

After a final check and a few more turns of the flywheel, the engine is ready for a trial run with a light gas flame. During this run the bottom end sealing cap is still not fitted, thus allowing any

"TUBA": ENGINE SPECIFICATIONS

	IMPERIAL SIZES	NEAREST "WORKING" METRIC EQUIVALENTS
Engine Cylinder	6⅝in long 2in OD 1¹¹⁄₁₆in ID	168mm 50mm 43mm
Power Cylinder liner	3³⁄₁₆in long 1¹³⁄₁₆in OD flanges 1¼in OD annulus 1in ID	80mm 46mm 32mm 25mm
Power Piston	1⅛in long 1in OD	28mm 25mm
Displacer hot end	2¼in long 1¹⁄₁₆in OD 1in ID	57mm 27mm 25mm
Displacer	2⁹⁄₃₂in long ³¹⁄₃₂in OD	58mm 24mm
Power Piston Stroke	⅝in	15.9 - 16mm
Displacer stroke	⅞in	22.2 - 22.5mm
Flywheel	4in - 5in diameter	100 - 125mm
Power unpressurised	- approx 2.5W at 650 RPM	
Pressurised to 20lb/sq.in. gauge	- at least 5W at same speed.	

slight degree of phase alteration that may be required when running the engine.

MOUNTING THE ENGINE

The engine can be mounted in a number of positions, flywheel on top (the flywheel can be replaced by a fan), the hot end cap on top, or the engine in a horizontal position. To mount the engine, two alternative methods are suggested - brackets screwed into the main aluminium tube, taking care not to introduce air leakage paths, or alternatively, one or two bands passed aroung the crankcase tube and clamped in place and to a base.

HEATING

For demonstration purposes the heat source can be a gas torch played on the hot end, or a solid fuel tablet with a simple lamp house to concentrate the heat in the hot cap, or, once the engine has been run -in and is working well, a night light or stub of candle.

To exploit the full potential of the engine a gas burner is required. If the engine is mounted with the hot cap downwards, or mounted horizontally, a ceramic burner such as supplied by Bruce Engineering Ltd. can be used. These burners use a special ceramic element which combines convection and radiant heat. If the engine is mounted with the hot cap uppermost, a ring type burner as described in Chapter 4 may be used.

For full power the optimum heat source seems to be one which will bring the first ¾in (20mm) of hot cap to a medium red heat.

RUNNING THE ENGINE UNDER PRESSURE

Once the engine has been running for some time with a soft gas flame, the test for pressurising follows. The tie-bolts are screwed into the inner liner flange, the sealing cap carefully placed with the "O" ring well seated, tight fitting washers with silicone compound or gasket cement sealing well the fitting. A blob of quick drying gasket cement covering the two nuts holding the sealing cap ensures an air tight connection.

The engine is ready for its first test of pressurisation - WITHOUT RUNNING. The crankcase is pumped by a few strokes of a hand bicycle pump, left for a few minutes and those parts that are subject to leakage dipped in a paraffin container. Any major leaks will show by tell-tale bubbles. The flywheel/crankshaft housing is the most probable culprit but a turn or two on the subsidiary housing set screws will eliminate most of the leakage.

The next test is to leave the crankcase under pressure for progressively longer periods, letting out the air through the valve needle. Practice will show how much air has remained in the body after each test.

Finally, when satisfield with the pressure tests, the engine may run for a full pressurisation test.

The goal with the crankshaft seal is to retain air pressure without any more seal friction than is necessary. Some leakage occurs and has to be made good by pumping. In use the engine can run pressurised or unpressurised. Increasing the pressure in the crankcase (buffer space) raises the mean cycle pressure, also the power at a given running speed provided the heat source is adequate.

PERFORMANCE

"TUBA" has a no-load speed of between 200 to 1500 RPM depending on the heat source, the torque curve is fairly flat and the optimum speed seems to be 400 to 700 RPM. Increasing the crankcase pressure to 15 - 20 lb/sq in doubles the output, but more pressure produces progressively smaller benefits. Tests are taking place to see whether this is because of crankshaft seal friction, or whether the limit of heat transfer through the small area of the plain hot cap is being reached.

A revised seal with a large diameter thread instead of a three stud gland may give better adjustment, and experiments with an inward sealing cup leather are scheduled.

This little engine is presented not as a definitive answer, but as a basic Stirling engine of reasonably efficient and simple design which can be used for small scale power, or as a basis for experiments.

C H A P T E R T W E N T Y T H R E E

How to Measure engine performance
(Speed, Torque, Power & Power Pressure)

No model engineer is satisfied with his efforts unless he finds out the actual performance of his engine. The two questions that come to mind are how fast? and what power? Measuring the revolutions of a hot air engine is no easy matter, as every modeller finds out sooner or later. The normal tachometer pushed against the shaft stops an engine dead. After all we are dealing with models of engines whose shaft power, even in the larger type of hot air engine, is always relatively low. In order, therefore, to obtain an accurate reading of the revolutions the modeller has to resort to a mechanical revolution counter which puts little or no friction on the engine, or to an electronic instrument which measures speed without any contact with the engine. There are a number of different revolution counters which are suitable and reliable. The one described here is one of the more accurate and easier to construct.

MECHANICAL REVOLUTION COUNTER

This counter consists of a worm and wheel assembly which when coupled to the engine output shaft causes the wheel to turn without effort. A stop watch is used to time a given number of turns. The construction is simple but precision is essential to ensure minimal friction.

A bracket is constructed from a brass strip ⅛in thick and ¼in wide, with space for the worm gear to turn without binding. Two holes are drilled at the same height in the lateral arms of the U-bend. The size of the holes depend on the shaft used on the worm gear. If a ⅛in shaft is used, a slightly smaller hole is drilled first and then a ⅛in hole is drilled from side to side. The holes are finished off with a reamer. Two holes are drilled in the bottom of the brackets to take 4 BA screws. The gear wheel is mounted on a dural base ¼in thick. A shaft to fit the wheel is screwed into the base. The wheel is then placed through the shaft with a couple of washers underneath, and the assembly is secured from above by a collar. The gear wheel should be free enough to revolve easily with the merest finger flick.

In the third stage of construction the U-bracket with the worm attachment is placed along the wheel and the securing holes marked for drilling. The holes are drilled slightly larger than the bolt diameter to allow for lateral adjustment of the bracket. Two important points should be kept in mind: The centre height of the worm should be that of the wheel and secondly the worm thread should just touch the teeth of the wheel. Finally the drive shaft of the worm is fitted with an adapter or a universal drive which also fits the engine drive shaft. A simple and fairly efficient drive may be made from a short piece of soft rubber tubing joining the two shafts (Fig 23.2)

One way to test the efficiency of this instrument is to insert a piece of cardboard in a slot in the adapter and to blow one side of the cardboard. A soft blow should be sufficient to turn the worm and wheel a few turns. Another revolution counter more suitable for the smaller engine (up to 10cc) can be constructed from parts of an electric meter which has seen better days. These meters usually have one or more worm and wheel sets. Greater

Fig 23.1 Revolution counters. The revolution counter on the left was constructed from parts of a junior engineering set while the one on the right is described in the text. Putting together the assembly was relatively easy.

precision is required in fitting together this counter due to the size of gears and shafts.

The revolution counter should be mounted on a stand with a heavy base. In constructing this stand allowance would be made for the counter to be adjusted for height. A typical stand can be made from a 1½in OD bar by 1in high into which a ¼in steel rod is inserted vertically. A collar with a grub screw supports the revolution counter base which is drilled to fit the steel rod. A grub screw fitted laterally in the base makes the assembly quite rigid.

In using the revolution counter the wheel and the base are marked with pointers to show the starting mark. The counter is placed against the engine shaft so that the shafts are exactly aligned and the universal drive fitted. The engine is run and when the speed to be calculated is reached, just as the pointers coincide, the stop watch is started. The watch is stopped when a predetermined number of turns of the wheel have been made. If the wheel has 95 teeth and has gone round 5 times in 20 seconds, the speed works out as follows :

(95 teeth by 5 turns/20 seconds) by 60 = rpm
i.e., 475/20 = 23.75 by 60 = 1425 rpm

ELECTRONIC REVOLUTION COUNTERS

Electronic revolution counters of the types described below have two distinct advantages over the mechanical types. The equipment does not touch the engine or create friction and setting up

the measuring equipment takes very little time.

The STROBOSCOPE has a probe or a wand with a flickering light placed near the moving mechanical drive (Fig 23.3). Unfortunately this has to be done in a darkened room for the flickering bulb in the probe to throw sufficient light on the moving parts. The method of operation is fairly simple - the engine is run, the equipment switched on and the probe placed near the mechanical drive (the connecting rods are the easiest 'readable' target). The control knob on the dial is shifted slowly until the moving parts appear stationary in the light of the probe. A reading is taken on a calibrated dial and the speed read off. Usually the pulses are set in cycles per second and any reading is therefore

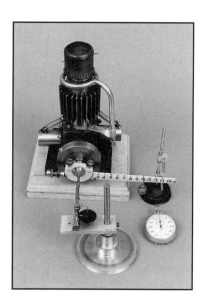

Fig 23.2 Test rig and accessories on engine.

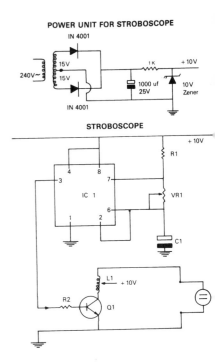

calibrated either in pulses and multiplied by 60, or the dial calibration is already translated into actual speed. Stroboscope components are listed in Appendix 2

The DIGITAL DISPLAY TACHOMETER Fig 23.5 utilizes an infrared source and sensor. The main requirement in operating the tachometer is to fit a piece of stiff cardboard in the shape of a long and narrow tongue bonded to the flywheel. During the revolutions the cardboard tongue slips between the infra red source and sensor serving as an interrupter. The source and sensor are fitted in a plastic holder and mounted on a stand which is placed adjacent to the flywheel. The instrument itself may be placed nearby where it can be read with ease. The digital display tachometer has two advantages over the stroboscope in that it can be operated in full light and there is no probe to hold. Components of this instrument are listed in Appendix 3.

The digital display gives a reading in cycles per second. therefore an 07 on the display means 7 by 60 = 420rpm. A display of 12 means 12 by 60 = 720rpm. The two figure display can show up to 99 (by 60 = 5,940rpm) which is higher than a model engine is likely to go. However with minor modifications to the circuit the display can be made read up to 4 figures, i.e., 9,999 cycles per second (by 60 = 599,940rpm).

HOW TO MEASURE TORQUE

The power generated by an engine is measured in watts or horsepower, (746W = 1hp). Power cannot, however, be measured directly as it is the product of two other engine parameters: speed (rpm) and torque, both of which can be measured directly at the engine crankshaft. The torque of an engine is the turning or twisting force it exerts at its shaft - the torque naturally varies with the engine speed.

To understand how torque is measured, one must imagine that the twisting force at the engine shaft (Fig 23.7a) is equivalent to a force W acting at a radius X (Fig 23.7b).

The torque is then equal to the product WX. In the SI system of units, W is measured in newtons and X in metres, so that the SI unit of torque is the newton-metre (Nm). For model engines this unit is much too large, so we express W in grams and X in centimetres, and we measure torque in gram-centimetres (gcm). This necessitates the use of a conversion factor when calculating power.

When an engine is running off load, i.e., nothing attached to the shaft, all the power generated is used to overcome internal friction. At this speed, the output power and hence the torque available at the shaft is zero. If a load, (e.g., a generator) is attached to the engine shaft, the speed of the engine decreases. Some of the power which was previously being used to overcome friction is now being delivered in the form of shaft power. At this stage the torque of the engine is exactly balanced by the equal and opposite torque exerted by the load. To measure the torque at this particular speed, we must remove the load (i.e., generator) and attach instead a torque measuring device, which will then be adjusted until the engine speed returns to its original level, that is at the generator

Fig 23.3 (Far left) Stroboscope.

Fig 23.4 (Middle) Stroboscope electrical circuit.

Fig 23.5 (Right) Tachometer (open case).

load level. This torque measuring device is called the 'torque testing rig', and its principle can be understood from fig 23.7 (a) and (b). The torque testing rig exerts a counter-torque by means of weight W_1 hanging form radius X_1. This counter-torque W_1X_1 balances exactly the engine torque WX when the engine is running at a steady speed. If W_1 is in grams and X_1 is in centimetres, the product W_1X_1 is the engine torque in gram-centimetres.

A typical test rig with its accessories is seen in Fig 23.8, while a rig assembled for engine testing is seen in Fig 23.2. The torque test rig consists of a brass drum which slides onto the engine shaft and is tightened by a grub screw. The drum rotates freely inside a PTFE, nylon or wooden friction clutch. The clutch is made in two halves. Two set screws can be used to tighten the two halves onto the drum to increase the friction. The clutch has an arm attached to one side and an adjustable counter-weight screwed on the other side. The arm is calibrated in distance (centimetres or inches) from the centre point of the drum. The torque test rig is mounted on the engine shaft and the drum tightened. The revolution counter is then fitted on to the engine shaft (see Fig 23.2).

To initiate the test a suitable small weight is placed on the arm, (e.g., 10 grams at a distance of 10cm), the clutch is loosened and the engine is started with the arm pointing downwards. Once the

Fig 23.6 (a) and (b) Tachometer electrical circuit.

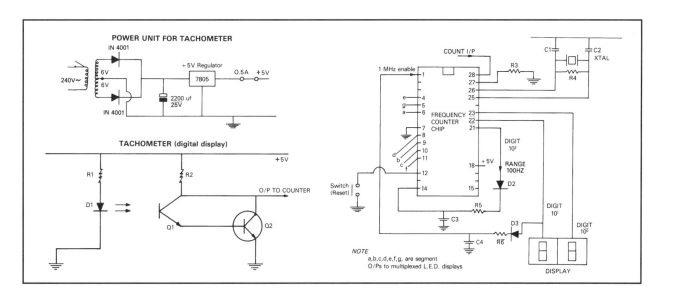

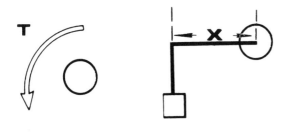

Fig 23.7 (a) Torque.   *23.7 (b)*
                               Weight x distance.

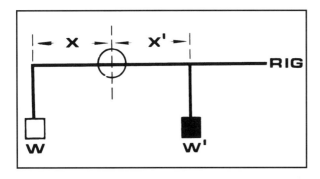

Fig 23.7 (c) (Above) Countertorque diagram.
Fig 23.7 (d) (Below) Graph.

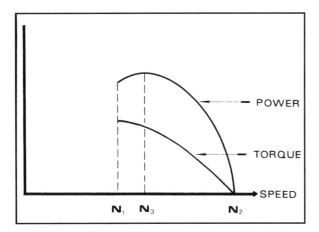

This procedure can be repeated for a range of different torques, (the torque being varied by either changing the mass or altering the radius-arm length). For each torque value, the engine speed is read and the power calculated. Three engine speeds of particular interest are N_1, N_2, and N_3 (Fig 23.7d). N_1 is the engine stalling speed, that is the lowest speed at which the engine can run. Any further increase in torque at this point will cause the engine to stop. N_2 is the no-load speed, and is the maximum speed at which the engine can run (since torque is zero at this point, the output power is also zero). Somewhere in between lies N_3, the speed at which the engine delivers maximum power. This speed is one of the most important parameters of any hot air engine.

A simple torque rig can be constructed in the following manner. Required are : A brass drum, a hardwood or PTFE block, an aluminium strip 6in long by ½in wide by 1/16in thick, two 4 BA studs; two fine compression springs to fit the studs. The size of the drum , although not critical, should in practice be about ¾in diameter. Machining the drum consists of drilling a bore to fit the engine crankshaft, stepping or recessing the drum and reducing the drum on both sides to obtain two collars, which are tapped to take grub screws. The hardwood or PTFE block is of the same thickness as the inner grooved part of the drum and is bored to fit the same diameter of the grooved drum. A fine saw cut is made across the diameter of the bore while the top corners of the block are sawn off. The top and bottom halves are drilled and the bottom half tapped to take the studs. The aluminium strip is bonded or riveted to the bottom part of the block so that the strip is perfectly in line with the bottom half. The arm is marked in cm/in distance from the mid-centre point of the drum bore in the block. The calibration, apart from the marking, is scored by notches on the arm.

It will be noticed that on assembly the weight of the arm will pull the arm downwards towards the perpendicular. Therefore a counterweight must be fitted on the side of the block opposite the arm to balance, so that when the instrument is mounted it remains perfectly horizontal, and when rotated by hand on the engine shaft it will regain this position repeatedly. There are several methods of fixing the counterweight. One is to insert a stud and add on nuts or other weights until a perfect balance is achieved. The rig is assembled with the drum into the block, the studs in place, the springs on the studs. The rig is now ready for the first test run. A simple device such as a wooden stand with an upright beam to which are fixed two dowels, placed near the end of the arm, will prevent the arm from excessive movement and allows fine adjustments to the calibration when friction is applied.

engine picks up speed, the clutch set screws are tightened. This causes an increase in frictional torque on the engine shaft and the engine speed to decrease. The screws are adjusted until the test rig is observed to fluctuate about a mean horizontal position. At this stage the engine rpm corresponding to the given torque (which is 10gm by 10cm = 100gcm) can be read off the revolution counter. If for example, a speed of 600 rpm is observed, then the engine power:

W = grams by centimetres by rpm by 0.00001026
W = 10gm by 10cm by 600rpm by 0.00001026
= 0.6 watts

Author's Note: this chapter has been enhanced by the following contribution by Mick Collins:

COMPUTERISED POWER PRESSURE INDICATOR

By F. M. Collins

To get some idea of what is actually happening inside a Stirling Engine an 'indicator' diagram is required. The indicator was one of James Watt's inventions and draws a figure representing the varying pressure on the piston throughout a revolution. From the area of this figure the mean pressure can be calculated and the effect of timing variation, etc. observed. Watt used it to study the performance of his steam engines and it has been used by engineers ever since to investigate steam, I.C. and Stirling engines. Indicators can take several forms, from the earliest using a pressure controlled pen drawing on a card oscillated by a mechanical connection to the piston rod, and still usable today for low speed engines, to the modern device using a pressure transducer read by a computer, which has the advantages of both coping with the highest engine speeds and also doing all the necessary calculations.

In full-sized engineering, both research and marine engineers are very familiar with indicating, but amongst model engineers, with a few notable exceptions, it is almost completely ignored. The attention of interested readers is drawn to an excellent little monograph by Professor W. Hall, published by the S.M.E.E., which details the use of a computer for indicating, together with programmes and circuit diagrams. It is, of course, possible to plod through a revolution calculating the pressures on the piston at close intervals using the simple Gas Laws to draw a theoretical "indicator" diagram, although until the advent of the computer this was very tedious indeed; during the last century Schmidt described an analytical method based on engine dimensions and peak pressure.

However, the availability of reasonably priced pressure transducers, eg. Maplin UH37s/ MPX100AP, now brings the possibility of building a real indicator, within the capability of most computer-hacking, hot air enthusiasts, (surely the product of two improbabilities?)

Since the output from a pressure transducer is an analogue variable voltage and the computer requires a digital input, the first move was to buy an analogue to digital converter card for an Archimedes A3000 computer - and the first disappointment was to discover that the ADC (analogue to digital converter) chip fitted to it was far too slow for the job. However, the card also included a "user port" giving direct access to an area of the computer's memory and it is thus possible to use a much faster, though marginally less accurate, ZN448E ADC on an external circuit board connected to the port. This board is also required to hold an amplifier and logic chips, and the indicator works as follows:-

The transducer is connected to the power cylinder of the engine and its output amplified before being fed to the ADC. A disc on the crankshaft has two

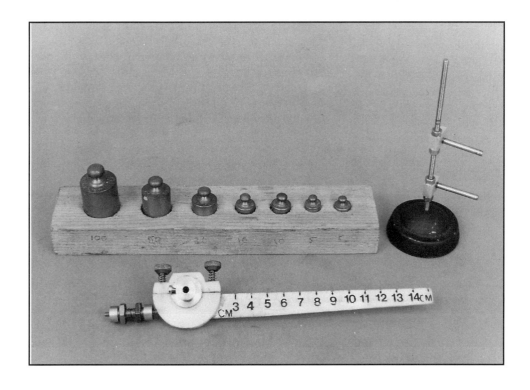

Fig 23.8 Test rig and accessories.

narrow slits in it to tell an optical sensor, type HOA2001, when the piston passes a dead centre. This signal is also passed to the computer.

In the computer, a Basic programme first stores details of the engine, cylinder bore/stroke, clearances, load etc. and then waits for a keystroke to start it indicating. This switches the programme to a much faster procedure written in machine code where it waits for the first dead centre signal, the arrival of which starts a clock to determine the engine speed during the following half revolution (stroke) and the rate at which it must sample pressures during the third stroke in order to take approximately 100 samples. The second signal from the disc stops the first clock and starts a second clock to calculate the sampling speed required during stroke four. Arrival of the fifth and last signal switches the computer back into the Basic programme which retrieves the readings from their stores to display them as a figure on the screen and completes the calculations required to display the mean pressure and indicated power. If required, the programme can now return to the machine code to deal with strokes 7 to 10, and "shadow bank" switching used to give a continuous "live" display - albeit of a previous revolution.

The figure shown (Fig 23.9) was taken from an 18cc engine, fired by a candle and pulling 0.27 watts on the brake. It is very close indeed to that obtained from a Schmidt analysis based on a peak pressure taken with a normal gauge via a non-return valve. From its area the computer has calculated the mean pressure on the piston as 1.21 PSI and the "indicated" power as 0.45 watts. The difference between this value and that obtained on the brake is the power absorbed by friction.

There are several snags with this indicator, the first being its use of illegal machine code to increase speed and cope with a sampling rate of up to 10,000/second to deal with engine speeds up to 3000 RPM; ("illegal" code is any crafty procedure specifically forbidden by the manufacturer as it will almost certainly be incompatible with future models of the computer - though it does no damage and it's not a hanging offence!)

The second objection is the use of only two synchronising signals and a free running time base

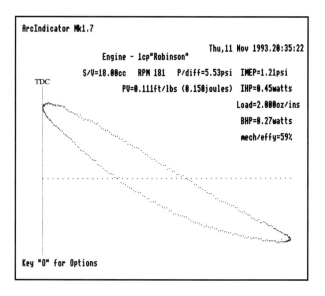

Fig 23.9 Screen dump taken from an experimental indicator. Diagram is of an 18cc, gamma type Stirling pulling a 2oz load on the brake. The horizontal dotted line is 14.7PSI (atmospheric pressure) and as the engine is non-snifting, the areas above and below this line are equal. The rough outline of the figure is due to electrical 'noise'.

during sampling. Whilst this is no worse than a normal oscilloscope indicator, it does assume sinusoidal piston motion and requires the engine speed (angular velocity) to remain constant for two revolutions. Possibly true enough with heavily flywheeled, low compression engines, but very unlikely with, say, a Rider or a Rhombic. The indicator detailed in Professor Hall's booklet overcomes this by using 180 slots.

The problem with "noise", due to very low output from the transducer, is also very apparent although its effect on the calculated mean is probably cancelled over the hundred or so readings. In view of these difficulties the MK1 indicator has now been abandoned and future developments will use a different ADC, accessing the computer via the printer port, similar to a "sound sampler".

PC owners may be interested to know that oscilloscope attachments which connect in this manner are available, although suitable synchronising arrangements would probably have to be made and software written.

APPENDIX 1

MATERIALS USED IN MODEL ENGINE CONSTRUCTION

Screws, nuts, bolts, washers, spring washers.
Silver steel or spindle steel rods - high quality precision for displacer rods and crankshafts. ¥in, ⁄in, ¢in mostly used.
Brass round bars - ¢in, ¥in, "in mostly used for bushes, bearings and guides.
Dural flat bars - different thickness, ⁄in to "in for flanges, cylinder plates, engine bases etc.
Dural round bars - different diameters, off cuts from ¢in to 2in, the latter for cooling fins.
Cast iron bars - off-cuts for making power pistons - around 1in to 1 "in.
Tubes - stainless steel, bright mild steel etc - ¢in to 1in OD for cylinder work; sometimes 1 ¢in to 1 ".
Shims - brass, for packing steel, steel, for regenerators if being used.
Brass tubes (as used in model boat propellor shafts) for small bushes and guides.
PTFE, Teflon, Rulon - off cuts to use for bushes, sealing rings etc.
Gasket material - various thicknesses up to ⁄in.
Other consumable items:
Very light fine lubricating oil.
Loctite products - nutlock, studlock, screwlock.
Bonding Agents; Loctite, Araldite, Super Epoxy etc.
Light grease, cutting oil, very fine grinding paste, polishing compound.

APPENDIX 2

STROBOSCOPE COMPONENTS LIST
(See also Fig 23.4)

R_1	10K o.5W oxide resistor
R_2	1K 0.5W oxide resistor
Q_1	BC 107 transistor
IC_1	555 timer
VR_1	100k variable potentiometer
C_1	2 microfarad electrolytic capacitor
L_1	Centre tapped transformer by selection
	Miniature neon

APPENDIX 3

TACHOMETER DISPLAY COMPONENTS LIST
(See also Fig 23.6)

R_1	270 ohm 0.5W oxide resistor
R_2	1.0K ohm 0.5W oxide resistor
R_3	100K ohm 0.5W oxide resistor
R_4	22 Meg ohm 0.5W carbon resistor
R_5	10K ohm 0.5W oxide resistor
R_6	10K ohm 0.5W oxide resistor
C_1	47 Picofarad polystyrene capacitor
C_2	47 Picofarad polystyrene capacitor
C_3	68 Picofarad polystyrene capacitor
C_4	68 Picofarad polystyrene capacitor
D_1	Infra-red source (RS 306 77)
D_2	IN 4148
D_3	IN 4148
Q_1	Infra-red sensor
Q_2	BC 107
Display	RS 2-digit 0.5in multiplexed display
Frequency	RS7216 C (RS 306 837)
Crystal	1MHz (RS 307 761)
Switch	Push-to-make

Note: RS = Radio Spares

Selected Bibliography

A number of books on the Stirling Engine, ranging from the purely academic to historical on to technical, have been published over the years. The following list is by no means comprehensive, rather it is a list of publications that the author has obtained, although not all are now in print. Some of these titles have a practical value to the newcomer to Stirling engines:

STIRLING ENGINES, by Prof. Graham Walker, published by the Clarendon Press, Oxford.

STIRLING ENGINES, by G.T. Reader and C. Hooper, published by E. & F. N. Spon, London and New York.

LIQUID PISTON STIRLING ENGINES, by Dr. Colin West, Ph.D., published by Van Nostrand Reinhold Co, New York.

STIRLING CYCLE ENGINES, by Andy Ross, published by Solar Engines, Phoenix, Arizona.

MAKING STIRLING ENGINES, by Andy Ross, published by Ross Experimental, Columbus, Ohio.

AN INTRODUCTION TO STIRLING ENGINES, by Prof. James R. Senft, published by Moriya Press, River Falls, Wisconsin.

RINGBOM STIRLING ENGINES, by Prof. James R. Senft, published by Oxford University Press, New York.

A HISTORY OF HOT AIR AND CALORIC ENGINES, by Robert Sier, published by Argus Books Ltd, Hemel Hempstead.

Interesting and informative papers are regularly presented at the "Intersociety Energy Conversion Engineering Conferences" and at the "International Stirling Engine Conferences". Your local University Library may be able to obtain selected items for a small fee.

The magazines "MODEL ENGINEER" and "ENGINEERING IN MINIATURE" in Britain, and "LIVE STEAM" and "MODELTEC" in America, often print articles by Stirling Engine enthusiasts and builders. These are well worth reading since they are a good source of knowledge and specific information, pooled and exchanged by experts. Newcomers especially are recommended to look into back numbers of these magazines for information.

Three articles which appeared in "PHILIPS TECHNICAL REVIEW "are of interest:

1947, Volume 9, No.4, pages 97-104 - "Fundamentals for the development of the Philips Air Engine", by H. de Brey, H. Rinia and F.L. van Weenan;

1947, Volume 9, No 5, pages 125-134 - "The construction of the Philips Air Engine" by F.L. van Weenan;

1959, Volume 20, No.9, pages 245-262 - "The Philips hot gas engine with rhombic drive mechanism" by R.J. Mejjer.

A number of historical and informative articles have appeared in "THE ENGINEER", mainly in the 19th century, but one particular more recent study is a must for engine modellers:

1959, Volume 207, pages 492-497, 522-527 and 720-723 - "Air Engines" by Dr. T. Finklestein.

STERLING STIRLING of Gwent publish a comprehensive leaflet which gives information on publications, models and supplies, and the publishers of this book, CAMDEN MINIATURE STEAM SERVICES, endeavour to keep all currently available books on the subject of Stirling engines in stock.

Index

Notes to the index: (1) Engine names are shown in *italics*.
(2) Page numbers in **Bold** indicate a main topic.